Elements of
Probability and Statistics

PRENTICE-HALL, INTERNATIONAL, INC., *London*
PRENTICE-HALL OF AUSTRALIA, PTY, LTD., *Sydney*
PRENTICE-HALL OF CANADA, LTD., *Toronto*
PRENTICE-HALL OF INDIA (PRIVATE) LTD., *New Delhi*
PRENTICE-HALL OF JAPAN, INC., *Tokyo*

Elements of
Probability and Statistics

ELMER B. MODE

Professor of Mathematics
Boston University

PRENTICE-HALL, INC.   *Englewood Cliffs, N.J.*

© 1966 by
PRENTICE-HALL, INC.
Englewood Cliffs, N.J.

Library of Congress Catalog Number 66-18390
Printed in the United States of America
26977C

Current printing (last digit):
10 9 8 7 6 5 4 3 2

Preface

In recent years there has been an increasing desire for the teaching of both probability and statistics in a single course—first, because probability in its own right has become a necessary tool in a multiformity of fields of intellectual activity, and second, because it is the cornerstone upon which the vast structure of modern statistics is based. The principal aim of this book is to develop the basic concepts and rules of mathematical probability and to show how these provide models for the solution of practical problems, particularly those of a statistical nature.

The text favors no particular area of application. Examples and exercises are chosen from many fields such as biology, education, economics, genetics, psychology, and sociology. Its mathematical prerequisite consists of the usual amount of high school mathematics—about two years of algebra as a minimum. However, in Section 9.6 it has seemed desirable to include a formal definition of the definite integral, but this can be omitted at the discretion of the instructor. The chapter on Markov chains more properly belongs with Chapters 2 to 5, on probability, but it seemed wiser to place it at the end of the book inasmuch as many courses cannot afford the time to include it.

The arrangement of material offers alternatives in the content of the course to be followed. Two of these are as follows.

(1) *A brief course in probability.* This could include Chapter 1 (Sections 1, 3, and 4), Chapters 2–5, Chapter 7 (Sections 1–3, 6, 8, 9), Chapter 8, Chapter 9 (Sections 6–8), Chapter 10 (Sections 1–10, 13), Chapter 11 (Section 1), Chapter 12 (Sections 3, 4), Chapter 13 (Sections 2, 3, 5),

Chapter 14 (Sections 1, 2, 4), Chapter 15 (Sections 1–10), Chapter 16 (Sections 3, 4), and Chapter 19.

(2) *A reduced course in probability and statistics.* This is suggested by the omission of Sections 5.4–5.6, 10.11, 10.12, 12.4, Chapter 14, Sections 15.7, 15.8, 15.11, and Chapter 19.

Generally speaking, the more complex topics such as bivariate probability functions, regression and correlation, and Markov processes appear at the end of the book.

The author is indebted to the Literary Executor of the late Sir Ronald A. Fisher, F.R.S., Cambridge, and to Oliver and Boyd, Ltd., Edinburgh, for their permission to reprint Tables Nos. III, IV, and V.A. from their book *Statistical Methods for Research Workers.* The author is also grateful to Professor Egon S. Pearson and the *Biometrika* trustees, to Professors Wilfrid J. Dixon and Alexander M. Mood, and to the McGraw-Hill Book Company for the use of charts or tables appearing in the back of the book. The author is again in debt to Professor Elizabeth A. Shuhany for her suggestions for clarifying the exposition of the manuscript.

E. B. M.

Contents

1

Introduction

Games of chance are probably as old as
the human desire to get something for
nothing; but their mathematical impli-
cations were appreciated only after
Fermat and Pascal in 1654 reduced
chance to law.

Eric T. Bell
The Development of Mathematics[1]

1.1. PROBABILITY

Many statements made in common parlance contain elements of
uncertainty: "It will probably rain tomorrow." "The American League
team is likely to win the World Series." "This new drug might be effective
in combating influenza." If you were to say "I'll bet you two to one that
it will rain," or "I'll give you odds of seven to three that the American
League team wins," then you would be attempting, in a crude way, to
measure your uncertainty. The theory of mathematical probability gives
us bases for constructing exact measures of uncertainty and provides the
necessary underpinning for the vast structure that modern statistics has now
become. Of course there are many areas where the uncertainties are not
amenable to mathematical analysis.

In the mid-sixteenth century, Girolamo Cardano, the Italian mathematician, physician, and gambler, wrote his *Liber de Ludo Aleae* ("The
Book on Games of Chance") in which appeared the first known study of the
principles of probability. About a hundred years later, the gambler Chevalier
de Méré proposed to Blaise Pascal the famous "Problem of the Points,"

[1] Copyright 1940, McGraw-Hill Book Company. Used by permission.

1

which may be described as follows: Two men are playing a game of chance. The one first gaining a certain number of points wins the stake. They are forced to quit before the game is completed. Given the number of points each has won, how should the stake be divided? This problem offered a real challenge to the wits of the two astute French mathematicians, Blaise Pascal and Pierre de Fermat. The methods employed by Cardano and Pascal represent the beginnings of the mathematics of probability, about which modern statistical theory centers today. The publication by Laplace in 1812 of the epoch-making *Théorie Analytique des Probabilités* laid a firm foundation for this theory.

1.2. STATISTICS

It is curious that the modern science of statistics traces its origin to two quite dissimilar human interests: political states and games of chance. In the mid-eighteenth century, statistics was born as a word describing the study of "the political arrangements of the modern states of the known world." The description of states was at first verbal, but the increasing proportion of numerical data in the descriptions gradually gave the new word the quantitative connotation that is associated with it now. From the rather restricted study of data pertaining to a state, statistics branched out into other fields of investigation.

Between 1835 and 1870, the Belgian astronomer, Quetelet, was applying the theory of probability to anthropological measurements. His conclusions may be summarized and extended by the statement: The same general laws of variation governing gambler's luck may be discovered in the statures of soldiers, the intelligence quotients of children, the blood pressures of adults, the speeds of molecules of a gas, and innumerable other aggregates of observations.

In more recent times, an English school of statisticians, under the leadership of Karl Pearson (1857–1936) and Sir Ronald A. Fisher (1890–1962), has made notable contributions to both theoretical and applied statistics. The power of general methods based on probability concepts became more clearly perceived, and as a result, applications have been made to many diverse fields of inquiry. An appreciation of the importance of the statistical method in man's attempt to come to grips with a marvelously complex physical and social world is a serious and legitimate aim of any educated person.

1.3. PROBABILITY AND STATISTICS

The theory of probability is a mathematical system composed of undefined and defined terms and a set of assumptions concerning them;

from all of this we draw logical conclusions, that is, we prove theorems. It is an abstract discipline which we use as a model in order to make deductions concerning events which possibly may occur in an actual or an imagined physical operation. For example, assume that we have in our possession two dice. One die, we think, is an honest die. That is, it seems to be a perfectly homogeneous cube with dots on its six faces—one dot on one face, two dots on a second face, three dots on a third face, and so on up to six dots on a sixth face. Because of its symmetry and homogeneity, we may believe that when we roll or toss it onto a flat surface it has just as good a chance of showing one face upward as any other, but our belief may not be fully justified. Nevertheless, we may *assume* that the probability of the appearance of a given number of dots is $\frac{1}{6}$. With this assignment of a probability number, $\frac{1}{6}$, to each face, we then develop laws of chance for dice games played with idealized dice. For example, as we shall see later, if two honest dice are tossed, the probability for the sum (of dots) 7 or 11 to appear is $\frac{2}{9}$. Thus the theory of probability enables us to make deductions from the mathematical model (idealized dice) which we hope are sufficiently accurate to be used in constructing patterns of behavior for honest dice games.

Now consider the other die, which we shall assume is a cube of non-homogeneous material—a loaded die. We cannot, by physical examination, estimate the chance of any one of the six faces appearing when the die is thrown. However, we can carry out an experiment such as rolling the die 100 times and noting how frequently the number (of dots) 1, 2, 3, 4, 5, and 6 appear. On the basis of our experimental result, we can make estimates of the chances of obtaining any one of these numbers on a single throw. These estimates (they cannot be otherwise), despite their incompleteness, have a desirable property, namely, that precise statements can be made concerning the probability of the estimate being correct. For example, if 5 dots appeared 25 times in 100 tosses, we should be tempted to guess that the probability for 5 is about $\frac{1}{4}$. This guess has the disadvantage that we cannot know how right or wrong it is, and for many practical uses it is not very helpful. However, statistical methods discussed later permit us to state that the probability of 5 appearing on the toss of this loaded die is between 0.17 and 0.33. This statement is almost sure to be correct.[2] If this estimate is not precise enough, we can roll the die a greater number of times. For example, if 5 dots appeared 250 times in 1000 rolls, the probability is estimated to be between 0.22 and 0.28.[2]

Statistics involves repetitive processes: For example, the die is rolled 100 times, 50 soldiers have their blood pressures recorded, 10 pieces of twine are tested for breaking strength, 247 students take a verbal aptitude test, and so on. One might say, then, that in the theory of probability we begin with assumed laws of chance and let them serve as models to guide us in predicting

[2] That is, it is correct about 95 per cent of the time. See Section 16.9.

the outcomes of certain experiments. In statistics we examine the outcomes of repetitive operations and then attempt to interpret them with the aid of estimated probabilities.

The preceding paragraphs constitute but a first and inadequate approach to an understanding of probability and statistics; however, they may be helpful in future chapters. Later chapters will elucidate more clearly the roles of these two interconnected fields of study.

1.4. APPLICATIONS

Aside from the vital role that probability plays in statistical theory and its applications, it has many uses in other fields, some of which are briefly described here: as

(i) *Genetic theory.* Random mating of individuals with similar or different physical and mental characteristics gives rise to offspring whose attributes we may wish to study. With appropriate measures of probability of occurrence of certain genes, useful predictions or conclusions involving inheritance can be made.

(ii) *Games of chance.* Games of cards, dice, coins, and so on are susceptible to analysis with a view to satisfying one's curiosity, governing one's strategy of play, or deciding on the fairness of the game. For example, books of the type, *How to Play Bridge*, contain many calculated probabilities of occurrence of certain combinations of cards.

(iii) *Military strategy.* The phrase "calculated risk" is often used, particularly with reference to problems of warfare. Idealized situations are subjected to probabilistic analysis, and strategies with maximum chances of success are worked out. In actual combat, sophisticated estimates involving probabilities and based on information gleaned from various sources may be used to determine appropriate actions.

(iv) *The physical sciences.* The kinetic theory of gases and the "random walk" phenomena are but two of many cases where probability or statistical laws operate.

(v) *Industry.* Telephone traffic, queuing theory (the problem of efficiently serving varying lines of people), and the theory of occurrence of runs of defective articles in a manufacturing process offer but a few illustrations of the operation of laws of chance in industrial processes or operations.

2

Sets

2.1. INTRODUCTION

The simple notion of a collection or set of objects is fundamental in the basic structure of mathematics, and it was first brought to the attention of mathematicians by Georg Cantor in the 1870's. Set theory has peculiar advantages in the formulation of definitions and the derivation of laws of probability. For this reason, we shall develop some of the elementary properties of sets. A satisfactory definition of a set cannot be given in terms of simpler concepts; hence, the word *set* must logically be taken as an undefined term. However, to characterize its properties, we do use descriptions or synonyms of the word such as collection, aggregate, class, and the German word Menge, introduced by Cantor.

Examples of sets follow:

    (i) The letters, a, b, c, d, e, f, g.
    (ii) The squares of the positive prime numbers less than 12.

[1] By a set M we understand a collection into a single whole of definite well-distinguished objects of our perception or of our thought which are termed the "Elements" of M.

(iii) The Ten Commandments.
(iv) The Presidents of the United States up to 1965.
(v) The positive integers.
(vi) Your living grandparents.
(vii) The basic colors of the spectrum.

Understand that a set consists of any number of distinguishable objects, distinguishable visibly or in the mind. For these objects we use a more appropriate mathematical term, *element*; and it is essential that the set be *well-defined*. This means that, given an object or element, one must be able to state unequivocally that it does or does not belong to the set.

One method of specifying a set is to make a list or roster of its members. Thus in (i) the elements are already listed; in (ii) the elements are 2^2, 3^2, 5^2, 7^2, and 11^2; in (iii) we may list the elements from the book of Exodus; in (iv) we may write Washington, Adams, Jefferson, and so on to the present; in (v) the roster is $1, 2, 3, , , ,$. Here the elements are infinite in number (as indicated by the succession of commas) since the counting process may go on indefinitely. In (vi), if you have no grandparents living, the set is an empty or *null* set, one that is devoid of members. This special set is quite useful for it plays a role in set theory which is similar to that played by zero in arithmetic; however—and this must be emphasized—a null set is not zero but the number of elements in it is.

In the notation of sets, a pair of braces { } is used to enclose the elements of a set. Thus we define the sets of our illustrations as follows:

(i) $L = \{a,b,c,d,e,f,g\}$.
(ii) $M = \{4,9,25,49,121\}$.
(iv) $P = \{$Washington, Adams, Jefferson, , , Johnson$\}$.[2]
(v) $I = \{1,2,3, , ,\}$.
(vii) $C = \{$red, orange, yellow, green, blue, indigo, violet$\}$.

In (iii), we could list the Commandments from the Bible; but it would be awkward and unnecessary unless required by your Sunday School teacher. In (vi), if you have no living grandparents, the empty set, G, of them is designated by a standard symbol, $\varnothing$. Thus $G = \varnothing$, the null set.

A second method of characterizing a set is to state the distinctive property or properties of its elements. In this manner we may write:

(i) $L = \{$the first seven letters of the English alphabet$\}$.
(ii) $M = \{x^2 \mid x$ is a positive prime number less than 12$\}$. Here the symbol " $\mid$ " is read "such that."

_____
[2] As of 1965.

(iv) $P = \{$the presidents of the U.S.A. from Washington to Johnson$\}$.

(v) $I = \{$the positive integers$\}$.

(vii) $C = \{$the basic colors of the spectrum$\}$.

As a further illustration, we take

$$A = \{x \mid x = 2k^2 + 5; k = 1,2,3, , ,\}.$$

Here the set of values is infinite and is obtained if we let k assume all positive integral values.

The members of a set sometimes consist of pairs of objects, of triples of objects, or in general, of *n-tuples* of them. Thus

$$\text{(viii)}\quad O = \{HH, HT, TH, TT\}$$

represents the set of possible outcomes, heads or tails, when two coins are tossed. Here the first letter of each pair refers to a specified coin, and the second letter to the other coin.

$$\text{(ix)}\quad B = \{(x,y,z), (x,z,y), (y,x,z), (y,z,x), (z,x,y), (z,y,x)\}.$$

Here the set is made up of the possible arrangements of the letters x, y, and z.

Note that a change of order of the members of a set does not alter the set. Thus, for example, in (i)

$$L = \{a,b,c,d,e,f,g\} = \{b,d,f,g,a,c,e\}$$

and in (vii)

$$C = \{r,o,y,g,b,i,v\} = \{v,i,b,g,y,o,r\}$$

where the letters are abbreviations for the colors. In this connection, notice that in (ix) a member is a triple; however, the letters x, y, and z are not elements of the set but are constituents of the elements. Furthermore, elements of a set must differ from one another; there should be no duplicate elements.

Sets are often specified with the aid of formulas or equations. Thus,

$$U = \{(x,y) \mid x^2 + y^2 = 1\}$$

defines the set of ordered numbers (x,y) such that $x^2 + y^2 = 1$; these ordered pairs correspond to points on the unit circle with center at the origin $(0,0)$. This again is an infinite set.

It is often advantageous to indicate what elements are and what elements are not members of a given set. In this connection we employ the symbol $\in$ to mean "is a member of" or "belongs to," and $\notin$ to mean "is not a member of" or "does not belong to."

Thus in (i) $c \in L$ but $h \notin L$;

(ii) $9 \in M$ but $10 \notin M$;

(iv) Lincoln $\in P$ but Bryan $\notin P$.

2.2. RELATIONS AND OPERATIONS

*Two sets **A** and **B** are said to be equal if every element of one is an element of the other.* In this case we write $A = B$. Thus if $A = \{a,b,c,d\}$ and $B = \{b,d,a,c\}$, then $A = B$.

*A set **A** is said to be a subset of a set **B** if every element of **A** is also an element of **B**.* The relation $A \subset B$ is read "*A* is contained in *B*" or "*A* is a subset of *B*." Note that this definition permits a set to be a subset of itself, so that $A \subset A$. If *A* is a subset of *B* but $A \neq B$, then *A* is a *proper* subset of *B*. For example in (i), $\{a,c,d\} \subset \{a,b,c,d,e,f,g\}$ and in (v), $\{2,4,6,\,,\,\} \subset \{1,2,3,\,,\,\}$. Here the even positive integers constitute a proper subset of the positive integers.

In (iii), the *unit set* (a set consisting of only one element) {Thou shalt not kill} $\subset$ {The Ten Commandments}. Also we define $\varnothing$ to be a subset of all sets: $\varnothing \subset A$ for every *A* and $\varnothing \subset \varnothing$.

*The union of two sets **A** and **B** is the set of all elements that belong either to **A** or to **B** or to both **A** and **B**.* It is symbolized by $A \cup B$ which may be read "*A* union *B*" or "*A* cup *B*."

EXAMPLE 1. If $A = \{a,b,c\}$ and $B = \{b,d,e\}$ then $A \cup B = \{a,b,c,d,e\}$.

EXAMPLE 2. If $M = \{$the male members of your family$\}$

and

$$F = \{\text{the female members of your family}\}$$

then

$$M \cup F = \{\text{the members of your family}\}.$$

EXAMPLE 3. Consider the two sets:

$$D = \{\text{Democrats in Massachusetts}\}$$

$$T = \{\text{Truck drivers in Massachusetts}\}.$$

Then

$$D \cup T = \{\text{Democrats or truck drivers or both in Massachusetts}\}.$$

Note that for all sets *A*,

$$A \cup \varnothing = A.$$

*The intersection of two sets **A** and **B** is the set whose elements belong to both **A** and **B**.* It is symbolized by $A \cap B$, and is read "*A* intersection *B*" or "*A* cap *B*." Thus for example 1, $A \cap B = \{b\}$. For example 2, $M \cap F = \varnothing$, and for example 3, $D \cap T = \{$Truck drivers who are Democrats in Massachusetts$\}$.

Note that for all sets A,

$$A \cap \varnothing = \varnothing.$$

Two sets A and B are said to be disjoint or mutually exclusive if they have no elements in common, that is, if $A \cap B = \varnothing$.

In example 2, the male and female members of your family form disjoint sets, that is, $M \cap F = \varnothing$.

In set theory, one refers frequently to certain basic or *universal sets*, much as one employs in logic the idea of a "universe of discourse." Such a set will be designated by the capital letter U. If, for example, we are analyzing the voting habits of the city of Boston we may let

$$U = \{\text{all voters of Boston}\}.$$

Referring to this set, we may be interested in many different subsets of U such as the male voters, the Independent voters, the Roman Catholic voters, the Independent voters who voted Republican in 1964, the voters of South Boston, and so on.

If M and M' are any two disjoint sets such that $M \cup M' = U$, they are said to be complementary (with respect to U). Thus if

$$U = \{\text{all voters in Boston}\}$$

$$M = \{\text{all male voters in Boston}\}$$

and

$$M' = \{\text{all female voters in Boston}\}$$

then M and M' are complementary with respect to U.

In example 2, M and F are complementary sets relative to the set $S = \{\text{the members of your family}\}$, since $M \cup F = S$, and $M \cap F = \varnothing$. Thus $M = F'$ and $F = M'$. Each subset, M or F, is a complement of the other.

If the universal set is (i) and $A = \{a,b,c\}$, then $A' = \{d,e,f,g\}$; if the universal set is (v) and $E = \{\text{the even integers}\}$ then $E' = \{\text{the odd integers}\}$.

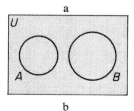

2.3. VENN DIAGRAMS

It is often very useful to represent the elements of a set by points, and the set itself by an aggregate of these points contained within a circle or other simple closed region. This device for deriving properties of sets was suggested by John Venn in 1881. The universal set is conveniently, but not necessarily, represented by a rectangle. Thus in Fig. 2-1a, the

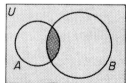

Figure 2-1

dots within the circular regions *A* and *B* represent two intersecting subsets of *U*. In Fig. 2-1b, *A* and *B* represent two disjoint sets. In Fig. 2-2, the three circles represent three mutually intersecting subsets *A*, *B*, and *C*.

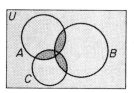

Figure 2-2

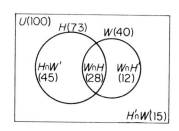

Figure 2-3

EXAMPLE 1. Suppose that a college freshman class consists of 100 students. Of these, 40 are women, 73 take history, and 12 are women not taking history. How many men do not take history?

Solution. If 12 women out of 40 do not take history, then 28 do. If 28 out of the 73 taking history are women, then 45 must be men taking history. Of the 100 − 40, or 60 men, there are 60 − 45, or 15, who do not take history. This simple problem can also be illustrated and solved with the aid of a Venn diagram (Fig. 2-3).

The steps in the solution are as follows:

Women not taking history $= W \cap H'$		12
Women taking history $\quad = W \cap H$		$40 - 12 = 28$
Men taking history $\quad = H \cap W'$		$73 - 28 = 45$
Men not taking history $\quad = H' \cap W'$	$100 - (45 + 28 + 12) = 15.$	

EXAMPLE 2. In a sample of 50 housewives, 35 had television sets, 20 had electric garbage disposals, and 15 had hi-fi radios; 15 had both television sets and disposals, 10 had television sets and hi-fi radios, and 12 had disposals and hi-fi sets. Eight housewives had all three of these appliances. How many had none of these?

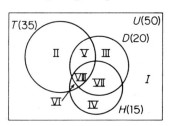

Figure 2-4

Solution. It is convenient to label the regions of the Venn diagram (Fig. 2-4) as shown and to work outward from the innermost region when possible. Then the numbers of housewives in the various subsets of U may be found as follows:

Region	Subset	Number of Housewives
viii	$(T \cap D) \cap H$	8
v + viii	$T \cap D$	15
vi + viii	$T \cap H$	10
vii + viii	$D \cap H$	12

By a series of subtractions we find the following results:

v	$(T \cap D) \cap H'$	7
vi	$(T \cap H) \cap D'$	2
vii	$(D \cap H) \cap T'$	4

Therefore

v + vi + viii		$7 + 2 + 8 = 17$

whence

ii	$(T \cap D') \cap H'$	$35 - 17 = 18$

Also,

v + vii + viii		$7 + 4 + 8 = 19$

whence

iii	$(D \cap T') \cap H'$	$20 - 19 = 1$

Likewise,

vi + vii + viii		$2 + 4 + 8 = 14$

whence

iv	$(H \cap D') \cap T'$	$15 - 14 = 1$

It follows then, that

ii + iii + iv + v + vi + vii + viii	$(T \cup D) \cup H$	41

whence

i	$((T \cup D) \cup H)'$	$50 - 41 = 9$

Therefore 9 housewives had none of these appliances.

2.4. THE ALGEBRA OF SETS

The Venn diagrams of the preceding section are useful as an intuitive approach to the algebra of sets. This algebra is a *Boolean algebra*, named after George Boole, an English mathematician whose book, *An Investigation of the Laws of Thought*, on which are founded the *Mathematical Theories of*

Logic and Probabilities, was published in 1854. This important work contained concepts and methods which permeate many branches of mathematics today.

There are numerous ways in which the assumptions underlying set algebra may be formulated. The following will be useful for our purposes. Assume a class K of sets A, B, C, , , and two operations $\cup$ and $\cap$, which we call union and intersection, respectively. $A, B, C, , ,$ are to satisfy the following postulates:

Postulate of Closure. If A and B are in K, then
(1a) $A \cup B$ *and* **(1b)** $A \cap B$ *are also in* **K**.

Commutative Postulates.
(2a) $A \cup B = B \cup A$
(2b) $A \cap B = B \cap A$

Associative Postulates.
(3a) $A \cup (B \cup C) = (A \cup B) \cup C$
(3b) $A \cap (B \cap C) = (A \cap B) \cap C$

Distributive Postulates.
(4a) $A \cap (B \cup C) = (A \cap B) \cup (A \cap C)$
(4b) $A \cup (B \cap C) = (A \cup B) \cap (A \cup C)$

Null Set. There exists a unique set $\varnothing$ such that
(5a) $A \cup \varnothing = A$
(5b) $A \cap \varnothing = \varnothing$

Universal Set. There exists a unique set U such that
(6a) $A \cup U = U$
(6b) $A \cap U = A$

Complementary Set. For each set A there exists a unique set A' such that
(7a) $A \cup A' = U$
(7b) $A \cap A' = \varnothing$

The similarity of postulates 1a and b, 2a and b, 3a and b, and 4a to those of the algebra of real numbers should be evident when we replace union by addition, $\cup$ by $+$, and intersection by multiplication, $\cap$ by $\times$. Note that postulates 4a and b affirm dual distributive laws in which intersection is distributive over union, and union is distributive over intersection. In ordinary algebra, multiplication is distributive over addition, $A(B + C) = AB + AC$; but addition is not distributive over multiplication, $A + BC \neq (A + B)(A + C)$. $\varnothing$ behaves like zero since $A + 0 = A$ and $A \times 0 = 0$. U behaves like unity in multiplication for $A \times 1 = A$.

The plausibility of the postulates becomes apparent when we represent the sets and their relations by means of Venn diagrams. On the basis of these postulates, it is possible to prove many theorems concerning the algebra of sets. Rather than give formal proofs, we shall verify some of these theorems with the aid of Venn diagrams.

Two theorems developed by the English mathematician De Morgan (1806–1871) are of interest also.

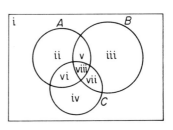

(8a) $(A \cup B)' = A' \cap B'$
(8b) $(A \cap B)' = A' \cup B'$

We shall now verify distributive law 4b and the first of De Morgan's laws by means of Venn diagrams.

Figure 2-5

Refer to Fig. 2-5. The subsets (regions) listed in the left column of the following list may be symbolized by the relations shown in the right column.

Subset (Region)	Notation
(a) vii + viii	$B \cap C$
(b) (ii + v + vi) + (vii + viii)	$A \cup (B \cap C)$
(c) ii + iii + $\underline{v}$ + $\underline{vi}$ + $\underline{vii}$ + $\underline{viii}$	$A \cup B$
(d) $\underline{ii}$ + $\underline{v}$ + $\underline{vi}$ + $\underline{viii}$ + iv + $\underline{vii}$	$A \cup C$

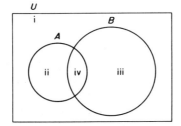

Figure 2-6

The numerals underlined in (c) and (d) represent the intersection or common region of $A \cup B$ and $A \cup C$; hence, line (e) follows:

(e)   ii + v + vi + viii + vii $(A \cup B) \cap (A \cup C)$

The regions of (e) are identical with those of (b); hence $A \cup (B \cap C) = (A \cup B) \cap (A \cup C)$, and the theorem is "proved."

To verify that $(A \cup B)' = A' \cap B'$, we set up the following from Fig. 2-6.

Subset (Region)	Notation
ii + iii + iv	$A \cup B$

Since $U = i + (ii + iii + iv)$, the subset whose region is i is the complement of the subset whose region is $(ii + iii + iv)$. That is:

i	$(A \cup B)'$
$i + iii$	A'
$i + ii$	B'
i	$A' \cap B'$

hence, $(A \cup B)' = A' \cap B'$.

2.5. CARTESIAN PRODUCTS

A pair of objects a and b may be examined with reference to their order so that we may state that the ordered pair (a,b) is different from the ordered pair (b,a). Thus we may treat (a,b) and (b,a) as two distinguishable elements of a set $\{(a,b), (b,a)\}$ and $(a,b) \neq (b,a)$. Similarly, $\{(a,b,c), (a,c,b), (b,a,c), (b,c,a), (c,a,b), (c,b,a)\}$ is a set comprised of six distinct ordered triples.

The preceding ideas are generalized to include sets of ordered n-tuples (an n-tuple is a group of n objects) which may be formed from the n objects $x_1, x_2, x_3, , , x_n$, so that any arrangement of these n objects may constitute an element of a set. The reader must distinguish clearly between the items comprising an ordered group and the elements of a set in which each element is an ordered group. Thus the second set of the preceding paragraph contains six elements or members, and each element is made up of an ordered group of the three letters a, b, and c.

We stated earlier that a set cannot comprise duplicate elements. However, ordered pairs, triples, , , n-tuples may. Thus we may have the set $\{HHT, HTH, THH\}$ whose elements (ordered triples) are all different (as they should be) from one another but which contain the same three letters H, H, and T. These letters may represent the outcomes, heads or tails, when a penny is tossed three times and produces two heads and one tail. If we were to inquire: "What are the possible outcomes when a coin is tossed three times in succession?" we find the answer conveniently represented by the set of ordered triples

$$\{HHH, HHT, HTH, THH, HTT, THT, TTH, TTT\}.$$

In each triple the first letter represents the outcome on the first toss, the second letter that for the second toss, and the third letter that for the third toss.

The Cartesian product set $A \times B$ is defined as the set consisting of all possible ordered pairs formed when the first element is taken from the set A

and the second element is taken from the set B. Thus, if $A = \{a,b\}$ and $B = \{c,d,e\}$, then

$$A \times B = \{(a,c), (a,d), (a,e), (b,c), (b,d), (b,e)\}.$$

Note that unless A and B are identical sets, $A \times B \neq B \times A$; thus the commutative law does not hold for Cartesian products. Note that

$$B \times A = \{(c,a), (c,b), (d,a), (d,b), (e,a), (e,b)\}.$$

The elements (ordered pairs) of $B \times A$ are not the same as those of $A \times B$; the orders are reversed.

As another example, consider $A = \{H,T\}$. Then

$$A \times A = \{HH, HT, TH, TT\}.$$

The elements of A represent the possible outcomes when a coin is tossed, and the elements of $A \times A$ represent the possible outcomes for either two successive tosses of a coin or for the toss of a pair of coins.

The Cartesian product set $A_1 \times A_2 \times A_3 \times \cdots \times A_k$ is defined as the set consisting of all possible ordered k-tuples formed when the first element is taken from set A_1, the second element from set A_2, , , and the kth element from A_k.

From the preceding two illustrations, it would appear that the number of elements in $A \times B$ equals the product of the number in A and the number in B, $2 \times 3 = 6$, and that the number in $A \times A$ equals the number in A, squared, $2 \times 2 = 4$. In fact, one may prove the following:

Theorem. If the set A_i contains n_i elements, where $i = 1, 2, \ldots k$, the number of elements contained in the Cartesian product set $A_1 \times A_2 \times \cdots A_k$ equals $n_1 n_2 \cdots n_k$.

The proof is quite simple. The first member of an ordered k-tuple can be selected from any one of the n_1 members in A_1; the second member can be selected from any one of the n_2 elements in A_2. That is, for any choice from A_1 there are n_2 choices from A_2; hence, the first two elements can be chosen in $n_1 \times n_2$ ways. The third element can be chosen in n_3 ways, any one of which can be placed with any one of the $n_1 \times n_2$ ordered pairs from $A_1 \times A_2$; hence, the first three elements can be chosen in $n_1 \times n_2 \times n_3$ ways. Clearly, this reasoning can be extended to all k sets. A completely rigorous proof may be obtained by mathematical induction but will not be included here.

The exposition of this theorem is aided by a *tree diagram*, a useful graphical device which we shall meet again. (See Section 4.5.) For example,

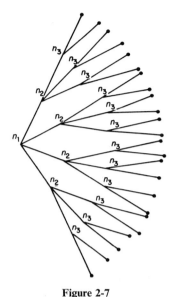

Figure 2-7

if $n_1 = 4$, $n_2 = 3$, and $n_3 = 2$, the tree assumes the form shown in Fig. 2-7. It is easily seen that the tree has $4 \times 3 \times 2$ or 24 branches emanating at the right.

Example. If a student may elect any one of five courses at nine o'clock, any one of three courses at ten o'clock, and any one of four courses at two o'clock, he may choose his three courses in 60 different ways, for each triple of course elections is an element of a Cartesian product set having $5 \times 3 \times 4$ elements.

2.6. PARTITIONS

A useful device for studying subsets of a larger or universal set is the partition. To illustrate this concept, let us assume that a club composed of 20 adults had the composition of its membership analyzed and exhibited the following data:

(a) Marital status: 10 married persons, 6 single women, 4 bachelors.
(b) Sex: 12 men, 8 women.
(c) Voting preference: 10 Democrats, 8 Republicans, 2 Independents.
(d) Educational background: 10 college graduates, 5 incomplete college education (no degree), 4 high school diploma only, 1 incomplete high school education.

Note that each of these four classifications has three simple but important characteristics. Take, for example, the marital status. (i) Each class, such as bachelors, is a subset of the larger set called the club. (ii) No member of the club belongs to two of the subsets comprising the marital classification. (iii) The three subsets constitute the entire club. Each of the other three categories—sex, voting preference, and educational background—possesses the same three characteristics. Mathematically, we state that the set of persons called the club has been partitioned in four different ways. Of course, we might add other ways: By age groups, church affiliations, residential sections, and so on. We now state the definition of a partition.

Let $E_1, E_2, , , E_n$, be subsets of the set S. These subsets are said to form a partition of S if the following properties are true:

(i) *Each E_i is a proper subset of S, that is,*

$$E_i \subset S, \qquad i = 1, 2, , , , n \quad but \quad E_i \neq S.$$

(ii) *The union of all the subsets E_i is S, that is,*
$$E_1 \cup E_2 \cup \cdots \cup E_n = S.$$
(iii) *The subsets E_i are pairwise disjoint, that is,*
$$E_i \cap E_j = \varnothing, \qquad i,j = 1, 2, 3, \,,\, n, \, i \neq j.$$

EXAMPLE 1. Let $U = \{a,b,c,d,e,f,g\}$. Then $E_1 = \{a,b\}$, $E_2 = \{c,d,e,f\}$, and $E_3 = \{g\}$ form a partition of U, because

  (i) $E_1 \subset U$, $E_2 \subset U$,   and $E_3 \subset U$.
  (ii) $E_1 \cup E_2 \cup E_3 = U$.
  (iii) $E_1 \cap E_2 = \varnothing$, $E_1 \cap E_3 = \varnothing$,   and $E_2 \cap E_3 = \varnothing$.

EXAMPLE 2. Suppose that we toss a pair of dice and note the sum of the dots appearing. Let $S = \{$all possible sums$\}$, $E_1 = \{$odd sums$\}$, $E_2 = \{$sums obtained when the dice show like faces$\}$, and $E_3 = \{$even sums obtained when the dice show unlike faces$\}$. Do E_1, E_2, and E_3 form a partition of S?

First, we observe that, although the two dice might look alike if they happen to be of the same size, material, and color, they nevertheless are different dice; so a sum such as 7, for example, may be obtained by a 3 on one die and a 4 on the other, or vice versa. We can symbolize these possibilities by means of the ordered pairs (3,4) and (4,3).

Since the first die can show any one of six different faces and for any one of these showing, the second die can also show any one of six different faces, there are 6 × 6 or 36 different ways in which the pair of dice can appear. These are given by the Cartesian product set, $D \times D$, where $D = \{1,2,3,4,5,6\}$.

$$D \times D = \{(1,1), (1,2), (1,3), (1,4), (1,5), (1,6), (2,1), (2,2), (2,3),$$
$$(2,4), (2,5), (2,6), (3,1), (3,2), (3,3), (3,4), (3,5), (3,6), (4,1), (4,2),$$
$$(4,3), (4,4), (4,5), (4,6), (5,1), (5,2), (5,3), (5,4), (5,5), (5,6), (6,1),$$
$$(6,2), (6,3), (6,4), (6,5), (6,6)\}.$$

From these we find that for possible sums,
$$S = \{2,3,4,5,6,7,8,9,10,11,12\}.$$

The odd sums are produced by the ordered pairs:

    (1,2), (1,4), (1,6), (2,1), (2,3), (2,5), (3,2), (3,4), (3,6), (4,1), (4,3),
    (4,5), (5,2), (5,4), (5,6), (6,1), (6,3), (6,5),
hence
$$E_1 = \{3,5,7,9,11\}.$$

The elements of E_2 stem from the pairs:

    (1,1), (2,2), (3,3), (4,4), (5,5), (6,6),
hence
$$E_2 = \{2,4,6,8,10,12\}.$$

The elements of E_3 stem from the ordered pairs:

$$(1,3), (1,5), (2,4), (2,6), (3,1), (3,5), (4,2), (4,6), (5,1), (5,3), (6,2), (6,4),$$

therefore

$$E_3 = \{4,6,8,10\}.$$

Condition (i) is satisfied for

$$E_1 \subset S, E_2 \subset S, \text{ and } E_3 \subset S.$$

Also, condition (ii) holds for $E_1 \cup E_2 \cup E_3 = S$. However, although $E_1 \cap E_2 = \varnothing$ and $E_1 \cap E_3 = \varnothing$, condition (iii) does not hold because $E_2 \cap E_3 = \{4,6,8,10\} \neq \varnothing$. Therefore, E_1, E_2, and E_3 do not constitute a partition of S.

2.7. THE DERIVATION OF SETS FROM OTHER SETS

In Section 2.5, we saw how sets of ordered pairs can be derived by forming Cartesian products. We shall often have under consideration a universal set from which we wish to form certain kinds of subsets or sets of ordered k-tuples. Also, we may wish to calculate the numbers of elements in these derived sets. Such calculations are frequently performed with the aid of some very useful formulas which we shall now develop.

2.8. FACTORIALS

We define *factorial N*, symbolized by $N!$, as $N(N-1)(N-2)\cdots 3 \cdot 2 \cdot 1$ where N is assumed to be a positive integer. Thus, $4! = 4 \cdot 3 \cdot 2 \cdot 1 = 24$ and $7! = 7 \cdot 6 \cdot 5 \cdot 4 \cdot 3 \cdot 2 \cdot 1 = 5040$. It follows that:

$$4! = 4 \cdot 3!$$
$$3! = 3 \cdot 2!$$
$$2! = 2 \cdot 1!$$

and if we carry this process forward in a mechanical manner, we should write:

$$1! = 1 \cdot 0!$$

In order for the symbol $0!$ to have meaning, it would seem that we should let $0! = 1!/1 = 1$. We shall therefore define $0!$ as equal to 1.

2.9. PERMUTATIONS AND COMBINATIONS

Each ordered group of elements is called a *permutation*. An unordered group of elements is called a *combination*. Thus the set $\{a,b,c\}$ can be viewed as a combination. If we form all possible different ordered triples from the elements of this set we obtain the following: (a,b,c), (a,c,b), (b,a,c), (b,c,a), (c,a,b), (c,b,a). Each of the six groups contains the same combination of letters, but each has a different arrangement from the others. There are represented, therefore, six different permutations of the same three letters, but only one combination of three.

On the other hand, if from the three letters abc we choose two letters at a time, we can make six ordered pairs or permutations, namely, ab, ba, ac, ca, bc, and cb. But the pairs ab and ba constitute the same combination of letters; likewise for ac and ca, and for bc and cb. Therefore only three combinations are possible, if we take only two letters at a time.

2.10. FUNDAMENTAL THEOREMS ON PERMUTATIONS

The number of distinct permutations of r objects taken from a set of N objects is:

$$P(N,r) = N!/(N - r)!. \tag{2.1}$$

This theorem may also be stated in the following form:

The number of different ordered r-tuples that can be selected from a set of N elements is given by formula (2.1).

Proof. We can choose the first element in N ways. Having chosen it in a given way, we can choose the second element in any one of the remaining $(N - 1)$ ways. Having chosen the first two elements, we have $(N - 2)$ left from which to choose the third. We continue in this manner until we choose the rth element in any one of $(N - \overline{r - 1})$ ways. By the theorem of Section 2.5, we conclude that the r elements may be selected in

$$N(N - 1)(N - 2) \cdots (N - \overline{r - 1})$$

ways. Since the next factor in order in this product would be $N - r$, we multiply this product by $(N - r)!/(N - r)!$ to obtain

$$\frac{N(N - 1)(N - 2) \cdots (N - \overline{r - 1})(N - r)!}{(N - r)!}.$$

But the numerator is equivalent to $N!$; hence, we have derived formula **(2.1)**.

Example. If five sprinters compete in the final race of a 100-yard dash, in how many ways may three prizes be won?

Here, the order in which they finish determines, of course, the first, second, and third prize awards. $N = 5$, $r = 3$; hence, by formula (2.1)

$$P(5,3) = 5!/2! = 60.$$

Therefore the prizes may be won in 60 different ways.

As a corollary to this theorem, we state the following:

The number of different ordered N-tuples that can be formed from a set of N elements is:

$$P(N,N) = N! \tag{2.2}$$

To prove this result we set $r = N$ in $(N - r)!$ to obtain $0! = 1$ as the denominator of formula (2.1).

The number of different ordered N-tuples that can be constructed from N elements consisting of k different groups such that n_1 elements are alike in the first group, n_2 are alike in the second group, . . . , and n_k are alike in the kth group, where $n_1 + n_2 + \cdots + n_k = N$, is given by the formula

$$P(N: n_1, n_2, \ldots, n_k) = N!/n_1! n_2! \cdots n_k!. \tag{2.3}$$

Proof. If the symbol on the left represents the desired number of ordered N-tuples (permutations), and if each n_i elements $(i = 1, 2, , , k)$ that are alike are replaced by n_i elements which are different from one another and from all the elements in the other groups, then the number of permutations of N different elements taken all at a time can be obtained by multiplying

$$P(N: n_1, n_2, , , n_k) \quad \text{and} \quad n_1! n_2! \cdots n_k!.$$

This is true because $n_i!$ represents the number of permutations possible from n_i different elements taken all at a time [formula (2.2)]. Thus,

$$P(N: n_1, n_2, , , n_k) n_1! n_2! \cdots n_k! = N!$$

whence formula (2.3) follows.

2.11. A FUNDAMENTAL THEOREM CONCERNING COMBINATIONS

The number of combinations of r objects selected from a set of N objects is:

$$C(N,r) = \frac{N!}{r!(N - r)!}. \tag{2.4}$$

This theorem may also be stated as follows:

The number of different subsets of r elements each which can be formed from a set of N elements is given by formula (2.4).

Proof. Any given combination of r different objects is susceptible to $r!$ permutations by formula (2.2); hence, if the total number of combinations is multiplied by $r!$, we obtain the total number of permutations, $P(N,r)$. Thus

$$P(N,r) = C(N,r)r!$$

whence,

$$C(N,r) = \frac{P(N,r)}{r!}$$

$$= \frac{N!}{(N-r)!r!}. \qquad (2.4)$$

EXAMPLE 1. A committee of 5 is to be chosen from a club of 12 members. In how many ways may the committee be chosen?

Solution. Since a different order of a given group of 5 does not constitute a different committee, the problem is to find the number of combinations of 5 people selected from 12. Using formula (2.4), we have

$$C(12,5) = 12!/5!7! = 792.$$

EXAMPLE 2. How many different subsets of five elements each can be formed from a set consisting of 12 elements.

Solution. This is simply another setting of the preceding example.

EXERCISES

1. Specify each of the following sets by making either a roster of its members or using the symbol $\varnothing$.
   (a) The divisors of 36 not including 1 and 36.
   (b) The coins of the United States now in use.
   (c) The even divisors of 27.
   (d) The positive unit fractions, that is, numbers of the form $1/a$ where a is a positive integer.
   (e) The regular solids.
   (f) The sum of the numbers of dots appearing when two dice are thrown.

2. Specify each of the following sets by making either a roster of its members or using the symbol $\varnothing$.
   (a) {the prime numbers between 20 and 40}.
   (b) $\{x^3 \mid x = 1,2,3,4,5\}$.
   (c) {possible numbers of heads appearing when 5 pennies are tossed}.
   (d) $\{x \mid x^2 = 3x - 2\}$.
   (e) {x is a real number $\mid x^2 = x^3$}.
   (f) {the unicorns of Africa}.

3. The members of each of the following sets are ordered k-tuples. Characterize each set by its roster.
   (a) {possible 3-digit numbers formed from 1,2, and 3}.
   (b) {possible 3-digit numbers formed from 5,5, and 7}.
   (c) {possible ordered pairs from the letters a,b,c, and d}.

4. A small regular tetrahedron has its four faces numbered 1, 2, 3, and 4. If this solid is tossed, the possible sums of the numbers appearing on the faces turned upward form a set. List the numbers of this set.

5. The genes that control the basic blood groups in man are conveniently referred to as either *A*, *B*, or *O* genes. The combination of two of these genes, one from each parent, produces a genotype of blood in the offspring. What is the set of possible genotypes?

6. Characterize each of the following sets by listing their members.
(a) {possible amounts of money that can be formed from a cent, a nickel, a dime, and a quarter}.
(b) {possible arrangements of the five signs: $+ + - + -$}.
(c) {different hands possible of three cards, each chosen from the ace, king, queen, jack, and ten of clubs}. Use symbols A, K, Q, J, and 10.

7. The *theory of runs* is frequently applied in industrial statistics. Suppose that a sample of four lamp bulbs is tested; a lamp is designated as *G* if it is a good bulb, and as *D* if it is a defective one. Characterize in roster form the set of all possible outcomes.

8. Given $U = \{v,w,x,y,z\}$; which of the following are subsets of U?
(a) $\{x,y,z\}$
(b) $\{u,v,w,x\}$
(c) $\{u,x,z\}$
(d) $\{v,w,x,y,z\}$
(e) $\varnothing$

9. Write all the subsets possible of the set $\{r,s,t\}$.

10. How many different subsets can be formed from the following?
(a) $\varnothing$
(b) $\{x_1\}$
(c) $\{x_1,x_2\}$
(d) $\{x_1,x_2,x_3\}$
(e) $\{x_1,x_2,x_3,x_4\}$
(f) Generalize these results for a set of n elements.

11. Given the sets $X = \{u,v,w,x,y,z\}$ and $Y = \{s,t,x,y,z\}$; find (a) $X \cup Y$; (b) $X \cap Y$; (c) $X \cup \varnothing$; (d) $Y \cap \varnothing$.

12. Given the sets $U = \{a,b,c,d,e,f,g,h\}$, $A = \{a,b,c,d,e\}$, and $B = \{c,d,e,f,g\}$; list the elements of the following sets: (a) $A \cup B$; (b) $A \cap B$; (c) $A \cap U$; (d) $A' \cap B'$; (e) $A' \cup B$; (f) $A' \times B'$.

13. Let $U = \{$quadrilaterals$\}$, $A = \{$parallelograms$\}$, and $B = \{$rectangles$\}$. Characterize the following sets: (a) $A \cup B$; (b) $A \cap B$; (c) $A \cap U$; (d) $B \cap U$; (e) $A \cup U$.

14. Let U represent the set of all voters in Ohio. Which of the following are subsets of U?
(a) {Republican voters in Ohio}.
(b) {Female Democratic voters in Ohio}.

(c) {Voters neither Republicans nor Democrats in Ohio}.
(d) {Male citizens of Ohio over 21 years of age}.
(e) {Women between the ages of 25 and 30 in Ohio}.

15. Which of the following are complementary sets of the given universal set U? If any are not, state why.
   (a) U = {voters of New York State}; {urban voters of New York State}; {rural voters of New York State}.
   (b) U = {quadrilaterals}; {trapezoids}; {parallelograms}.
   (c) U = {all males}; {smokers}; {nonsmokers}.
   (d) U = {rational numbers}; {integers}; {quotients of integers}.

16. Of 150 soldiers in a battle, 80 lost an eye, 70 lost an ear, and 20 escaped injury. How many lost both an eye and an ear?

17. Of 150 soldiers in a fierce battle, 80 lost an eye, 70 lost an ear, 50 lost a leg, 20 lost an eye and an ear, 25 lost an eye and a leg, 30 lost an ear and a leg, and 10 lost an eye, an ear, and a leg. How many escaped injury? (Adapted from Lewis Carroll.)

18. In a class of 30 selected science students, 20 had A in mathematics, 23 had A in chemistry, 18 had A in physics, 15 had A in mathematics and chemistry, 12 had A in mathematics and physics, and 14 had A in chemistry and physics. There were none without an A. How many had A's in all three courses?

19. An automobile agency sold 47 cars in March, 1965. Twenty-three of these had power steering, 27 had automatic shifts, and 20 had radios. Seven had power steering, automatic shifts, and radios; three had power steering and automatic shifts but no radio; two had automatic shifts and radios but no power steering; and four had power steering and radios but no automatic shifts. How many cars were sold with only one of these accessories?

20. In a test of some electric light circuits, 10 were found to be defective. Of these, seven had broken filaments, five had faulty connections, and four had broken wires. One had both a broken filament and a faulty connection, but good wires; one had a faulty connection and a broken wire but good filaments; two had both broken filaments and wires but good connections; and three had only broken filaments. (a) How many were defective by virtue of all three faults? (b) How many had broken wires only?

21. Use Venn diagrams to verify each of the following:
   (a) $(A \cap B)' = A' \cup B'$.
   (b) $A \cap (B \cup C) = (A \cap B \cup (A \cap C)$.
   (c) $A \cup (B \cup C) = (A \cup B) \cup C$.

22. If $A = \{b,c\}$ and $B = \{d,e,f,g\}$, find $A \times B$.

23. If $A = \{a,b,c,d\}$ and $B = \{e,f,g\}$, find $A \times B$.

24. If $A = \{H,T\}$, find $A \times A \times A$. Interpret your result.

25. If $C = \{r,w,b\}$ and $D = \{g,y,o\}$, find $C \times D$.

26. A small regular tetrahedron had 1, 2, 3, and 4 dots on its faces. Represent by means of a Cartesian product the possible outcomes (pairs) when the tetrahedron

is tossed twice. By an outcome we shall mean the number of dots on the face that lands downward.

27. Give reasons why each of the following sets do or do not form partitions of the set $U = \{r,s,t,u,v,w,x,y,z\}$.
   (a) $A_1 = \{r,s,t,u,v\}$, $A_2 = \{w,x\}$, $A_3 = \{y,z\}$.
   (b) $A_1 = \{r,t,v,x,z\}$, $A_2 = \{s,u,w,y\}$, $A_3 = \{x,y,z\}$.
   (c) $A_1 = \{r\}$, $A_2 = \{s,t\}$, $A_3 = \{u,v,w\}$, $A_4 = \{x,y,z\}$.

28. Do the following sets form a partition of the set $U = \{$executives in the ABC company$\}$?
   (a) $A = \{$executives with salaries under \$7000$\}$;
   (b) $B = \{$executives with salaries greater than \$7000 and less than \$10,000$\}$;
   (c) $C = \{$executives with salaries greater than \$10,000$\}$.

29. List all the possible partitions that can be formed from the set (a) $U = \{a,b,c\}$; (b) $U = \{a,b,c,d\}$. Do not include $\varnothing$.

30. Let $U = \{$all voters in town $X\}$. Which of the following form partitions of U?
   (a) {Republican voters}, {Democratic voters}, {all other voters}.
   (b) {Male voters}, {female voters}.
   (c) {Protestant voters}, {Roman Catholic voters}, {Jewish voters}.
   (d) {Those who voted in person}, {those who mailed absentee voter ballots}.

31. In example 2 of Section 2.6 replace the dice by a pair of small regular tetrahedrons with faces on each containing 1, 2, 3, and 4 dots. Discover if E_1, E_2, and E_3, modified accordingly, constitute a partition. The dots to be noted as outcomes are those on the face not showing.

32. Let $R = \{$real numbers$\}$, $A = \{$rational numbers$\}$, $B = \{$irrational numbers$\}$, $C = \{$integers$\}$, $D = \{$zero$\}$. Do A, B, C, and D form a partition of R? Why?

33. Consider the set S of possible outcomes in terms of ordered triples when three pennies are tossed.

$$S = \{HHH, HHT, HTH, THH, HTT, THT, TTH, TTT\}.$$

Partition S according to:
   (a) the frequency of occurrence of heads.
   (b) the position of the first head to appear.

34. Partition each of the following sets into at least 3 subsets.
   (a) $\{a,b,c,d,e,f,g,h\}$.
   (b) {the 52 cards of a bridge deck}.
   (c) {the sums that can appear when two dice are rolled}.
   (d) {the girls in your probability class}.

35. If a club had four candidates for president, three for vice-president, and two for secretary-treasurer, in how many ways may the officers be elected?

36. An examination contains three groups of questions. Group A contains five questions, group B, two, and group C, two. One question is to be answered from each group. In how many different ways may a student select his questions?

37. Find the number of permutations that can be made from the letters *a*, *b*, *c*, *d*, *e*, and *f* taken (a) four at a time; (b) all at a time.

38. How many different arrangements can be made from the letters of the word *distance* if we take (a) five at a time? (b) all at a time?

39. Twenty sprinters compete in a race for which there are first, second, and third prizes. In how many ways may the prizes be awarded?

40. Find the number of permutations that can be made from the letters of the word *Oshkosh* taken all at a time.

41. When a penny was tossed eight times in succession, a head appeared three times and a tail five times in the following order: *T H H T H T T T*. In how many other orders could they have appeared?

42. A true-false test consisted of ten statements of which seven were false and three were true. If a student knew this but merely guessed at the answers, in how many ways might he have listed his answers?

43. In how many ways may a committee of four be chosen from a club of nine members?

44. In an examination paper, any three questions may be omitted from the ten questions given. In how many ways may selections be made?

45. A lunch counter has seven seats in a row. If four persons, strangers to one another, occupy seats at random, in how many different ways may the three remaining seats be empty?

46. How many three-digit numbers can be formed from the digits 1, 2, 3, 4, and 5 (a) if no digits are repeated? (b) if digits may be repeated?

47. The letters *A*, *B*, and *O* are used to denote certain basic blood characteristics in man. If a person has inherited two *A* genes, one from each parent, he is designated as *AA*. If he inherits an *A* gene from one parent and an *O* gene from the other, he is designated as *AO*.   Thus we have any one of six genotypes possible, *AA*, *AO*, *BB*, *BO*, *AB*, and *OO* in any person. (a) How many different matings of genotypes are possible? (b) One such mating is illustrated by the genetic formula for the mating of *AO* with *BO*.

	$AO \times BO$	
	A	*O*
B	*AB*	*BO*
O	*OA*	*OO*

Construct at least four other genetic formulas.

48. How many different four-digit numbers can be formed from the digits 4, 5, 6, 7, 8, and 9 if repeated digits are not permitted?

49. A witness to a bank robbery said that the license number of the criminals' automobile was a six-figure number of which the first three figures were 487.   He

did not recall the last three figures but was positive that all three were different. How many automobile license numbers must the police check?

50. (a) In how many ways may an assignment of five problems be made from a group of 12 problems? (b) How many times will the most difficult problem be assigned?

51. How many different arrangements can be made of the signs from the following succession: $+ - + - - - + + -$?

52. Seven competitors enter a fancy skating contest in which first, second, and third prizes are to be awarded. In how many different ways may these prizes be given?

53. In how many ways may a committee consisting of five men and four women be chosen from 10 men and seven women?

54. Three soldiers are to be selected by lot from 10 volunteers for a dangerous mission. In how many ways may they be chosen?

55. How many different numbers can be formed from the numerals 5, 6, 6, 7, 7, 7, 8, 8, if we use them all?

3

Probability

3.1. EXPERIMENTS, EVENTS, AND RANDOM VARIABLES

In the study of mathematical probability, we are concerned with the derivation of the laws of chance and with the the outcomes they determine. Thus, if we toss a penny ten times, we can calculate the probability that no head will appear, one head will appear, two heads will appear, and so on. Likewise, if a sample of 100 Christmas tree lights are selected at random from a shipment and tested, and if we know that such lights average three per cent defective, then we can compute the probability that this sample will contain at least five defective lights. These are illustrations of experiments which can be carried out in actuality or in our imagination; and experiments are important ingredients of the processes employed in probability. The results or outcomes of such experiments are called *events*.

A *random* or *chance variable*, X, is so named because its value is determined by the result of an experiment; such results are due to the operation of unpredictable or chance causes. Probability, as well as statistics, is often defined as the study of random variables. The outcome when two dice are rolled, the length of life of a 40-watt light bulb, the number of mice dying when ten are inoculated with comparable doses of digitalis, the number of coast-to-coast calls placed in a given day in a telephone exchange—all these are chance variables. A more precise definition of a random variable is given in Section 3.4.

The variables studied in probability and statistics fall into two classes: discrete and continuous variables. A variable is *discrete* if the set of all possible values it may have is finite, that is, countable in the ordinary sense of the word, or denumerably infinite. A set is *denumerably infinite* if it is capable of being placed in one-to-one correspondence with the infinite sequence of positive integers, 1, 2, 3, , , . This means that each member of the infinite set will eventually be included in the count, since the count continues without end.

The possible outcomes in terms of sums appearing when two dice are rolled comprise the finite set (Section 2.6)

$$\{2,3,4,5,6,7,8,9,10,11,12\}.$$

The possible outcomes (number dying) when 10 mice are given dosages form the finite set

$$\{0,1,2,3,4,5,6,7,8,9,10\}.$$

The set of possible frequencies of coast-to-coast telephone calls might be

$$\{0,1,2, , , 300\}$$

if 300 is the long-distance capacity of the telephone exchange. The number of tosses necessary to give to five coins before all of them show heads simultaneously form the denumerably infinite set

$$\{1,2,3, , ,\}$$

since, conceivably, we might never succeed in obtaining all heads on a throw of five coins.

Just now the study of probability will be restricted to discrete random variables. Later, in Chapter 9, we shall discuss continuous random variables and some of their more important probability laws. For the present, we might note that man's stature is a continuous variable since, as it increases from one given height, say 62 inches, to another, say 65 inches, it assumes all possible numerical values between 62 and 65. Such possible values could be represented by all the points on a line segment from 62 to 65. A similar property is characteristic of lives of light bulbs, weights of potatoes, concentrations of a salt solution, and ages of men and women, to state but a few examples.

3.2. SAMPLE SPACE

Since random events are the results of chance and vary from observation to observation or from experiment to experiment, we shall employ the symbol X for a random variable and x, for the actual value of X.

Let us take some illustrations. Let the number of dots that could appear when a die is rolled be represented by X. The values of X are limited to 1, 2, 3, 4, 5, and 6. The set of possible outcomes is, therefore,

$$S = \{1,2,3,4,5,6\}.$$

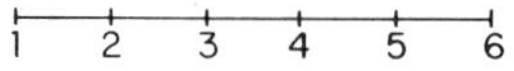

Figure 3-1

This set of numerals could be represented by points on a line as in Fig. 3-1. Such a set or such a configuration of points representing all possible events is called an event space or, more commonly, a *sample space* which we shall usually denote by S. Each element represents a simple event or outcome, so that a simple event is a unit subset of S. The outcome "x is even," we might denote by

$$E = \{2\} \cup \{4\} \cup \{6\}$$

or

$$E = \{2,4,6\}$$

which is a proper subset of S, $E \subset S$. This outcome constitutes a compound event, so that a compound event is a union of two or more simple events. *Thus, any event, simple or compound, is merely a subset of S.*

Let us take another illustration. A machine tests the dimension of a critical element in an instrument automatically. If the dimension is correct, a green light flashes (g); if it is not, a red light flashes (r). A sample space for the testing of three such elements might be defined as the set of ordered triples:

$$S = \{ggg, ggr, grg, rgg, grr, rgr, rrg, rrr\}.$$

This, however, is not a unique sample space for this experiment because our interest might be only in the number of possible faulty elements. Then

$$S = \{0,1,2,3\}.$$

A third illustration arises if we make a random toss of two pennies and observe each pair of outcomes. Four simple events may occur: they may both show tails, the first may show a tail and the other a head, the other may show a tail and the first one a head, or both may show heads. These four simple events may be symbolized by TT, TH, HT, and HH respectively. Another useful method of designating them is by means of the ordered pairs (x,y), where $x = 0$ or 1 and $y = 0$ or 1, so that

$$S = \{(0,0), (0,1), (1,0), (1,1)\}$$

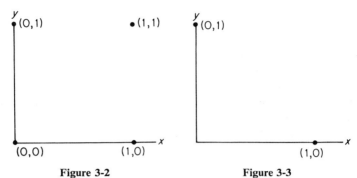

Figure 3-2   **Figure 3-3**

or

$$S = \{(x,y) \mid x = 0,1; y = 0,1\}$$

where the first digit in each pair represents the number of heads appearing on penny A and the second represents the number of heads appearing on penny B. These pairs of numbers may be plotted as points (x,y) on a plane (Fig. 3-2). Such a configuration or set of ordered pairs constitutes a sample space for the experiment of tossing two pennies. These four points represent all possible outcomes and the geometric sample space is conveniently chosen as two-dimensional.

As an example of a compound event, we may consider the possibilities that the two pennies show differently. This compound event, the appearance of different faces, may occur in two ways, by means of the two simple

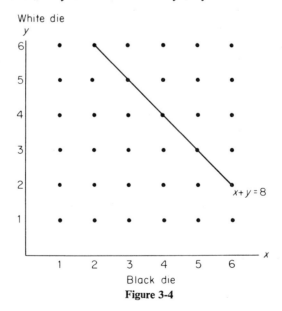

Figure 3-4

White die

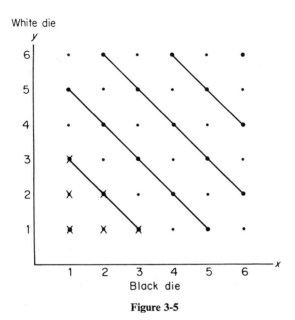

Black die

Figure 3-5

events: *TH* or (0,1) and *HT* or (1,0). The compound event is thus represented by a portion or subset of the sample space as shown in Fig. 3-3.

Consider next, the experiment of throwing a pair of dice; say one is black, the other, white. Note that the difference in color merely emphasizes the fact that they are different dice. There will be 36 simple events possible, namely those given by the Cartesian product set, $D \times D$ where $D = \{1,2,3,4,5,6\}$ as discussed in Section 2.6. The totality of such possible outcomes may be represented by the sample space of Fig. 3-4, consisting of the lattice of 6×6 or 36 points. As an example of a compound event for a pair of dice, we consider "the sum 8." This sum may be obtained in only the following ways:

Black die	White die
x	*y*
2	6
6	2
3	5
5	3
4	4

Thus there are five simple events constituting the compound event, "the sum 8." The subset $\{(2,6), (6,2), (3,5), (5,3), (4,4)\}$ of points lying on the diagonal from (2,6) to (6,2) represents the compound event, $x + y = 8$.

As another illustration, we may consider first the compound event "an even sum" ($x + y =$ an even number). This is represented by the larger dots in Fig. 3-5 lying on the alternate diagonals extending downward from left to right. Secondly, "a sum less than 5" ($x + y < 5$) is pictured by means of the six crossed dots in the lower left-hand corner. Finally, the compound event, "an even number sum less than 5" is shown by means of the dots both large and crossed. These dots constitute the intersection of the two subsets, $\{x + y = \text{an even number}\}$ and $\{x + y < 5\}$.

For the remainder of this book, we shall use the words "element" and "point" of sample space interchangeably, for it is frequently convenient to conceive of sets and subsets of elements as aggregates of geometric points.

3.3. CONTINUOUS SAMPLE SPACE

It might be helpful to examine briefly a sample space for a continuous variable. Let X stand for the number of years of age of a husband. Let us further assume that there are no husbands younger than 15 nor older than 100 years. Then the sample space for ages of husbands may be defined as

$$H = \{15 \leq x \leq 100\}, x \text{ a real number}$$

and represented by all points on the x-axis from 15 to 100 (Fig. 3-6). If we make a similar convention for ages of wives,

$$W = \{15 \leq y \leq 100\}, y \text{ a real number}$$

(points on the Y-axis from 15 to 100), then the sample space S, for ages of married couples is the set

$$S = \{(x,y) \mid 15 \leq x \leq 100, 15 \leq y \leq 100\}, x, y \text{ real numbers.}$$

This is conveniently represented by all points within the rectangle bounded by the two vertical lines at $x = 15$ and $x = 100$, and by the two horizontal lines at $y = 15$ and $y = 100$.

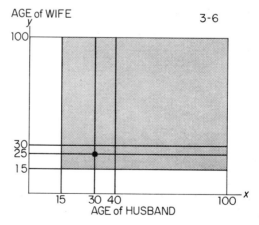

Figure 3-6

The simple event for a couple, "husband of age 30 and wife of age 25," is represented by the single point (30,25). The compound event, "husbands between 30 and 40 with wives between 25 and 30," is represented by the subset of points in the small rectangle shown in Fig. 3-6. The compound event, "married couples with husbands older than 40 and wives older than 30," is represented by the subset of points in the upper right-hand rectangle.

3.4. RANDOM VARIABLES AND PROBABILITY

A random variable X is a function defined over a sample space S: $\{e_1, e_2, , , e_n\}$. This means that to each element e_i of S there corresponds a unique real number, namely, the value of X. Thus we may write

$$X(e_i) = x_i.$$

The outcome e_i determines one and only one value of the function which we shall call x_i.

For example, a random variable might be the number of heads appearing when two pennies are tossed. Then

$$S = \{HH, HT, TH, TT\}$$

or better,

$$S = \{(1,1), (1,0), (0,1), (0,0)\}.$$

Then

$$X(1,1) = 2, \ X(1,0) = 1, \ X(0,1) = 1, \quad \text{and} \quad X(0,0) = 0.$$

As another example, when two dice are rolled the sample space consists of 36 ordered pairs (see Section 2.6). If the random variable X is the sum of dots appearing, then

$$X(1,1) = 2, \ X(1,2) = X(2,1) = 3$$

$$X(1,3) = X(3,1) = X(2,2) = 4$$

and so on. Note that each outcome always determines one and only one value of the random variable X, but a given value of X may correspond to more than one outcome.

It should be observed that often $X(e_i) = e_i$. Thus, when 10 mice are given dosages, the possible outcomes (number dying) form the set

$$\{0, 1, 2, , , 9, 10\}$$

and each element of this set is a possible value of the random variable X, the number dying.

If we return to the sample space for the tossing of two pennies (Fig. 3-2), we sense intuitively that any one of the four possible outcomes TT, TH, HT,

HH, is as likely to happen as any other; and therefore, it seems reasonable to assign the same probability number to each of these outcomes. In fact, if we were to toss a pair of pennies a large number of times, say 1000, we would find that each of the four possible events would occur roughly about 250 times or about 25% of the time, provided the pennies were not badly worn, mutilated, or otherwise biased. On the other hand, when the author repeatedly tossed a pair of thumb tacks on to a table top and recorded the number of occurrences of each of the four possible outcomes, *DD, DU, UD, UU*, where *D* symbolizes "point down" and *U*, "point up," he found that "point up" occurred less frequently than "point down," so that he felt confident that these four events were not equally likely. In this case, to each possible outcome or sample point we could not reasonably assign the same probability number. In an experiment with 100 tosses, the author made preliminary estimates of probabilities as follows: $P(DD) = 0.34$, $P(DU) = 0.25$, $P(UD) = 0.21$, $P(UU) = 0.20$.

In view of the foregoing remarks, we shall now more formally assume that every conceivable outcome or simple event corresponds to just one point in sample space, and that every compound event corresponds to a subset of two or more sample points belonging to the sample space. For the discrete case:

The probability $P(E_i)$ of a simple event E_i will be defined as a non-negative number associated with a point E_i of sample space S such that

$$P(E_1) + P(E_2) + \cdots + P(E_n) = 1$$

where

$$S = E_1 \cup E_2 \cup \cdots \cup E_n.$$

Thus, for the toss of two pennies,

$$P(TT) + P(TH) + P(HT) + P(HH) = \frac{1}{4} + \frac{1}{4} + \frac{1}{4} + \frac{1}{4} = 1.$$

For the toss of two thumb tacks,

$$P(DD) + P(DU) + P(UD) + P(UU) = 0.34 + 0.25 + 0.21 + 0.20 = 1.$$

Here the four probabilities are suggested by the author's experiment but cannot be regarded as accurate.

The preceding definition of probability is extended to include countably infinite sample spaces where, above, *n* becomes infinite.

In many cases, a probability number cannot be assigned to a simple event by any process of inspection or geometric analysis, as we do in the case of a penny or a die. Instead, we assume that if *N* is the number of repetitions made under identical conditions, and *f*, the frequency of occurrence of an event *E*, then for large *N*, the ratio f/N is defined as $P(E)$. The vast field of insurance—life, casualty, medical, etc.—is built upon probabilities defined in just this manner.

Examples of "probability numbers" assigned to simple events follow:

(a) The probability that a penny shows head is $\frac{1}{2}$.
(b) The probability that two pennies both show heads is $\frac{1}{4}$.
(c) The probability that a pair of dice, one black, the other white, shows 3 on the black die and 5 on the white, is $\frac{1}{36}$.

The reader may wish to refer to the appropriate space diagrams in order to see the reasons for defining the probabilities in (b) and (c).

If a compound event A consists of the simple events E_1, E_2, , , E_k, that is, if $A = E_1 \cup E_2 \cup \cdots \cup E_k$, we define its probability $P(A)$ by means of the equation:

$$P(A) = P(E_1) + P(E_2) + \cdots + P(E_k).$$

The following are examples of this definition.

(d) For the toss of two pennies, the probability that they show the same faces is $P = P(HH) + P(TT) = \frac{1}{4} + \frac{1}{4} = \frac{1}{2}$.

(e) In the toss of a pair of dice, the probability of obtaining the sum 6 is:

$$P(x = 6) = P(1,5) + P(5,1) + P(2,4) + P(4,2) + P(3,3)$$

$$= \frac{1}{36} + \frac{1}{36} + \frac{1}{36} + \frac{1}{36} + \frac{1}{36}$$

$$= \frac{5}{36}.$$

(f) For a pair of dice, the probability of obtaining a sum less than 13 is:

$$P(x + y < 13) = P(x + y = 2) + P(x + y = 3) + \cdots$$
$$+ P(x + y = 12)$$
$$= P(1,1) + [P(1,2) + P(2,1)] + [P(1,3) + P(3,1)$$
$$+ P(2,2)] + \cdots + P(6,6) = 1$$

and the probability of obtaining the sum 13 is:

(g) $P(x + y = 13) = 0$.

It is evident that mathematical probability is a number restricted to values from 0 to 1 inclusive. In symbols,

$$0 \leq P(A) \leq 1.$$

In (f) the probability, 1, is associated with certainty: a sum less than 13 *must* occur when a pair of dice is thrown. In (g) the probability of an impossible event is zero.

It seems wise at this point to clarify some of the last statements. Since an event is defined as a subset of sample space and the null set $\varnothing$ is always such a subset, we state:

(i) If $E = \varnothing$, then $P(\varnothing) = 0$, and the event E is said to be impossible.
(ii) If $E = S$, then $P(S) = 1$, and the event E is said to be certain.

Note, however, that in (i) we did not say that if $P(E) = 0$, the event is necessarily impossible. The reason for this seeming paradox is that, in dealing with a continuous sample space where the number of possible outcomes is infinite, the probability of obtaining any one particular simple outcome is zero although that outcome is not an impossible one. To illustrate more concretely, consider all the real numbers between 0 and 1; they are infinite and nondenumerable. Let these numbers be represented by points on a line segment from 0 to 1. (Fig. 3-7) If we conceive of an infinitely thin needle dropped at random across this line segment, the probability that its intersection with the line segment corresponds to some definite number such as, say, 0.73723 is zero, since this is merely one among an infinity of numbers between 0 and 1. Note that $E = \{0.73723\} \neq \varnothing$, but $P(E) = 0$.

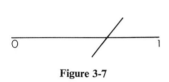

Figure 3-7

3.5. FURTHER EXAMPLES

It should become clear from some of the examples given in Section 3.4, that a common type of sample space is one in which all the points are assigned the same probability. Thus, for the toss of two unbiased pennies, each event $\{TT\}$, $\{TH\}$, $\{HT\}$, and $\{HH\}$ is assigned a probability of $\frac{1}{4}$. For the roll of a pair of dice, each of the 36 points of the sample space is assigned a probability of $\frac{1}{36}$. In many problems where there is no valid reason for assuming otherwise, the points of an appropriate sample space will be given the same probability number. Once the sample space has been properly defined, there remains essentially a counting problem: the count of the points in the sample space so that probabilities may be assigned, and the count of the points in the subset, the event.

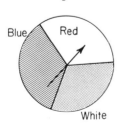

Figure 3-8

(i) A dial, shown in Fig. 3-8, is divided into three equal sectors, one painted red, one white, and the other blue. A pointer, pivoted at the center of the dial, is given two successive spins. What is the probability that it points to the same color each time?

The sample space consists of nine points or color pairs which we shall symbolize by means of the initial letters of the colors.

$$S = \{RR, RW, RB, WW, WR, WB, BB, BW, BR\}$$

$$E = \{RR, WW, BB\}$$

Since the sectors are all equal, and the outcome of a spin is entirely due to chance and does not affect the next spin, we assign a probability of $\frac{1}{9}$ to each of the nine points of S. Then

$$P(E) = \frac{3}{9} = \frac{1}{3}.$$

(ii) If a hand of five cards is dealt from a well-shuffled, standard, 52-card deck, what is the probability that it contains three diamonds and two clubs?

The number of possible hands (combinations) of five cards each is given as 52!/5!47! or 2,598,960. It is natural to assume that any combination of five cards is as likely to be dealt as any other; hence, each point of the sample space has a probability of 1/2,598,960 attached to it. The number of ways in which a combination of three diamonds can arise from thirteen diamonds is $C(13,3) = 13!/3!10!$. Similarly, for clubs $C(13,2) = 13!/2!11!$. Then the event, "three diamonds and two clubs," consists of a subset of (13!/3!10!) × (13!/2!11!) points. The probability sought is, therefore,

$$\frac{13!}{3!10!} \times \frac{13!}{2!11!} \bigg/ \frac{52!}{5!47!} = \frac{429}{49,980} = 0.00858.$$

(iii) In Section 3.2, we defined S for the machine testing of three elements

$$S = \{ggg, ggr, grg, rgg, grr, rgr, rrg, rrr\}.$$

If the three elements are chosen at random from a production line, the expectation is that most of the elements will have the correct dimensions and, hence, the light will flash green. Suppose that, as a rule, 5% of the elements are found to be defective. What is the probability that in a test of three random elements, not more than one is found defective? Here,

$$E = \{ggg, ggr, grg, rgg\}.$$

The eight points of S do not have equal probabilities. The probability for all three to have correct dimensions is much greater than the probability for all three to have incorrect dimensions. For reasons to be discussed in the next chapter (see exercise 4.36), the respective probabilities to be assigned to the triples of S listed before are, computed to four-place decimals,

0.8574, 0.0451, 0.0451, 0.0451, 0.0024, 0.0024, 0.0024, 0.0001.

Note that these probabilities add to unity as they should. The required answer is:

$$P(E) = 0.8574 + 0.0451 + 0.0451 + 0.0451 = 0.9927.$$

EXERCISES

1. A die has three faces numbered 1, two faces numbered 2, and one face numbered 3. Make a diagram of the sample space for the possible outcomes when the die is thrown. Label each point with its appropriate probability.

2. Two dice have the same color on opposite faces of each and the colors red, white, and blue appear on each die. Construct a sample space diagram of the possible color outcomes when the pair of dice is thrown. What is the probability (a) that they show different colors? (b) that white does not show?

3. Three unbiased pennies are tossed. (a) Write the sample space for this experiment as triples of letters as, for example, *HHT*. What is the probability that (b) just two tails show? (c) at least two tails show? (d) at least two of the same face show?

4. A committee of three is to be selected from five people, A, B, C, D, and E. Specify a sample space and assign appropriate probabilities to its elements. What is the probability that (a) B is selected? (b) A and B are selected? (c) neither A nor C is selected?

5. Two objects A and B are distributed at random in three numbered cells. Specify an appropriate sample space for this experiment. Use subscripts to denote the cell numbers, e.g., A_1B_3 means that A is in cell 1 and B in cell 3. What is the probability that (a) cell 2 is left empty? (b) two cells are left empty?

6. Three objects A, B, and C are distributed in two numbered cells. Specify an appropriate sample space for this experiment. Use subscripts as suggested in the previous exercise. What is the probability that (a) cell 2 is left empty? (b) A and B are in the same cell?

7. Refer to exercise 9.1 and find the probability that an employee chosen at random from the group has a salary (a) between $8000 and $10,000; (b) greater than $12,000.

8. Refer to exercise 7.4 and calculate the probability that a student chosen at random had more than three mistakes. Which would be more probable: that this student had more than two or fewer than two mistakes?

9. What is the probability that the toss of three coins shows all three heads or all three tails?

10. What is the probability that the throw of two dice is (a) 8? (b) under 5? (c) greater than 8?

11. If a pair of dice is tossed, what is the probability that the sum is either 5 or 6?

12. What is the probability of obtaining the sum 11 when three dice are tossed?

13. In dealing a hand of five cards from a standard deck, what is the probability that they are all spades?

14. In dealing a hand of four cards from a standard deck, what is the probability that they are all of different suits?

15. A pair of dice is tossed. What is the probability that an odd number of dots appears on each die?

16. A student is asked to name the kind of taste three different drugs have— tart, sweet, or bitter, each of which is present in one of the drugs. He has no knowledge of drugs and has a defective sense of taste so he guesses. What is the probability that he guesses all three correctly?

17. From a group consisting of six men and four women, a committee of three is to be chosen by lot. What is the probability that (a) all three are men? (b) two are men and one is a woman?

18. A box contains nine tags numbered consecutively from 1 to 9. If two tags are drawn at random, what is the probability that the sum of their numbers is 10?

19. A committee of four men is to be chosen by lot from seven men, two of whom are brothers. What is the probability that (a) the brothers are on the committee? (b) at least one of the brothers is on the committee?

20. A bag contains three red balls, four white balls, and five blue balls, all of the same size and material. If three balls are drawn at random, what is the probability of drawing a patriotic combination of them?

21. What is the probability that of six cards taken from a bridge deck, three will be black and three red?

22. Six dice are thrown. What is the probability that all faces shown are different from one another?

23. If the letters *a b c c d* are rearranged at random, what is the probability that the *c*'s stand together?

24. "A lady declares that, by tasting a cup of tea made with milk, she can discriminate whether the milk or the tea infusion was first added to the cup." An experiment consisting of mixing eight cups of tea, four in one way and four in another, and presenting the cups in random order to the subject is carried out. If a subject has no faculty of discrimination, what is the probability that she judges each cup correctly? (From Fisher, R.A., *The Design of Experiments*, 2nd ed., London: Oliver and Boyd, 1937. p. 13.)

25. A committee of five men is drawn by lot from eight Americans, five Englishmen, and three Frenchmen. What is the probability that the committee will be composed of two Americans, two Englishmen, and one Frenchman?

4

Probability Theorems

4.1. ADDITION THEOREMS OF PROBABILITY

Let $P(A)$ and $P(B)$ be the probabilities for two events, A and B. Then $P(A \cup B)$ denotes the probability that either A or B occurs or both occur. Let the events A and B be represented by points of the two regions marked A and B within the sample space S, as shown in Fig. 4-1. These two regions or subsets, we shall assume, have a common portion, or intersection, $A \cap B$. With each point is associated a probability. The sum of the probabilities for the points in A yield $P(A)$, and the sum for the points in B yield $P(B)$. Then

Theorem 4.1.

$$P(A \cup B) = P(A) + P(B) - P(A \cap B) \quad (4.1)$$

where $P(A \cap B)$ designates the probability for both A and B to occur. The addition of the probabilities $P(A)$ and $P(B)$ results in including the points of $A \cap B$ twice; hence,

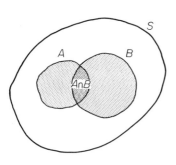

Figure 4-1.

$P(A \cap B)$ must be subtracted from the sum $P(A) + P(B)$. Equation (4.1) may be called the *either-or* theorem of probability.

If A and B are disjoint sets so that $A \cap B = \varnothing$, they cannot occur simultaneously; they are defined to be *mutually exclusive* events, and

$$P(A \cap B) = 0.$$

In this case, the either-or theorem reduces to the *addition theorem*, sometimes called the theorem of *total probability*;

Theorem 4.2.

$$P(A \cup B) = P(A) + P(B). \qquad (4.2)$$

Here the two regions A and B in Fig. 4-2 have no points in common. This theorem is essentially the same as the definition of a compound event as given in Section 3.4.

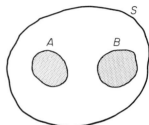

EXAMPLE 1. What is the probability that in the toss of two dice we obtain the sum 7 or 11?

Figure 4-2

It is helpful to recall first the set of 36 ordered pairs defined by the Cartesian product set $D \times D$ in Section 2.6, which set constitutes a sample space for the toss of two dice. From this set of 36 points (x,y), we find that the sum 7 is given by any member of the subset A, of six points, where

$$A = \{x + y = 7\} - \{(1,6), (6,1), (2,5), (5,2), (3,4), (4,3)\}$$

and that the sum 11 is given by either member of the subset B, of two points

$$B = \{x + y = 11\} = \{(5,6), (6,5)\}.$$

Therefore $P(A) = \frac{6}{36}$ and $P(B) = \frac{2}{36}$. These two sets are disjoint or, in other words, the events are mutually exclusive; hence Eq. (4.2) applies:

$$P(A \cup B) = \frac{6}{36} + \frac{2}{36} = \frac{2}{9}.$$

The geometric representation of the sample space $S = D \times D$ is shown in Fig. 3-4.

EXAMPLE 2. What is the probability that in the toss of two dice we obtain an even sum or a sum less than five?

It is helpful to refer to Section 3.2 and Fig. 3-5.

$$P(A) = P(x + y = \text{an even number}) = \frac{18}{36} = \frac{1}{2},$$

because the 18 larger points in the sample space correspond to an even sum and each point has a probability of $\frac{1}{36}$ attached to it.

$$P(B) = P(x + y < 5) = \frac{6}{36} = \frac{1}{6}$$

because the six crossed points correspond to sums less than 5.

$$P(A \cap B) = \frac{4}{36} = \frac{1}{9}$$

because the points both crossed and large correspond to the simultaneous occurrence of A and B. By the either-or theorem,

$$P(A \cup B) = \frac{18}{36} + \frac{6}{36} - \frac{4}{36} = \frac{5}{9}.$$

In many problems, it will not be necessary to list the elements of the sets involved in order to obtain probabilities; but whenever there is the slightest doubt concerning the constituency of such sets, they should be spelled out in roster form.

A generalization of Eq. (4.1) is:

$$P(E_1 \cup E_2 \cup \cdots \cup E_n) = \sum_{i=1}^{n} P(E_i) - \sum_{i,j=1}^{n} P(E_i \cap E_j)$$

$$+ \sum_{i,j,k=1}^{n} P(E_i \cap E_j \cap E_k) - \cdots \pm P(E_1 \cap E_2 \cap \cdots \cap E_n) \quad \textbf{(4.1a)}$$

where

$$1 \le i < j < k \le n,$$

and of Eq. (4.2)

$$P(E_1 \cup E_2 \cup \cdots \cup E_n) = P(E_1) + P(E_2) + \cdots + P(E_n)^{(1)} \quad \textbf{(4.2a)}$$

The proof of Eq. (4.1a) is left an exercise for the student. (See exercise 8.) The proof of Eq. (4.2a) follows.

We make use of the method of mathematical induction. Equation (4.2a) has been shown to be true for $n = 2$. Assume that it is true for $n = k$ and let us prove that it must then be true for $n = k + 1$. Thus we assume that

$$P(E_1 \cup E_2 \cup \cdots E_k) = P(E_1) + P(E_2) + \cdots + P(E_k) \quad \textbf{(4.3)}$$

Let E denote the event $E_1 \cup E_2 \cup \cdots \cup E_k$. Then

$$P(E \cup E_{k+1}) = P(E) + P(E_{k+1})$$

by Eq. (4.2). This last equation may be written

$$P(E_1 \cup E_2 \cup \cdots \cup E_k \cup E_{k+1}) = P(E_1 \cup E_2 \cup \cdots \cup E_k) + P(E_{k+1})$$

$$= P(E_1) + P(E_2) + \cdots + P(E_k) + P(E_{k+1})$$

---

[1] Students not familiar with the Σ notation for sums should read Section 6.5. In order to amplify the definition there, we note that when $n = 3$, Eq. (4.1a) becomes

$$P(E_1 \cup E_2 \cup E_3) = P(E_1) + P(E_2) + P(E_3) + P(E_1 \cap E_2) + P(E_1 \cap E_3)$$

$$+ P(E_2 \cap E_3) + P(E_1 \cap E_2 \cap E_3).$$

because of Eq. (4.3). Thus, if the equation is true for $n = k$, it is also true for $n = k + 1$. But it is true for $n = 2$, therefore it must be true for $n = 3$; if it is true for $n = 3$, it is also true for $n = 4$, and so on.

4.2. CONDITIONAL PROBABILITY

For the experiment of rolling a pair of dice, we represented the sample space conveniently by means of a square array of 36 points (Fig. 3-4). Suppose that we now ask, "If a pair of dice shows an even sum, what is the probability that this sum is less than 5?" We are now restricting the sample space to a subset of points corresponding to even sums only (18 such points) and asking, "Which of these possible points (outcomes) represent a sum less than 5?" There are 4 of these points out of the 18, and all have equal probabilities; hence, $P = \frac{1}{18} + \frac{1}{18} + \frac{1}{18} + \frac{1}{18} = \frac{2}{9}$. Note that we have set down the condition that the sum, $x + y$, is even (event A), and then requested the probability for $x + y$ to be less than 5 (event B). This *conditional probability* is symbolized by $P(B \mid A)$, which may be read "P of B line A" or in words, "the probability for the event B under the condition that event A has occurred," Here A is the event "$x + y$ is even" and B is the event "$x + y < 5$." The probability $\frac{2}{9}$, above, was obtained when we divided the number, $N(A \cap B)$, of points in the subset $\{x + y$ is even and less than 5$\}$ by the number, $N(A)$, of points in the subset $\{x + y$ is even$\}$, so that

$$P(B \mid A) = \frac{N(A \cap B)}{N(A)} = \frac{N(A \cap B)/N}{N(A)/N} = \frac{P(A \cap B)}{P(A)} \qquad \textbf{(4.4)}$$

where N is the number of points in the entire sample space. Of course, $N(A)$ is assumed not to be 0.

Equation (4.4) has been derived for the special case where all points of S have the same probability, $\frac{1}{36}$. In many cases, this equality of probabilities does not hold; so we shall obtain the formula in a different manner. If B could be a subset of a number of different sample spaces R, S, T, and so on, and we wished to make it clear that S was the sample space of immediate concern, we could write $P(B) = P(B \mid S)$. Now $P(B) = P(B \cap S)$ [from Section 2.4, postulate (6-b)] and $P(S) = 1$; therefore

$$P(B \mid S) = \frac{P(B \cap S)}{P(S)} .$$

If, however, we chose to reduce the sample space S to A, then it would be natural to write

$$P(B \mid A) = \frac{P(B \cap A)}{P(A)} \qquad \textbf{(4.5)}$$

which is the same as Eq. (4.4). In Fig. 4-3, $A \cap B$ bears the same relation to the restricted sample space A, that B bears to the original sample space S. These relations are not necessarily identical but are similar in concept. Equation (4.5) will constitute our formal definition of conditional probability.

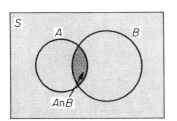

Figure 4-3

4.3. MULTIPLICATION THEOREMS

In the practical applications of Eq. (4.5), it is usually $P(A \cap B)$ that is difficult, if not impossible, to calculate; so a very useful form is obtained when we clear the equation of fractions. We have, then, the important multiplication theorem.

Theorem 4.3.

$$P(A \cap B) = P(A)P(B \mid A). \tag{4.6}$$

Stated in words this reads "The probability for the simultaneous occurrence of the events A and B equals the probability that A occurs multiplied by the probability that B occurs, provided A has already occurred."

EXAMPLE 1. Let us consider an urn containing five balls, alike in every observable respect, save color. If three of these balls are white and two are black and we draw two balls at random from this urn without replacing them, what is the probability that the first ball drawn is white and the second, black?

Equation (4.6) may be written

$$P(W \cap B) = P(W)P(B \mid W).$$

The probability, $P(W)$, that the first ball drawn is white is $\frac{3}{5}$. If the first ball drawn is white, then four balls remain, of which two are black; hence the probability, $P(B \mid W)$, that the second ball is black, provided the first is white, is $\frac{2}{4}$. Then

$$P(W \cap B) = \left(\frac{3}{5}\right)\left(\frac{2}{4}\right) = \frac{3}{10}.$$

Also

$$P(B \cap W) = P(B)P(W \mid B)$$

$$= \frac{3}{10}.$$

Since the drawing of a white ball followed by a black, and the drawing of a black ball followed by a white, are mutually exclusive events, the probability that the two balls drawn are of different color is, by Eq. (4.2), $\frac{3}{10} + \frac{3}{10} = \frac{3}{5}$.

EXAMPLE 2. Suppose that we have two boxes. In box No. 1, there are five sealed envelopes; three of them contain $1 bills, and two of them, $5 bills. In box No. 2, there are ten sealed envelopes; seven of them contain $1 bills, and three, $5 bills. If a box is selected at random and from it an envelope is chosen, what is the probability that it contains a $5 bill?

The chance of selecting box No. 1 is $\frac{1}{2}$, and if this is done, the probability of getting a $5 bill is $\frac{2}{5}$. Then by Eq. (4.6),

$$P_1 = \left(\frac{1}{2}\right)\left(\frac{2}{5}\right) = \frac{1}{5}.$$

Similarly for box No. 2,

$$P_2 = \left(\frac{1}{2}\right)\left(\frac{3}{10}\right) = \frac{3}{20}.$$

Since P_1 and P_2 are the probabilities for two mutually exclusive events, the probability for either one event or the other to occur is, by the addition theorem,

$$P_1 + P_2 = \frac{1}{5} + \frac{3}{20} = \frac{7}{20}.$$

4.4. INDEPENDENT EVENTS

If the occurrence of the event B is not influenced or conditioned by a second event A, for which $P(A) \neq 0$, so that

$$P(B \mid A) = P(B) \tag{4.7}$$

then B is said to be independent of A.

Theorem 4.4. If $P(A) \neq 0$ and $P(B) \neq 0$ and B is independent of A, then A is independent of B. In this case, A and B are said to be mutually independent.

Proof. By Eq. (4.6)

$$P(A \cap B) = P(A)P(B \mid A)$$

and

$$P(B \cap A) = P(B)P(A \mid B).$$

However $A \cap B = B \cap A$ by the commutative law [postulate (2b) of Section 2.4], and $P(A \cap B) = P(B \cap A)$; therefore,

$$P(A)P(B \mid A) = P(B)P(A \mid B).$$

But because of Eq. (4.7),

$$P(A)P(B) = P(B)P(A \mid B)$$

whence

$$P(A) = P(A \mid B)$$

and A is independent of B.

*Theorem 4.5. A necessary and sufficient condition for two events, **A** and **B**, to be mutually independent is that*

$$P(A \cap B) = P(A)P(B) \tag{4.8}$$

provided $P(A) \neq 0$ and $P(B) \neq 0$.

First we note that if the events are mutually independent, $P(B \mid A) = P(B)$; whence Eq. (4.8) follows immediately from Eq. (4.6).

Second, we note that if

$$P(A \cap B) = P(A)P(B)$$

then by Eq. (4.6)

$$P(A)P(B \mid A) = P(A)P(B). \tag{4.9}$$

Dividing Eq. (4.9) by $P(A)$, we obtain

$$P(B \mid A) = P(B)$$

whence B is independent of A by Eq. (4.7). Thus A is independent also of B, by Theorem 4.4. Equation (4.8) becomes a very useful definition of two independent events, because it holds even when we remove the restriction of nonzero probability for A and B.

Two events A and B are defined to be independent if and only if $P(A \cap B) = P(A)P(B)$.

The generalization of this definition is as follows:

The events $E_1, E_2, , , E_n$ are said to be independent if and only if the multiplication rule

$$P(E_1 \cap E_2 \cap \cdots \cap E_k) = P(E_1)P(E_2) \cdots P(E_k)$$

holds for every k-tuple of events; $k = 2, 3, , , n$.

The necessity for the conditions stated in this definition will not be discussed in this book. See, for example, Reference 4.

> EXAMPLE 1. Assume two coins are tossed; one is a penny, the other a dime. Let A be the event that the penny shows head, and let B be the event that the coins show different faces. Are A and B independent?
>
> $$S = \{HH, HT, TH, TT\}$$
>
> where the first letter of each pair refers to the outcome for the penny, and the second, to the dime.
>
> $$A = \{HH, HT\} \qquad \text{hence } P(A) = \tfrac{1}{2}$$
>
> $$B = \{HT, TH\} \qquad \text{hence } P(B) = \tfrac{1}{2}$$
>
> $$A \cap B = \{HT\} \qquad \text{hence } P(A \cap B) = \tfrac{1}{4}$$
>
> Since $P(A \cap B) = P(A)P(B)$, A and B are independent events.

EXAMPLE 2. Let us refer to example 1 of Section 4.3. If A is the event that the first ball drawn is white and B the event that the second ball drawn is black, are A and B independent?

$$P(A) = \frac{3}{5}, \qquad P(B) = P(B \mid A) + P(B \mid B)$$

$$= \frac{2}{4} + \frac{1}{4} = \frac{3}{4}$$

and

$$P(A)P(B) = \frac{9}{20}\,; P(A \cap B) = \frac{3}{5}\cdot\frac{2}{4} = \frac{6}{20}\,.$$

But $P(A \cap B) \neq P(A)P(B)$, hence A and B are dependent.

4.5. A THEOREM INVOLVING PARTITIONS

Let $\{E_1, E_2, \,, E_n\}$ be any partition of the sample space S (See Section 2.6), and let E be any event. Then

Theorem 4.6.

$$P(E) = \sum_{i=1}^{n} P(E_i)P(E \mid E_i) \qquad (4.10)$$

provided $P(E_i) \neq 0$, $i = 1, 2, \,, n$.

The understanding of the proof will be facilitated by Fig. 4-4. In all that follows, $i = 1, 2, \,, n$. E is represented by the shaded region within S.

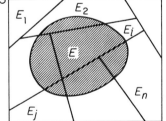

Figure 4-4

$$S = E_1 \cup E_2 \cup \cdots \cup E_n$$

$$E = E \cap S$$

$$= E \cap (E_1 \cup E_2 \cup \cdots \cup E_n)$$

$$= (E \cap E_1) \cup (E \cap E_2) \cup \cdots \cup (E \cap E_n)$$

because of an extension of postulate (4a). $(E \cap E_i) \cap (E \cap E_j) = \varnothing$, $i \neq j$, because $E \cap E_i \subset E_i$, and the E_i's are disjoint by definition of a partition. Hence by Eq. (4.2a),

$$P(E) = P(E \cap E_1) + P(E \cap E_2) + \cdots + P(E \cap E_n)$$

$$= P(E_1)P(E \mid E_1) + P(E_2)P(E \mid E_2) + \cdots + P(E_n)P(E \mid E_n)$$

$$= \sum_{i=1}^{n} P(E_i)P(E \mid E_i). \qquad (4.10)$$

EXAMPLE 1. Let us refer to the club of 20 members in Section 2.6 and add the information that six of the married persons, three of the single women, and one of the bachelors, are Democrats. If a member of the club is picked at random, what is the probability that he is a Democrat?

The answer to this question may be obtained very easily. Since there are $6 + 3 + 1$ or 10 Democrats in the club of 20, the desired probability is merely $\frac{10}{20}$ or $\frac{1}{2}$. However, most problems involving partitions cannot be solved as readily and recourse to Eq. (4.10) is desirable.

In Fig. 4-5

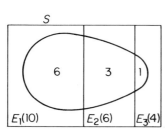

Figure 4-5

$E_1 = \{\text{married persons}\}$

$E_2 = \{\text{single women}\}$

$E_3 = \{\text{bachelors}\}$

$E = \{\text{Democrats}\}$

$P(E) = P(E_1)P(E \mid E_1) +$

$\qquad\qquad P(E_2)P(E \mid E_2) + P(E_3)P(E \mid E_3)$

$\qquad = \dfrac{10}{20} \cdot \dfrac{6}{10} + \dfrac{6}{20} \cdot \dfrac{3}{6} + \dfrac{4}{20} \cdot \dfrac{1}{4} = \dfrac{1}{2}.$

EXAMPLE 2. In Wellville, 55% of the voters are registered Republicans and 45% are registered Democrats. There are two candidates for mayor: R, a Republican and D, a Democrat. In the election, 80% of the Republicans and 10% of the Democrats voted for R. Twenty per cent of the Republicans, and 90% of the Democrats voted for D. If a voter is selected at random what is the probability that he voted for D?

Let E_1 be the event that the voter is a Republican, E_2 that he is a Democrat, E the event that the voter cast his ballot for D, and $\bar{E}$ that he

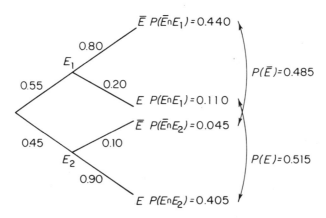

Figure 4-6

cast his ballot for R. Then by Eq. (4.10),

$$P(E) = P(E_1)(P(E \mid E_1) + P(E_2)P(E \mid E_2)$$
$$= 0.55 \times 0.20 + 0.45 \times 0.90 = 0.515.$$

The tree diagram in Fig. 4-6 is useful here.

4.6. BAYES' RULE

The following theorem was advanced by the English clergyman, Thomas Bayes (?–1761).

Theorem 4.7. Let the set of events $\{E_1, E_2, , , E_n\}$ form a partition of the sample space S, where $P(E_i) \neq 0$, $i = 1, 2, , , n$. Then for any event E for which $P(E) \neq 0$ and for $1 \leq k \leq n$,

$$P(E_k \mid E) = \frac{P(E_k)P(E \mid E_k)}{\sum\limits_{i=1}^{n} P(E_i)P(E \mid E_i)} . \tag{4.11}$$

Proof. From Eq. (4.5)

$$P(E_k \mid E) = \frac{P(E_k \cap E)}{P(E)} .$$

We now replace the numerator by its equivalent in Eq. (4.6) and the denominator by its equivalent in Eq. (4.10).

$$P(E_k \mid E) = \frac{P(E_k)P(E \mid E_k)}{\sum\limits_{i=1}^{n} P(E_i)P(E \mid E_i)} .$$

Example. Refer to example 2 of the preceding section. If a voter is selected at random and is found to have voted for D, what is the probability that he is a Democrat? By Eq. (4.11),

$$P(E_2 \mid E) = \frac{P(E_2)P(E \mid E_2)}{P(E_1)P(E \mid E_1) + P(E_2)P(E \mid E_2)}$$
$$= \frac{0.45 \times 0.90}{(0.55 \times 0.20) + (0.45 \times 0.90)} = 0.786.$$

It will be fruitful to comment on this problem. If the only information concerning the voters of Wellville consisted of the fact that 55% were Republicans and 45% were Democrats, and we asked "What is the chance that a voter selected at random is a Democrat?" we should reply, "The probability is 0.45." However, if we increase our knowledge by means of the additional facts stated in our original problem and by the important item that the random voter was found to have voted for *D*, then our probability value rises from 0.45 to about 0.79. This illustrates the reason for the assertion "But if our probability is a measure of the importance of our state of ignorance it must change its value whenever we add new knowledge."[2]

Bayes' rule is sometimes termed the formula for "inverse probability" or for "probabilities of hypotheses." The events $E_1, E_2, , , E_n$ constitute *n* a priori hypotheses or "causes" used to account for the event *E*. $P(E_1), P(E_2)$, , , $P(E_n)$ are the corresponding a priori probabilities; $P(E_i \mid E), i = 1, 2, , , n$, are a posteriori probabilities for the same hypotheses. The latter are probabilities based on an event *E* that is assumed to have already happened. There is some controversy as well as misunderstanding concerning Bayes' formula, but we shall not attempt to discuss them here. The formula is an exceedingly useful one and has wide acceptance. Inferences which aim to decide what hypothesis is true when a certain event or combination of events has occurred are desirable in many problems in probability and statistics. The logic underlying Bayes' formula is similar to that employed in establishing confidence limits in statistics (see Section 16.6.)

EXERCISES

1. Of 150 patients examined at a clinic, it was found that 90 had heart trouble, 50 had diabetes, and 30 had both diseases. What percentage of the patients had either heart trouble or diabetes?

2. A die has three black faces numbered 1, 2, and 3; the others are white and numbered 4, 5, and 6. If this die is tossed, what is the probability that either an even number or a white face shows?

3. The registration cards of 200 students were examined with reference to certain languages. It was found that 100 had elected French, 80 had elected Spanish, and 60, both of these languages. If a student were selected at random from these 200, what is the probability that he had elected either French or Spanish or both?

4. If a pack of cards is cut, what is the probability that an ace, a king, a queen, a jack, or a diamond shows?

5. In a certain college for men, 5% of the senior students were elected to Phi Beta Kappa, 10% of the class were veterans, and 10% of the veterans were elected to Phi Beta Kappa.   What is the probability that a senior chosen at random was either a veteran or a Phi Beta Kappa man?

6. Of 100 college seniors, 60 had studied biology, 20 had studied geology, and 10 had studied astronomy. Fifteen had studied both biology and geology,

[2] T. C. Fry, *Probability and Its Engineering Uses* (Princeton N.J.: D. van Nostrand Co., Inc., 1928), pp. 118–119.

seven, both biology and astronomy, and three, both geology and astronomy. Three had studied all three subjects. What is the probability that a randomly selected senior had studied at least one of these three subjects?

7. Without the use of a Venn diagram, prove that if

$$P(A \cup B) = P(A) + P(B) - P(A \cap B)$$

then

$$P(A \cup B \cup C) = P(A) + P(B) + P(C) - [P(A \cap B) \\ + P(A \cap C) + P(B \cap C)] + P(A \cap B \cap C).$$

8. Prove Eq. (4.1a) by mathematical induction.

9. In a throw of two honest dice, what is the probability of obtaining a sum less than 7?

10. A box contains three red balls and eight black balls, all of the same size and material. If two balls are drawn in succession without replacement, what is the probability that both are red?

11. From a bag containing five black and three white balls, three balls are drawn in succession without replacements. What is the probability that all three are black?

12. A box contains five red balls, 10 white balls, and 15 blue balls, all of the same size and material. If three balls are drawn in succession without replacements, what is the probability that they are all a different color?

13. For the *ABO* blood group system, the probability of a man in the United States having *AB*-type blood is 0.030. If such a man has an *O*-type wife, the probability that his child is of type *A* is $\frac{1}{2}$. What is the probability that a woman of group *O* marries a man of group *AB* and has a child belonging to group *A*?

14. The faces of a die numbered 1, 2, and 3 are colored red; the faces numbered 4 and 5 are colored white, and the face numbered 6 is blue. What is the probability that on a toss of this die (a) it shows red or 5? (b) it shows red or an odd number? (c) it shows 2 on the condition that it shows red?

15. The faces of a die numbered 1, 2, and 3 are white, and the faces numbered 4, 5, and 6 are black. (a) When this die is rolled what is the probability that if the die shows black it also shows an odd number? (b) If two such dice are rolled what is the probability that both show the same color or that both show the same number?

16. A club consisting of 10 married couples is to choose a president by lot and then a secretary. What is the probability that (a) both are men? (b) they are of opposite sex? (c) a married couple is chosen?

17. There are three types of repairs that a certain kind of radio amplifier is likely to require during its first year of use, and the probabilities for them are 0.05, 0.04, and 0.02. What is the probability that a random amplifier needs repair during its first year of use? Each type of repair is independent of the other two types.

18. The probabilities of an accused man in the United States being exonerated

of a false charge of paternity by means of a blood group test in the *ABO* system is 0.165; in the *MN* system it is 0.274, and in the *Rh* system, 0.256. These tests are independent of one another. What is the probability that such a man may be exonerated if all these blood group systems are used?

19. Five boxes contain 100 flash bulbs each. Two of the boxes have 10 defective bulbs each, two of them have 5 defective bulbs each, and one has 2 defective bulbs. If a box is chosen at random and from it a bulb is selected, what is the probability that the bulb is defective? Make a tree diagram.

20. A commando operation is to begin at 11 P.M. on a certain night. Six hours before, rain is estimated to fall with a probability of 0.8. If it rains, the chance of the operation being successful is estimated to be 0.75. If it does not rain, the chance is estimated to be 0.6. What is the probability of success? Make a tree diagram.

21. Jack Wood of the Black Sox baseball team has been hitting fairly consistently with a batting average of 0.300. He has had 70 hits of which 20 were two-baggers. In his next time at bat, what is the probability that he will hit a two-bagger?

22. If 60% of American males of age 20 and 65% of American females of age 20 live to be 70, what is the probability that an American couple married when they were 20 years old will live to celebrate their golden wedding anniversary?

23. In New England, the distribution of the four basic blood groups has been found to be as follows: *O*, 45%; *A*, 40%; *B*, 10%; *AB*, 5%. What is the probability, for a random New England couple, that (a) both are of type *A*? (b) neither is of type *O*? (c) the wife is of type *A* and the husband of type *B*? (d) one is of type *A* and the other of type *B*? (e) they are of different types?

24. Assume that a thumbtack lands "point down" 60% of the time. Make a diagram of the sample space for the possible outcomes when two thumbtacks are dropped on the floor. Label each point with its appropriate probability. Let 0 denote "point down" and 1, "point up."

25. A fair game of chance is one in which there is a probability of ½ for a player to win. Which, if any, of the following are fair games? If the game is not fair, what is the probability of a player winning?
  (a) A well-shuffled bridge deck of cards is cut. If a diamond, an ace, a king, a queen, or a jack shows, the cutter wins.
  (b) A small regular tetrahedron has its four faces numbered 1, 2, 3, and 4. A player tosses it twice. If the sum of the numbers showing is even he wins.
  (c) A pair of dice is tossed. If the sum 7 or 12 appears, or if a 5 appears on either or both of the dice, the player wins.

26. As a rule, 10% of a certain type of Christmas tree bulb are defective. If a random sample of 10 such bulbs is selected from a lot and tested, what is the probability that none are defective? You do not need to compute the answer decimally.

27. In a large club, there are twice as many women as men. If three committee members are to be chosen by lot, what is the probability that two are men and one is a woman? If the club consisted of only nine members with the same ratio of sexes as before, what would your answer be?

28. An unbiased penny is tossed three times. Let A be the event "not less than two tails." Let B be the event "at least one of each face." Are A and B independent events?

29. A box contains five white and two black balls. A second box identical with the first, contains three white and five black balls. One box is chosen and a ball withdrawn from it. What is the probability that this ball is white?

30. In example 2 of Section 4.5, who won the election?

31. In Wellville, 48% of the voters are registered Republicans, 42% are Democrats, and 10% are Independents, not registered for either party. There are three candidates for mayor: R, a Republican, D, a Democrat, and I, an Independent. Eighty per cent of the Republicans, 5% of the Democrats, and 10% of the Independents voted for R; 10% of the Republicans, 80% of the Democrats, and 10% of the Independents voted for D; 10% of the Republicans, 15% of the Democrats, and 80% of the Independents voted for I. (a) If a voter is selected at random and declares truthfully that he voted for I, what is the probability that he is a Republican? (b) Who received the largest percentage of the vote?

32. A class in advanced mathematics contains 10 juniors, 30 seniors, and 10 graduate students. Three of the juniors, 10 of the seniors, and 5 of the graduate students received A in the course. If a student is chosen at random from this class and is found to have earned an A, what is the probability that he is a graduate student?

33. A storeroom contains 80 boxes of fuses, 100 per box. Twenty boxes contain fuses produced by machine A, 30 boxes have fuses produced by machine B, and 30 have fuses produced by machine C. The boxes are piled, hit or miss, without regard to the machine source. Machine A produces, on an average, 5% defective fuses, machine B, 3%, and machine C, 2%. If a box is selected at random, and a fuse in it tested and found to be defective, what is the probability that it was manufactured by machine B?

34. The probability of a child belonging to blood group A, genotype AO, when the mother belongs to group O, is $\frac{1}{2}$ if the father is of genotype OA, 1 if the father is of genotype AA, and $\frac{1}{2}$ if of genotype AB. The probabilities that a male belongs respectively to these three genotypes are 0.352, 0.069, and 0.015. If a child of an O mother is found to belong to genotype OA, what is the probability that its father has blood of type AB?

35. A bag contains two half-dollars, three quarters, four dimes, and three nickels, all wrapped individually in identical packages. A man draws one package at a time until the sum drawn equals fifty cents or more. What is the probability that he draws exactly fifty cents?

36. Verify the probabilities listed in example (iii) of Section 3.5, p. 37.

37. The Yankees and the Red Sox are playing a series of three games. A Yankee fan estimates the probability as 0.6 that the Yankees win an individual game regardless of previous outcomes. What should the Yankee fan calculate the probability to be that the Yankees win just two out of three games?

38. A Bostonian returning from Europe plans to see, if possible, a ball game the day following his return. He does not know the schedule but hopes that he can see the Boston Red Sox play the New York Yankees. The probability that a game is scheduled in Boston is $\frac{1}{2}$, that New York is the scheduled team is $\frac{1}{7}$, and that rain will cancel a scheduled game is $\frac{1}{20}$. If Boston plays New York, the chance of Boston winning is estimated to be $\frac{2}{5}$; if Boston plays any other team, the chance of winning is estimated to be $\frac{1}{2}$. What is the probability (a) that the Bostonian sees the Red Sox beat the Yankees? (b) that this Bostonian sees his team lose to the Yankees, or (c) the game with the Yankees is canceled because of rain?

39. A woman was assaulted by a man who, in the ensuing struggle, left blood stains on the floor. The victim did not get a clear view of her assailant's face but was positive that he was a white man with red hair, and well over six feet in height. A test of the blood showed it to be of type *AB* and to contain evidence of syphilis. Assume that *AB* blood occurs in only 3% of the population, about 5% have red hair, not more than 1% of white males have syphilis, and about 10% of adult males are over six feet tall. What is the probability that a random white adult American male possesses all these characteristics?

40. Assume that the winner of a World Series between New York and Cincinnati must capture two out of three games, and that a New York fan estimates a probability of 0.6 that New York wins an individual game regardless of previous outcomes. Draw a tree diagram for the possible outcomes in the series, and compute their probabilities. What is the New York fan's probability that his team wins the series?

5

Some Miscellaneous Problems

How hadde the cherl this ymaginacioun
To shewe swich a probleme to the frere.

GEOFFREY CHAUCER
The Sompnoures Tale

5.1. THE BIRTHDAY PROBLEM

What is the probability that in a group of N people, at least two of them will have the same birthday?

With 365 different birthdays possible, excluding leap years, intuitively it would seem that the chance for coincident birthdays in a group of, say, 40 persons would be quite small. Let us see how good our intuition is.

The desired probability is most easily obtained if we first find the chance that no two persons have the same birthday and then subtract the result from 1. A random individual might have any one of the 365 days of the year as a birthday; a second individual may likewise have any one of 365 birthdays; and so on. Hence, by the theorem of Section 2.5, the sample space consists of 365^N points, to each of which is attached the same probability. The number of ways possible for none of the N birthdays to coincide is:

$$365 \cdot 364 \cdot 363 \cdots (365 - \overline{N-1}) = \frac{365!}{(365 - N)!}$$

because if a given person may have any one of the 365 days of the year as his birthday; the next person may have any one of the remaining 364 days as his birthday; a third person may have any one of the remaining 363 days as his birthday; and so on until the Nth person's possible birthdays are $365 - \overline{N-1}$ in number. The probability for no two birthdays to coincide is, therefore,

$$\frac{365!/(365 - N)!}{365^N} \cdot$$

Finally, the probability that at least two individuals have the same birthday is

$$P = 1 - \frac{365!}{(365 - N)!365^N} \cdot \qquad (5.1)$$

Let us compute P for $N = 40$. We make use of a table of logarithms of factorials.[1]

log 365!	778.3997
log 325! = 676.8715⎫	
40 log 365 = 102.4916⎭	779.3631
	9.0366 − 10

We have subtracted the sum of the logarithms of the two factors in the denominator of Eq. (5.1) from the logarithm of the numerator to obtain $9.0366 - 10$. The corresponding antilogarithm is 0.1088, whence

$$P = 1 - 0.109 = 0.891.$$

Thus, there is almost a 90% chance of finding at least two persons with the same birthday in a group of 40.

For $N = 23$, 30, and 50, $P = 0.51$, 0.71, and 0.97 respectively. Clearly, there is approximately an even chance when $N = 23$ that at least two birthdays coincide; and when $N = 50$, the coincidence is almost certain to occur.

5.2. THE GAME OF CRAPS

This famous dice game is played as follows: A person throws a pair of dice. He wins if

    (i) 7 or 11 appears;

    (ii) 4, 5, 6, 8, 9, or 10 appears, and the same sum reappears before 7 does in succeeding throws of the dice. He loses if

    (iii) 2, 3, or 12 appears;

    (iv) 4, 5, 6, 8, 9, or 10 appears, and 7 appears before the sum first obtained reappears in succeeding throws of the dice.

---

[1] See, for example, *Tables of Applied Mathematics in Finance, Insurance, Statistics,* by James W. Glover, George Wahr, Publisher, Ann Arbor, Michigan, 1923.

We seek the probability of the player winning. Before solving this problem, it is desirable to consider briefly an extension of the definition of probability given in Section 3.4. If instead of a finite sample space we have one consisting of a denumerable infinite set of elements (Section 3.1):

$$S = \{E_1, E_2, , ,\}$$

then the probability $P(E_i)$ of a simple event E_i is defined as a non-negative number associated with E_i such that

$$\lim_{n \to \infty} \sum_{i=1}^{n} P(E_i) = 1.$$

A compound event may consist of a finite subset of S such as

$$\{E_1', E_2', , , E_k'\}$$

or an infinite subset such as

$$\{E_1'', E_2'', , ,\}.$$

The probability of a compound event A consisting of a finite subset is given by

$$P(A) = P(E_1') + P(E_2') + \cdots + P(E_k').$$

For an infinite subset,

$$P(A) = P(E_1'') + P(E_2'') + \cdots = \lim_{k \to \infty} \sum_{j=1}^{k} P(E_j'').$$

For the game of craps, a listing of the elements of the sample space would be a laborious operation, but it could be done systematically as follows:

(i) The game is decided by a single throw of the dice if 7, 11, 2, 3, or 12 appears.

(ii) The game ends with two tosses if they result in (4,4), (5,5), (6,6), (8,8), (9,9), (10,10), (4,7), (5,7), (6,7), (8,7), (9,7), or (10,7).

(iii) The game ends with three tosses if they result in (4,2,4), (4,3,4), (4,5,4), , , (5,2,5), (5,3,5), , , (4,2,7), (4,3,7), (4,5,7), , , (5,2,7), (5,3,7), , , and so on.

The enumeration of the possible outcomes is a tedious process and leads to a denumerable infinite set of outcomes constituting the sample space. It is not necessary, however, to carry out this enumeration in order to solve the problem.

(i) The probability for 7 or 11 on the first throw equals $\frac{6}{36} + \frac{2}{36} = \frac{2}{9}$.

(ii) The probability for 4 on the first throw is $\frac{3}{36}$ or $\frac{1}{12}$; the probability of not getting a 7 or a 4 on a given throw equals $1 - (\frac{6}{36} + \frac{3}{36})$ or $\frac{3}{4}$. The probability, then, of winning on throw number $r + 2$ by getting a 4 on the first throw is

$$\frac{1}{12}\left(\frac{3}{4}\right)^r \cdot \frac{1}{12}, \qquad r = 0, 1, 2, 3, , , .$$

Hence the probability of winning by getting a 4 on the first throw and not getting a 7 before 4 reappears is

$$P = \frac{1}{12^2} + \frac{1}{12}\left(\frac{3}{4}\right)\frac{1}{12} + \frac{1}{12}\left(\frac{3}{4}\right)^2\frac{1}{12} + \frac{1}{12}\left(\frac{3}{4}\right)^3\frac{1}{12} + \cdots$$

$$= \frac{1}{12^2}\left[1 + \frac{3}{4} + \left(\frac{3}{4}\right)^2 + \left(\frac{3}{4}\right)^3 + \cdots\right].$$

The limit of the sum of the terms of the infinite geometric progression in parentheses is $1/(1 - \frac{3}{4}) = 4$; hence,

$$P = 4(\tfrac{1}{12})^2 = \frac{1}{36}.$$

The remaining probabilities are calculated in a similar fashion and are left as exercises. In this connection, it should be noted that the probability for winning by scoring 10 on the first throw is the same as that for 4. Similar symmetric relationships aid in shortening the calculations. The probability that the player wins a crap game can be shown to be 0.4928. The game is essentially a fair one, provided the dice are not loaded; though there is a very small bias in favor of the opponent not tossing the dice. (See exercises 3–5.)

5.3. THE HAT PROBLEM

Imagine that an inebriated checkroom girl gets all the hats mixed up and then distributes them at random to the guests. What is the probability that at least one guest receives his own hat?

This famous problem was first proposed and solved by Pierre Raymond de Montmort (1678–1719). It has appeared in many disguises and has led to problems of a more general nature. In a more prosaic form, the problem is this: Assume that an urn contains N counters marked 1 to N and that the counters are withdrawn at random, one at a time, until the urn is exhausted. What is the probability that at least one of the numbers drawn matches the number of counters drawn, for example, that the eighth counter drawn is numbered 8?

Let E_1 be the event that the number i is selected on the ith drawing. Then the remaining $N - 1$ numbers may be drawn in any one of $(N - 1)!$ orders. Since the sample space consists of $N!$ orders,

$$P(E_1) = \frac{(N - 1)!}{N!} = 1/N.$$

Let E_2 be the event that the numbers i and j appear on the ith and jth drawings, respectively. Then the remaining $N - 2$ numbers may be drawn in any one of $(N - 2)!$ orders. Therefore,

$$P(E_2) = \frac{(N - 2)!}{N!}.$$

Similarly, for a given set of r matchings,

$$P(E_r) = \frac{(N - r)!}{N!}.$$

There are N possible numbers such as i, $[N!/2!(N - 2)!]$ possible pairs of numbers i, j, and, in general, $[N!/r!(N - r)!]$ possible r-tuples of numbers. It follows that

$$\sum P(E_1) = N\left(\frac{1}{N}\right) \qquad\qquad = 1;^{(2)}$$

$$\sum P(E_2) = \frac{N!}{2!(N - 2)!} \cdot \frac{(N - 2)!}{N!} = \frac{1}{2!};$$

$$\sum P(E_3) = \frac{N!}{3!(N - 3)!} \cdot \frac{(N - 3)!}{N!} = \frac{1}{3!};$$

$$P(E_N) = \frac{1}{N!}.$$

The events E_1, E_2, , , E_N are not mutually exclusive so Eq. (4.1a) applies. Hence the probability sought is

$$P = 1 - \frac{1!}{2!} + \frac{1}{3!} - \cdots \pm \frac{1}{N!}.$$

For $N > 5$ the value of P, computed to three decimal places, remains constant at 0.632. It may seem strange that the value of N has so little influence on the probability for all but small values of N. The chance of at least one match for ten counters is the same as that for a thousand. The reason for this stems from the fact that the contributions of the terms of the series following $1/6!$ are so small that they do not affect the first three decimal places in the value of P. More precisely, we may add that the value of e^{-1}, where e is the base of the natural system of logarithms, can be defined by the infinite series:

$$e^{-1} = 1 - 1 + \frac{1}{2!} - \frac{1}{3!} + \frac{1}{4!} - \cdots.$$

[2] The symbol $\sum P(E_1)$ is interpreted as the sum of the probabilities of all possible events E_1, which events might occur when the number 1 is selected on the first drawing, the number 2 on the second drawing, , , or the number N on the Nth drawing. Similar interpretations follow for the remaining sums. Section 6.5 deals with this notation in greater detail.

This series converges to 0.368 approximately. It follows that $P = 1 - e^{-1} = 0.632$, approximately.

Other forms of de Montmort's problem include the matching of two well-shuffled bridge decks of cards against each other, the guessing of the denomination of each card of a set of N different cards before each card is turned up, and the following unrealistic form. "If all of the inhabitants of Chicago should meet together in one place and get extremely drunk, and then try to go home by guesswork, the chances that at least one would get back to his own bed are almost two out of three."[3]

5.4. RANDOM DIGITS

The property of randomness is assumed or sought in many probabilistic and statistical experiments. This property implies that a selection has been made of an element or set of elements from a given population in such a manner that each element of the population is as likely to be selected as any other element. Such a condition is expected to subsist whenever we draw a marble from a bag containing well-mixed uniform marbles; whenever we deal a card from a well-shuffled deck of cards; whenever we ask a student to tell us the day and the month of his birthday, and so on. Any one of the marbles in the bag, any card in the deck, and any one of the 365 days of a non-leap year is as likely to result as any other. When each member of a sample is randomly drawn, the sample is said to be a *random sample*. (See Section 6.2 for a more exact definition.)

Many investigations begin with sampling, and obtaining a truly random sample is sometimes the major problem of an experiment. Consider, for example, the difficulties encountered in the sampling of the fish population of a lake, the trees of a pine forest, the red cells of the human blood, and the voting population of the United States.

Because of the extreme care that must sometimes be exercised in the selection of a sample, statisticians frequently employ a table of random digits. These digits have been produced by a mechanical or electronic process that ensures that each digit obtained is independent of the digits previously obtained and is the result of pure chance. A specimen page of random digits is shown in Table 5.1. This page was selected from a well-known and useful table, "A Million Random Digits," prepared by the Rand Corporation. (See Reference 23.) One method of using such a table will be illustrated.

Imagine that a file of college student record cards consists of 1000 cards arranged alphabetically. Let these be numbered 000, 001, 002, 003, , , and so on up to 997, 998, and 999. To draw a random sample of 25 cards from

[3] Julian L. Coolidge, *An Introduction to Mathematical Probability* (Oxford: Clarendon Press, 1925), p. 25.

TABLE 5-1

A PAGE OF RANDOM DIGITS

70079	99064	97423	68793	91763	14940	55550	19900	36879	27718
74372	99540	00119	55063	97512	73665	45331	93614	49512	08359
43658	71456	63894	28132	98307	83300	08001	11186	21446	35864
72448	27714	10704	36331	68905	18477	42727	72133	25167	41601
43269	47963	88026	79532	82919	03920	10924	02018	13708	05281
66360	47852	32769	59586	00133	72584	26480	00245	48371	37526
22043	77224	26075	68778	87332	83287	54373	96391	82132	89338
78519	43251	18412	30777	14380	13550	37902	46169	27785	10488
58454	13026	26618	18537	44015	73261	42001	06096	21918	94440
00666	78245	32662	03375	54485	89848	90606	55556	49481	35329
80043	26080	72508	53576	49390	35273	86769	07108	66688	24636
53787	10007	66163	88811	21977	92078	95503	43655	57975	25768
88907	42653	05541	13459	89731	89459	98306	55222	32363	68675
76654	24020	67332	62362	65014	18061	92185	08657	92167	47793
11675	96819	10965	31214	39215	29883	34235	27113	22919	31278
90066	91253	59174	58312	84990	52539	64054	34864	00483	17913
29480	78114	48305	67868	85176	50048	62792	82816	52055	93273
93992	71132	91042	96303	11372	13817	15490	19452	08265	57612
79938	37498	27019	18573	88617	31245	60208	53962	52981	04301
20506	31384	51173	33453	93156	43166	33599	98112	09422	48744
43006	16020	49784	09917	50236	59837	18739	85767	49111	51512
45186	04205	76923	06181	81538	68226	73500	60779	65584	24305
49966	94867	62902	43090	37205	72584	78048	98669	83267	13303
62224	77713	14540	24003	20499	32752	42271	75891	45681	44445
73217	21643	46106	73942	02936	45948	74850	17297	44957	31068
11219	20296	59367	31426	31166	66247	54764	91861	83130	37507
02164	54666	21868	65824	97370	23627	39822	29285	31387	17045
73171	27920	41254	60089	00693	58712	88187	56810	92728	07894
48435	58944	61989	84538	67060	69031	28814	31405	82384	77694
45687	46494	61920	26751	54241	09903	71831	98113	33094	99925
64573	28270	63695	16900	25980	61906	38832	44327	01141	37889
36345	24793	88754	95921	99442	30336	07705	41314	53028	07381
37402	15236	64920	25909	25085	85456	00198	32419	54583	83635
27358	35142	91012	35570	50420	30509	44150	99868	77894	05250
17222	24172	26021	79527	44721	19041	04399	74266	15134	17952
48436	19800	03441	60218	83099	10869	27264	06777	70388	34992
08752	26430	45080	80472	35599	34343	90581	46482	13441	74151
79075	92335	12474	33423	72174	02953	37198	97172	98019	92623
73073	26360	19111	65852	87760	41988	77620	83328	24394	23932
48418	80642	09023	48310	25218	79006	12709	39456	02883	83600
01362	30222	93728	16044	23187	40562	71067	13330	11022	17378
38148	24320	87981	57518	37136	04182	67913	88235	61865	24638
27411	82008	23860	45246	03403	97639	28686	67623	00542	63666
48322	46340	31022	55657	58297	36244	25091	75297	14695	75932
38823	78043	75095	58043	95125	74783	24693	06360	66853	66663
87891	01449	19122	70232	38118	30249	76453	20802	76374	83474
11627	55036	51014	95142	41014	28968	77021	79801	95957	87132
43277	09284	89837	17654	84726	49893	29601	02749	77246	21271
18946	64377	60317	28724	82044	03820	25767	53052	43304	70629
04996	65987	16738	51367	54872	93628	69984	29220	58652	06087

this population of 1000 cards, we turn to a table of random sampling numbers, open it at any page and, without looking at this page, place a pencil point among the digits. Assume that the page opened is that shown in Table 5-1. and that the pencil point landed on the twentieth digit in the twenty-ninth row, namely, 8. This is followed, row-wise, by the successive digits 6 7 0 6 0 6 9 . . . . We begin by listing the successive trios of digits 867, 060, 690, 312, 881, 431, 405, 823, and so on, row by row, until 25 different three-digit numbers are obtained. The desired random sample consists of the cards bearing these numerals. In the case of repetitions of a numeral, we merely omit them and continue our listing. More refined methods of selecting the page and the initial point are explained in the published tables.

There are interesting, as well as, important questions which can be raised in reference to a table of random digits. We shall present a few of these questions.

(i) What is the probability of the occurrence of a succession of just n identical digits, that is, of a numeral of the form $a\,a\,a\cdots a$? Such a numeral constitutes a *run* of n digits. The probability for a given run, say for $4\,4\,4\cdots 4$, is clearly $(0.1)^n$, and ten such different runs of such a type are possible; hence,

$$P(aaa\cdots a) = 10(0.1)^n = (0.1)^{n-1}.$$

But if there are to be exactly n identical digits, no more and no less, the probability for the digits immediately preceding and immediately following the run to be different from a digit in the run is 0.9 in each case; hence, the probability sought is:

$$(0.9)(0.1)^{n-1}(0.9) = 81 \times (0.1)^{n+1}.$$

For example, for a run of just five digits,

$$P = 81(0.1)^6 = 0.000081.$$

In a block of 50,000 digits, we would expect to obtain a run of just five digits; $50,000 \times 0.000081$ or 4.05 times.

In the Rand table, runs of 1, 2, 3, 4, and 5 digits were counted in the first block of 50,000 digits. The results follow:

Length of Run	Expected Frequency	Observed Frequency
1	40,500	40,410
2	4,050	4,055
3	405	421
4	40.5	48
5	4.05	5

Note that the agreement between the expected and the observed frequencies is very good and that the discrepancies are of such magnitude as to be attributable to the usual chance errors. This assertion can be verified by a more refined test of agreement known as the Chi-square test. (See Chapter 11.)

(ii) When a table of random digits is constructed, are we sure that the resulting successions of digits have been produced in a random manner? One test employed for randomness is the run test just discussed. Another test is the *poker test*, a method based upon permutations of digits analogous to the classes of hands described in the card game of poker. Because the Rand table was conveniently printed in columns of five-digit numerals, each such numeral was treated as a poker hand. The million digits yielded, therefore, 200,000 poker hands with results shown in the following table.

Class	Symbol	Expected Frequency	Observed Frequency
Busts	abcde	60,480	60,479
Pairs	aabcd	100,800	100,570
Two Pairs	aabbc	21,600	21,572
Threes	aaabc	14,400	14,659
Full House	aaabb	1,800	1,788
Fours	aaaab	900	914
Fives	aaaaa	20	18
		200,000	200,000

Let us verify, for example, the expected frequency for a pair, that is, a group of five digits in which two and only two are alike, and which we symbolize by $a\,a\,b\,c\,d$. If we consider first the particular order, $a\,a\,b\,c\,d$, there are $10!/6!$ possibilities of choice of the four digits, $a, b, c,$ and d. To obtain the number of different orders, we consider the number of ways in which the pair of a's may be distributed among five positions. This is $5!/2!3!$. Since there are 10^5 possible arrangements of five digits chosen from the available ten, the final probability sought is:

$$P = \frac{\dfrac{10!}{6!} \cdot \dfrac{5!}{3!2!}}{10^5} = 0.50400.$$

For 200,000 poker hands the expected number of pairs is $200,000 \times 0.50400 = 100,800$. It turns out that this type of hand is more likely to occur than any other.

5.5. A PROBLEM INVOLVING A 2×2 TABLE

Let us assume that we have N balls in an urn; c_1 are marked A and c_2 are marked $\bar{A}$. The balls are alike in every other respect. After being thoroughly mixed, the balls are drawn at random and put into a row of N boxes, one to each box, of which r_1 boxes are marked B and r_2 are marked $\bar{B}$. What is the probability of obtaining just a balls marked A in boxes marked B?

	A	$\bar{A}$	
B	a	b	r_1
$\bar{B}$	c	d	r_2
	c_1	c_2	N

Fig. 5-1

This eventuality is conveniently represented by means of a 2×2 or four-fold table, as in Fig. 5-1. It is apparent that the specification of a balls in the AB cell immediately determines the numbers of balls in the remaining three cells, $\bar{A}B$, $A\bar{B}$, $\overline{AB}$, since the "marginal totals" r_1, r_2, c_1, and c_2 are assumed to be known. Thus $b = r_1 - a$, $c = c_1 - a$, and $d = c_2 - b$.

The number of ways of having

(1) a A's among r_1 B's is $\qquad \dfrac{r_1!}{a!b!}$;

(2) c A's among r_2 $\bar{B}$'s is $\qquad \dfrac{r_2!}{c!d!}$;

(3) c_1 A's among N boxes is $\qquad \dfrac{N!}{c_1!c_2!}$.

Hence the probability of having exactly the cell frequencies shown is:

$$P = \frac{\dfrac{r_1!}{a!b!} \cdot \dfrac{r_2!}{c!d!}}{\dfrac{N!}{c_1!c_2!}} = \frac{r_1!r_2!c_1!c_2!}{N!a!b!c!d!} . \qquad (5.2)$$

This probability model involving balls and boxes is useful in analyzing problems associated with a 2×2 table, as in the following.

Example. Of a total of 24 persons, eight were inoculated against typhoid fever and 16 were not; nine were attacked by the disease and 15 were not. Assuming that this type of inoculation does *not* influence one's susceptibility to typhoid, what is the probability that only one person inoculated will be attacked? Note that in the urn and ball model the markings on the balls had no influence on the type of boxes into which they were placed. For this reason we hypothesize the independence of inoculation and susceptibility to attack.

The information given leads us to construct the 2 × 2 table shown in Fig. 5-2. We note that the marginal totals in the table were fixed, given in

	A Inoculated	$\bar{A}$ Not inoculated	
B Attacked	1	8	9
$\bar{B}$ Not attacked	7	8	15
	8	16	24

Fig. 5-2

advance, and that knowledge of the single cell frequency, 1, enables us to supply the other three cell frequencies. Then,

$$P = \frac{9!15!8!16!}{24!1!8!7!8!} = 0.0787.$$

Two-by-two tables have many uses in statistics; but in their application one must be cognizant of the probability model underlying the assumptions made. In the model and the example given here, the four marginal totals were assumed or given fixed in advance. (See Section 11.10.)

5.6. THE LIARS

In 1934, the English scientist, Sir Arthur S. Eddington, discussed the following problem: "If A, B, C, D, each speak the truth once in three times (independently), and A affirms that B denies that C declares that D is a liar, what is the probability that D was telling the truth?" This tricky problem has provoked interesting discussions. It has also been discovered to be intimately related to other problems of a very practical nature.

Instead of solving the four liar problem, we shall solve a simpler three liar problem, stated as follows: "If B, C, and D each speak the truth once in three times (independently) and B denies that C declares that D is a liar, what is the probability that D was telling the truth?"

There are two possible statements that might actually have been made and which B could deny (or affirm). These are:

(i) C declares that D is truthful or, its equivalent, C denies that D is a liar, and

(ii) C declares that D is a liar or, its equivalent, C denies that D is truthful.

We shall use T and L to denote a truth and a lie respectively. Then if D actually lies we symbolize the preceding statements thus:

(i)' LL and (ii)' TL.

On the other hand, if D really tells the truth, then we have correspondingly

(i)'' TT and (ii)'' LT.

Revert now to the original statement. If B denies that C declares that D is a liar and D really is a liar, then B is telling the truth about (i) and we amend (i)' to read TLL. If D really tells the truth and (i) is the statement actually uttered, then B's original denial is again equivalent to a truth and we amend (i)'' to read TTT. Corresponding to statement (ii) we amend, similarly, (ii)' to LTL and (ii)'' to LLT.

If we assume that each person makes three statements of which two are lies and one is a truth, the frequencies with which the statements are made are indicated by the numbers below the following symbols:

(i)'	(i)''	(ii)'	(ii)''
TLL	TTT	LTL	LLT
4	1	4	4

The restricted sample space consists of 13 combinations of statements of which 5 correspond to a truthful D. The desired probability is $\frac{5}{13}$.

The original problem of the four liars provides an interesting challenge to the reader. The answer for this case is $\frac{13}{41}$.[4] The problem can also be solved by a more sophisticated method which treats the succession of statements as a Markov chain (see Section 19.5).

EXERCISES

In some of the following problems, it may be necessary to employ tables of factorials, of logarithms of factorials, and of powers of numbers.

1. Calculate the probability that at least two persons have birthdays in the same month when they are in a group of (a) 5; (b) 8; (c) 15. Assume all months of equal length.

[4] See The *American Mathematical Monthly*, Vol. 57, No. 1, January, 1950, pp. 43–45, and Vol. 58, No. 9, November, 1951, pp. 606–608.

2. Verify the probability (a) 0.51 for $N = 23$, and (b) 0.97 for $N = 50$, given near the end of Section 5.1.

3. In the crap game of Section 5.2, find the probability that the player wins by getting on his first throw a (a) 9; (b) 6.

4. In the crap game of Section 5.2, find the probability that the player wins by getting on his first throw a (a) 2, 3, or 12; (b) 5; (c) 10.

5. Find the probability that a player wins a crap game.

Exercises 6 through 8 refer to a table of random digits arranged in groups of five.

6. What is the probability for an arithmetic progression of five digits with a common difference of $+1$, e.g., 12345?

7. What is the probability for a group of five digits, all of which are (a) odd and different? (b) odd and making a full house?

8. What is the probability for each of the following poker hands?

(a) A bust   *abcde*
(b) Pairs   *aabcd*
(c) Two pairs   *aabbc*
(d) Threes   *aaabc*
(e) Full house *aaabb*
(f) Fours   *aaaab*
(g) Fives   *aaaaa*

9. Given the following 2×2 table, what is the probability for just six individuals in the category $\bar{A}B$?

	A	$\bar{A}$	
B			6
$\bar{B}$			4
	2	8	

10. In a test on 13 patients critically ill with the same disease, a new drug was administrated to 7 of them. The results are shown in the following 2×2 table. If we assume that the drug has no influence on the patients, what is the probability for such a result? Assume the marginal totals to be fixed.

	Improved	Not improved	
Drug	5	2	7
No Drug	0	6	6
	5	8	13

11. A random sample of 16 college girls showed the following characteristics:

Hair Color

		Light	Dark	
Eye Color	Blue	6	4	10
	Brown	2	4	6
		8	8	16

Assuming hair and eye color to be independent characteristics, what is the probability for such a result? Assume the marginal totals fixed.

12. In the preceding exercise, what is the probability for two or fewer girls with brown eyes and light hair?

13. The number of defective articles produced under two manufacturing processes are shown. If we assume that each process usually produces about the same percent of defectives, what is the probability that under Process *B* there will be as few as two defective articles or fewer? Assume the marginal totals fixed.

	Defective	Not Defective	
Process A	5	3	8
Process B	2	6	8
	7	9	16

14. If you select three successive digits at random from a table of random digits, what is the probability that they are (a) 538? (b) 666? (c) all different? (d) all alike? (e) contain only two digits alike?

15. For a table of random digits, find the probability for a run of just (a) three digits; (b) one digit; (c) six digits.

6

Introduction to Statistics

In 1786, I found that in Germany they were engaged in a species of political inquiry, to which they had given the name of Statistics. . . an inquiry for the purpose of ascertaining the political strength of a country, or questions respecting matters of state.

SIR JOHN SINCLAIR
The Statistical Account of Scotland, Vol. 21(1791–1799)

6.1. THE MEANING OF STATISTICS

In the opening chapter of this book, we described one of the most important aspects of statistics as the examination of the outcomes of repetitive operations with a view to their interpretation by means of the laws of probability. It would be well to broaden this definition in the light of the many facets of interest that statisticians have in gathered data.

The layman frequently conceives of statistics as a mass of figures or a collection of data such as we might find in the publications of the United States Census Bureau, among the records of a school principal, or in the files of a large hospital. The often repeated phrase "Statistics show . . . " is likely to imply that a given mass of figures contains salient and unalterable characteristics that can easily be discerned among the mass by any person of normal intelligence. That the word *statistics* may apply to certain aggregates of figures is not to be denied, but that important facts contained therein are easily detected is by no means always true.

A second meaning of *statistics* is simply the plural of *statistic*, where a statistic is a certain kind of measure used to evaluate a selected property of the collection of items under investigation. The average weight of a football squad, for example, may be found if we add the weights of the individual players and divide by their number. The average thus obtained is a *statistic*.

A third meaning of *statistics* is of prime concern to us in this book. It is the science of assembling, analyzing, characterizing, and interpreting collections of data. In this sense, statistics is a field of study, a doctrine concerned with mathematical characterizations of aggregates of items.

Statistics, as a science, is fundamentally a branch of applied mathematics, just as mechanics is mathematics applied to problems connected with bodies subjected to forces. In statistics, the applications may be made to almost any aggregate of observations or measurements. For this reason, it is useful in business, economics, sociology, biology, psychology, education, physics, chemistry, agriculture, and related fields.

6.2. SAMPLE AND POPULATION

A *population* is any group of objects which we use as the universe of discourse in a statistical investigation. Often a population consists of numerical values associated with these objects. Head lengths of criminals, test scores of pupils, thicknesses of washers, lengths of life of electric light bulbs, or the number of negative replies on a questionnaire may constitute populations of measurements or observations. Such aggregates may be finite or infinite, real or fictitious.

A random sample taken from a population was described in Section 5.4. More formally, we state:

If x_1, x_2, , , x_N denote a finite population of N objects and the probability of selection is:

$$P(x_1) = P(x_2) = \cdots = P(x_N) = 1/N,$$

then a selection of an object made under this condition is said to be random.

If a group of k objects is drawn in such a way that after each selection the object is replaced, then the group is said to be a sample drawn *with replacement*. Moreover, if x_1' denotes the first object drawn, x_2' the second, and so on, and if the probability of drawing the sample x_1', x_2', , , x_k' is given by the formula

$$P(x_1', x_2', , , x_k') = P(x_1')P(x_2') \cdots P(x_k') = \frac{1}{N^k},$$

then the sample is said to be random.

On the other hand, if, after the first selection is made, the object is withheld from the population and a second choice made, the second object withheld and a third choice made, and so on until k objects are chosen in this manner, the resulting sample is said to be a random sample obtained *without replacement.* Note that after each selection the probability changes:

$$P(x_1') = \frac{1}{N}, P(x_2') = \frac{1}{N-1}, P(x_3') = \frac{1}{N-2}, \, , \, , P(x_k') = \frac{1}{N-k+1} \, .$$

If N is very large with respect to the sample size k, sampling with and without replacement are essentially alike. The definition of random sampling from infinite populations is best understood after one has studied the probability density function in Chapter 9. A suitable definition may be found, for example, on page 132 of Reference 6.

Because some objects may have identical measurements, one *measurement* is not necessarily as likely to occur as another. A group of ten washers taken from a box constitutes a sample from this aggregate of, say, 1000 washers, or from the even larger potential product of the machine that manufactured them. This sample will not necessarily be random unless selected with some care. The ten washers should be selected from different parts of the box, not from a particular part such as the top. If a sample of student records is to be selected from an alphabetically arranged card file, it would be risky to select all the records from the same portion of the file. Student names might reflect racial factors. A sample of soil should be synthesized from several areas of the garden plot.

In more elaborate analyses, samples must be scientifically constructed so as to include appropriate numbers of different representative groups. Thus, the sample taken in an election poll must contain different economic, geographic, social, racial, or other groups if it is to reflect the voting tendencies of the country as a whole. The problem of obtaining an adequate sample is often solved only after careful study and subsequent testing. In many statistical investigations, the sample is drawn with the aid of a table of random digits (see Section 5.4).

6.3. THE NATURE OF STATISTICS

The field of statistics is extensive and varied; therefore, it may be helpful to describe it in terms of certain dichotomies that characterize it.

Statistical investigations may be *descriptive* or *inferential.* Generally the former type involves fairly simple techniques; the latter demands a somewhat higher order of critical judgment and mathematical methods.

Suppose that we are confronted with a set of measurements or observations actually obtained from life. Such a set usually represents a complex of data from which it is possible to extract an almost unlimited amount of information. For example, the weekly wages of a group of steel workers may yield information of the following kinds: the total wage received by the group, the highest wage, the lowest wage, the most frequent wage, the range of wages, the average wage, the number of wages below $75, the number above \$100, the number between \$75 and \$125, and so on. The task of the statistician is to select a few procedures and measures by means of which the significant aspects of the given data may be thrown into high relief. These aspects may be obtained by means of *classification, graphing*, and *averaging*. Because we are concerned only with an effective characterization of the given data themselves as they come to us through observation, and not with estimates or conclusions involving theoretically related populations, we shall distinguish this type of statistical analysis by means of the word *descriptive*. This analysis, confined exclusively to the data before us, deals with methods of recording or tabulating the constituent items, with their visual presentation, with the properties of various kinds of measures, with devices for computing them, and, in fact, with all means of giving a summary description of the data themselves.

The second type of statistical investigation is concerned with conclusions about the population that may be drawn from the data in the sample. If the data are on a large scale they may be treated as practically equivalent to the population and the properties of the sample may be considered to be like those of the population. Sometimes the sample data may constitute the population itself. If the data form a small sample drawn from the population, we usually seek to derive the properties of the population from the limited information contained within the sample. It is clear that in any case, we must make certain assumptions and interpret our results in the light of them. Theoretical analysis of this type is based upon the mathematical theory of probability. It has important applications, for instance, in industry, medicine, agriculture, education, and the social sciences.

A second dichotomy arises in a consideration of the theoretical and the practical aspects of statistics. *Mathematical* or theoretical statistics seeks to derive the laws which various populations of data and samples derived from them obey, these populations being more or less definitely specified. *Applied* or methodological statistics uses the theoretical results as models for the solution of practical problems.

A third dichotomy occurs when we consider the source of the data to be analyzed. If the data are already gathered and you have had no control over them, then you must find out what you can from what you have available. On the other hand, you may consider the objectives of your investigation first and then plan an appropriate experiment from which you can collect significant data. Here you have some control over the kind and amount of data desired. Problems connected with efficiently planned statistical experiments come under the heading of *The Design of Experiments*. In agriculture, industry, and medicine, for example, appropriate designing is highly desirable and indeed, necessary. Large sample methods are most useful when the data are already in; small sample techniques predominate when you gather information from an appropriate experiment.

6.4. AVERAGES

Many statistical inferences concerning a population have to be made from a random sample. The first step in drawing such inferences consists of describing the numerical characteristics of the sample. The description usually involves averages that summarize the central tendency of the data and their variability. An average is a typical or representative value; it is a single number that is employed to replace a set of numbers. There are many different kinds of averages, each with its own peculiar properties. The *median* or middle value of an ordered group, the *mode* or most frequent value, and the *arithmetic mean* are three of the most useful measures of central tendency. We shall discuss the arithmetic mean in detail, but only mention the properties of the other two averages by means of optional exercises. (See exercises 45 and 46 of this chapter and exercise 11 of Chapter 7.)

The *range*, the *mean deviation*, the *standard deviation*, and the *quartile deviation* are concerned with the degree of variability of data. These may evaluate the dispersion of the data about a central value or, perhaps, their complete spread. Some of these measures will be treated later.

6.5. A SYSTEM OF NOTATION

Suppose that the following amounts represent the salaries of the teachers in a certain school:

$6400, 5500, 4600, 6100, 5300, 8700, 4100, 6700, 5700, 5200.

To obtain the average salary known as the *arithmetic mean*, we merely add the ten amounts and divide by ten;

$$\frac{1}{10}(58,300) = 5830.$$

Thus the mean salary is $5830.

In this illustration, *salary* is the variable factor which we designate by the letter x. The observed ten salaries constitute the values of the variable and are called the *variates*. Variates are usually represented by the symbol for the variable with subscripts attached. Thus, above, $x_1 = 6400$, $x_2 = 5500$, $x_3 = 4600$, . . . , $x_{10} = 5200$. These symbols are read: x sub-one, x sub-two, x sub-three, . . . , x sub-ten.

It is necessary at this point to introduce an important notation for variates and other quantities associated with them. Because the calculation of many statistical measures requires the sum of a number of variates, we introduce a standard symbol, the capital Greek letter *sigma*, Σ, to denote a sum, as illustrated below:

$$\sum_{i=1}^{N} x_i = x_1 + x_2 + x_3 + \cdots + x_N.$$

The symbol on the left may be read "summation x_i, i taken from 1 to N," and means that the subscript i is a discrete variable whose values are the integers from 1 to N inclusive. These values are attached to x as subscripts, and the sum of the resulting x's taken. In like manner,

$$\sum_{i=1}^{10} x_i^2 = x_1^2 + x_2^2 + x_3^2 + \cdots + x_{10}^2;$$

$$\sum_{i=1}^{N} x_i y_i = x_1 y_1 + x_2 y_2 + \cdots + x_N y_N;$$

and

$$\sum_{j=1}^{8} f_j(x_j + y_j) = f_1(x_1 + y_1) + f_2(x_2 + y_2) + \cdots + f_8(x_8 + y_8).$$

Note that the variable in the summation is indicated below the summation sign, Σ. In the last three lines, the variable subscripts are i, i, and j, respectively.

There are a few basic theorems involving summations whose proofs follow immediately from the definition of the summation symbol.

Theorem 6.1. The summation of the product of a constant and a variable equals the product of the constant and the summation of the variable, that is:

$$\sum_{i=1}^{N} kx_i = k\sum_{i=1}^{N} x_i.$$

Proof.

$$\sum_{i=1}^{N} kx_i = kx_1 + kx_2 + kx_3 + \cdots + kx_N$$

$$= k(x_1 + x_2 + x_3 + \cdots + x_N)$$

$$= k \sum_{i=1}^{N} x_i.$$

Theorem 6.2. The summation of the sum (or difference) of two variables equals the sum (or difference) of their summations, that is:

$$\sum_{i=1}^{N} (x_i \pm y_i) = \sum_{i=1}^{N} x_i \pm \sum_{i=1}^{N} y_i$$

Proof.

$$\sum_{i=1}^{N} (x_i \pm y_i) = (x_1 \pm y_1) + (x_2 \pm y_2) + \cdots + (x_N \pm y_N)$$

$$= (x_1 + x_2 + \cdots + x_N) \pm (y_1 + y_2 + \cdots + y_N)$$

$$= \sum_{i=1}^{N} x_i \pm \sum_{i=1}^{N} y_i.$$

Theorem 6.3. The summation of a constant taken from **1** *to* **N** *equals the constant multiplied by* **N**, *that is:*

$$\sum_{i=1}^{N} k = Nk.$$

Proof. Since the constant, k, is unaffected by a subscript,

$$\sum_{i=1}^{N} k = k + k + k + \cdots + k$$

$$= Nk.$$

When no ambiguity arises it is common practice to omit the subscripts associated with summation terms. Exercises 27–30 at the end of this chapter are examples of such usage.

6.6. THE ARITHMETIC MEAN

The arithmetic mean $\bar{x}$ *(read "x-bar") of a set of variates* $x_1, x_2, \ldots, x_N$ *is defined by the formula,*

$$\bar{x} = \frac{1}{N} \sum_{i=1}^{N} x_i. \tag{6.1}$$

This average is not only the most familiar one in use today, but it is also the most basic in theory and the most useful in practice. Unless otherwise stated, the word *mean* customarily denotes the *arithmetic mean.*

The mean of the schoolteachers' salaries calculated at the beginning of the previous section was obtained by formula (6.1). As a further illustration, consider the diameters in centimeters of 13 steel tubes:

2.57, 2.59, 2.64, 2.60, 2.62, 2.57, 2.55, 2.61, 2.50, 2.63, 2.64, 2.56, 2.61.

Their mean diameter is:

$$\bar{x} = \tfrac{1}{13}(2.57 + 2.59 + 2.64 + \cdots + 2.61)$$

$$= \tfrac{1}{13}(33.69)$$

$$= 2.5877.$$

We shall state the mean diameter as 2.59 cm.

When the number of items is large, the precision of the mean may exceed somewhat the common precision of the separate items. In fact, the arithmetic mean of N items of common accuracy can be shown to be roughly $\sqrt{N}$ times as accurate as the items themselves.

6.7. A MATHEMATICAL PROPERTY OF
THE ARITHMETIC MEAN

The *deviation*, d_i, of a variate, x_i, from a mean, $\bar{x}$, is defined by the formula,

$$\mathbf{d}_i = \mathbf{x}_i - \bar{\mathbf{x}}. \tag{6.2}$$

Thus if x_i exceeds $\bar{x}$ the deviation is positive; if x_i is less than $\bar{x}$, the deviation is negative; if $x_i = \bar{x}$ the deviation is zero. The following property involving deviations has important uses in statistics.

Theorem 6.4. The sum of the deviations of a set of variates from its arithmetic mean is zero.

We shall first illustrate this theorem with the data on teachers' salaries (Section 6.5) where $\bar{x} = 5830$.

TABLE 6-1

x_i	$d_i = x_i - 5830$
6400	570
5500	−330
4600	−1230
6100	270
5300	−530
8700	2870
4100	−1730
6700	870
5700	−130
5200	−630
	4580
Totals....................	−4580
	0

We see from the second column of Table 6-1 that the sum of the deviations from the mean is exactly zero.

A formal proof of Theorem 6.4 follows.

$$\Sigma\,(x_i - \bar{x}) = \Sigma\,x_i - \Sigma\,\bar{x} \qquad \text{by Theorem 6.2;}$$

$$= \Sigma\,x_i - N\bar{x} \qquad \text{by Theorem 6.3;}$$

$$= \Sigma\,x_i - N\!\left(\frac{1}{N}\,\Sigma\,x_i\right) \text{ by Definition 6.1;}$$

$$= \Sigma\,x_i - \Sigma\,x_i = 0.$$

6.8. USES OF THE ARITHMETIC MEAN

In general, the arithmetic mean is a fairly stable average. It is not unduly affected by a few moderately small or moderately large values, and this stability increases with the total frequency, N. However, one or more extreme values may, at times, profoundly affect its value and render it of doubtful use. The general stability of the mean makes it a highly desirable statistical measure. It has a multitude of uses such as: in meteorology, for obtaining the average temperature or rainfall; in medicine, for discovering the average duration of a disease; in anthropology, for estimating certain average characteristics of a group of human beings; in economics, for computing average wages, prices, index numbers, and so on.

The arithmetic mean is dependent upon the *total* of the variates involved; hence, it is particularly useful in business statistics, as, for example, in averaging sales, production, prices, and so forth, over a specified period. In time series, totals are usually given for the week, month, or year, and from these we may find the mean daily, weekly, or monthly figures.

6.9. THE WEIGHTED ARITHMETIC MEAN

The *weight* of a variate is a numerical multiplier assigned to it in order to indicate its relative importance.

Suppose that a student receives grades of 88, 81, 78, 74, and 73 in courses carrying credit hours of 2, 3, 4, 3, and 3 hours, respectively. To find his average grade, we multiply each grade by the number of hours of credit assigned to it. The sum of the weighted values thus obtained is divided by the sum of the weights (the hours of credit), to obtain the weighted mean. Thus,

$$\bar{x} = \frac{(2 \times 88) + (3 \times 81) + (4 \times 78) + (3 \times 74) + (3 \times 73)}{2 + 3 + 4 + 3 + 3}$$

$$= 78.1.$$

The *weighted arithmetic mean* may therefore be defined by the formula:

$$\bar{x} = \frac{\sum\limits_{i=1}^{n} w_i x_i}{\sum\limits_{i=1}^{n} w_i}, \tag{6.3}$$

where w_i is the weight assigned to x_i.

It is often desirable to find the mean of sample means derived from samples of unequal sizes. Thus, if samples of $N_1, N_2, \ldots, N_k$ have means

$\bar{x}_1, \bar{x}_2, \ldots, \bar{x}_k$ respectively, the *over-all* mean of the k samples is:

$$\bar{x} = \frac{\sum\limits_{i=1}^{k} N_i \bar{x}_i}{\sum\limits_{i=1}^{k} N_i}. \tag{6.4}$$

Here the weights are the sample numbers, N_i. See, for example, exercise 50.

6.10. THE MEAN DEVIATION

A rather natural measure of variation is found when we average the deviations from the mean, where these deviations are taken without regard to sign. If, in Table 6-1, we change all the minus signs in the second column to plus, we find that the sum of these absolute deviations is 9160. The *mean deviation* is:

$$\text{M.D.} = \tfrac{1}{10}(9160) = 916.$$

Thus the salaries deviate "on an average" by \$916 from the mean salary of \$5830.

The *absolute value* of a number is its numerical value, and we indicate this by enclosing the numeral with two vertical bars. For example,

$$|-4| = 4, \ |7| = 7, \text{ and } |5 - 11| = 6.$$

We may now give a formal definition of the mean deviation.

*The **mean deviation, M.D.**, of a set of N variates, $x_1, x_2, x_3, \ldots, x_N$, is defined as the arithmetic mean of their absolute deviations from their arithmetic mean.*

$$\text{M.D.} = \frac{1}{N}\sum_{i=1}^{N} |x_i - \bar{x}|. \tag{6.5}$$

The mean deviation is not an important statistic; but it is occasionally used, for example, in laboratory measurements and in tests for the normality of a distribution. (See Section 10.12.) Although it is a sound measure of the dispersion of the data, it is not readily susceptible to algebraic treatment.

6.11. THE VARIANCE OF A SAMPLE

In calculating the mean deviation, we converted all minus signs to plus before averaging the deviations. Another method of eliminating minus signs is to square the deviations and then average these squares.

*The variance, s^2, of a sample of N variates, $x_1, x_2, \ldots, x_N$, with arithmetic mean, $\bar{x}$, is **1/Nth the sum of the squares of their deviations from the mean.**[1]*

[1] Many statisticians prefer to replace N by $N-1$ in the denominator of formula (6.6) for the reason stated in Section 16.5.

Thus,

$$s^2 = \frac{1}{N} \sum_{i=1}^{N} (x_i - \bar{x})^2. \tag{6.6}$$

The reasons for the use of a *sum of squares* are, (1) it is easily calculated, and (2) it may often be broken down into two or more component sums of squares yielding useful statistical information.

TABLE 6-2

Temperatures x_i	$x_i - \bar{x}$	$(x_i - \bar{x})^2$	x_i^2
47	7	49	2209
38	-2	4	1444
32	-8	64	1024
35	-5	25	1225
41	1	1	1681
39	-1	1	1521
45	5	25	2025
40	0	0	1600
42	2	4	1764
43	3	9	1849
43	3	9	1849
35	-5	25	1225
Totals....480	0	216	19,416

As a simple example of the use of formula (6.6), let us refer to the first three columns of Table 6-2, which lists the maximum temperatures at 12 selected towns of a certain region on a given date.

The mean temperature is readily found to be $\frac{480}{12}$ or $40°$. The deviations are given in column two, and they yield a sum of zero. This affords a check on our work. The squares of the deviations appear in the third column with a sum of 216. Then,

$$s^2 = \tfrac{1}{12}(216) = 18.$$

In most problems the calculation is not as easy as might appear from this example and may be expedited by the following:

Theorem 6.5. The variance of a sample of N variates equals 1/Nth the sum of their squares minus the square of their mean, that is,

$$s^2 = \frac{1}{N} \Sigma x^2 - \bar{x}^2. \tag{6.7}$$

Proof.

$$s^2 = \frac{1}{N} \Sigma (x - \bar{x})^2$$

$$= \frac{1}{N} \Sigma (x^2 - 2x\bar{x} + \bar{x}^2)$$

$$= \frac{1}{N} \Sigma x^2 - 2\bar{x} \cdot \frac{1}{N} \Sigma x + \frac{1}{N} \cdot N\bar{x}^2$$

$$= \frac{1}{N} \Sigma x^2 - 2\bar{x}^2 + \bar{x}^2$$

$$= \frac{1}{N} \Sigma x^2 - \bar{x}^2.$$

If we apply formula (6.7) to the temperature readings in Table 6-2, we may obtain from a table of squares (Table A of the Appendix) the values shown in the fourth column. Then,

$$s^2 = \tfrac{1}{12}(19,416) - 40^2$$
$$= 1618 - 1600$$
$$= 18.$$

As another illustration of the use of formula (6.7), consider the salaries of Section 6.5. The sum of the squares of these ten numbers (salaries) is found with the aid of Table A of the Appendix to be 354,590,000. The mean was previously found to be 5830. Then,

$$s^2 = \tfrac{1}{10}(354,590,000) - 5830^2$$
$$= 35,459,000 - 33,988,900 = 1,470,100.$$

6.12. THE STANDARD DEVIATION
OF A SAMPLE

The positive square root of the variance is defined as the *standard deviation*. Thus,

$$s = \left[\frac{1}{N} \Sigma (x - \bar{x})^2 \right]^{1/2}. \tag{6.8}$$

Since the variance of the 12 temperatures of Table 6-2 is 18, their standard deviation is $\sqrt{18} = 4.24$. Similarly, the standard deviation for the teachers' salaries is found from the variance:

$$s = (1,470,100)^{1/2} = 1212.$$

The standard deviation is, perhaps, the most important and the most widely used measure of variability. A relatively small value of s denotes close clustering about the mean; a relatively large value, wide scattering about the mean. A powerful reason for its usefulness arises from the fact that sums of squares are amenable to simple algebraic manipulation and give rise to useful and interesting relationships. A sum of absolute values, such as occurs in the mean deviation, is not as responsive to mathematical treatment. The standard deviation constitutes a convenient statistical unit for use in the construction of other statistics and in the comparison of these with one another. In other words, many measures are expressed in terms of the standard deviation as a unit.

A good working rule in computing s is to save, at most, one more decimal place than occurs in most of the individual variates. Thus, for the 12 temperatures we could write $s = 4.2°$. In general, however, three-digit accuracy is desirable. School teachers' salaries are represented by exact numbers, so we may state that their standard deviation is $1212.

EXERCISES

1. A 10-gram sample of coal from a carload of soft coal is to be analyzed in the chemical laboratory for ash content. How would you select this sample?

2. What are the objections, if any, to the use of a sample of public opinion obtained by the following methods? (a) Asking questions by telephone. (b) Mailing questionnaires. (c) Interviewing persons on the street. (d) Broadcasting a request for persons to send in their opinions.

3. From the list of dairies in each of 27 counties of a state, 20 dairies were selected at random. Was the resulting sample of 540 dairies a random one for the state as a whole? Why?

4. In the 1960 presidential campaign, a chain of popcorn stands sold popcorn in bags labeled Kennedy or Nixon, according to the preference of the purchaser. The relative sales of the two kinds of bags were used to estimate voting trends. Criticize this method of polling.

5. A school principal told a certain teacher that her class was below the average for the school. He said that he wanted no classes below the average. Criticize the principal's statement.

6. A prize drawing was made from a box containing several thousand uniform slips of paper upon which the names of the contestants were written. The slips were stirred with a spoon and then a blindfolded person reached into the box and drew out one slip of paper. Would you call this a random drawing? Why?

7. How would you draw a random sample of 50 student record cards from a file of 2000 cards arranged in alphabetical order, without the use of a table of random digits?

8. Using the first 200 pages of this book as a population, with the aid of Table 5-1, draw a random sample of 25 pages. Count the number of letters in the

last word on each page and record these 25 numbers. Find the mean number of letters in this sample.

9. Refer to the previous exercise and count the number of letters in the last word of every eighth page, beginning with page 8 and ending with page 200. Compare the mean number of letters in this sample with that obtained in exercise 8.

10. Turn to a five-place table of logarithms where the numbers, N, run from 100 to 999. With the aid of Table 5-1, select at random 10 such numbers. Record the frequency of occurrence of the digits 0, 1, 2, , , 9 in the last three places of the 10 five-figure logarithms (mantissas) in the rows corresponding to the N's chosen. There should be 300 digits in all.

In exercises 11–16, expand the term given.

11. $\sum_{i=1}^{N} F_i$ 12. $\sum_{i=1}^{9} f_i$ 13. $\sum_{i=1}^{n} f_i y_i$

14. $\sum_{i=1}^{7} x_i^2$ 15. $\sum_{i=1}^{6} f_i(x_i + y_i)$ 16. $\sum_{i=1}^{m} (x_i - x_0)$

In exercises 17–23, write the sums of terms as summations using Σ.

17. $X_1 + X_2 + X_3 + \cdots + X_{10}$

18. $f_1 x_1^2 + f_2 x_2^2 + \cdots + f_n x_n^2$

19. $\dfrac{f_1}{N} + \dfrac{f_2}{N} + \dfrac{f_3}{N} + \cdots + \dfrac{f_n}{N}$

20. $(x_1 - x_0) + (x_2 - x_0) + \cdots + (x_{15} - x_0)$

21. $f_1(y_1 + z_1) + f_2(y_2 + z_2) + \cdots + f_m(y_m + z_m)$

22. $f_1(x_1 - \bar{x})^2 + f_2(x_2 - \bar{x})^2 + \cdots + f_n(x_n - \bar{x})^2$

23. $x_1 y_1 + x_2 y_2 + \cdots + x_{50} y_{50}$

In exercises 24 and 25 write each in a simple form without the use of Σ.

24. $\sum_{i=1}^{10} a$.   25. $\sum_{i=1}^{N} \bar{x}$.

26. Prove that $\sum_{i=1}^{N} (x_i - x_0) - N(\bar{x} - x_0) = 0$.

Given the pairs of values of x and y in the following tables.

A		B		C		D	
x	y	x	y	x	y	x	y
1	−2	2	3	2	2	2	1
3	0	4	−1	−3	−1	−3	3
5	1	−3	2	5	3	1	−2
6	−1	0	6	0	4	3	0
5	7	5	3			4	1

27. In Table A, compute (a) Σx; (b) Σy; (c) Σx^2; (d) Σy^2; (e) Σxy; (f) $\Sigma x \Sigma y$; (g) $\Sigma (x - y)$.

28. In Table B, compute (a) Σxy; (b) $(\Sigma y)^2$; (c) Σx^2; (d) $\Sigma x \Sigma y$. Are the values of (a) and (d) equal?

29. In Table C, find the value of $\Sigma x \Sigma y - \Sigma xy$. What is the value of the difference between $\Sigma x^2 - \bar{x}^2$ and $\Sigma (x^2 - \bar{x}^2)$?

30. In Table D, calculate $\Sigma x \Sigma y - (\Sigma x)^2$; calculate $\Sigma xy + \Sigma y^2$.

31. Prove that $\left(\sum_{i=1}^{N} x_i \right)^2 \neq \sum_{i=1}^{N} x_i^2.$

32. Prove that $\sum_{i=1}^{N} x_i \sum_{i=1}^{N} y_i \neq \sum_{i=1}^{N} x_i y_i.$

33. A man invested the same amount of money in each of ten stocks. At the end of the year, the incomes from these, expressed in per cent, were as follows:

$$4.3, 5.1, 6.2, 5.4, 4.9, 1.2, 2.3, 6.4, 5.0, 3.3.$$

Find the mean per cent of income to the nearest 0.01.

34. In a chain of eight drug stores, the percentages of the total prescriptions that were refilled prescriptions in each store were 56, 49, 53, 45, 52, 55, 47, and 51. Find the mean per cent for the chain.

35. The tolerances or fatal doses of strophanthus in 0.01 cc per kg for seven cats were found to be as follows:

$$1.55, 1.58, 1.71, 1.44, 1.24, 1.89, 2.34.$$

Find the mean tolerance.

36. The changes in blood pressure of 12 patients after a short period of treatment were as follows:

$$-8, 0, 12, 5, -3, 0, -2, 20, -12, -9, -1, 3.$$

(a) What was the mean change? (b) What would the mean change be if all minus signs were changed to plus?

37. A sample of five aspirin tablets showed weights of 4.82, 4.77, 5.03, 4.90, and 5.14 grains. Find (a) the mean weight, and (b) the standard deviation to the nearest 0.01 grain.

38. In five plantings of 100 seeds each, 16, 10, 20, 15, and 12 seeds failed to germinate. Find (a) the mean number of failures, and (b) the variance.

39. In a psychological experiment with six adults, the numbers of seconds required for them to complete a certain operation were as follows: 26, 23, 25, 20, 27, 24. Calculate to the nearest 0.1 (a) the mean time, and (b) the standard deviation.

40. Given the following two groups of scores:

$$A: 80, 75, 70, 65, 60$$

$$B: 72, 71, 70, 69, 68$$

(a) What are the mean scores? (b) Which of the two groups is more variable? Why?

41. Eight samples of a halibut liver oil product were tested for Vitamin A content. The amounts, x, of Vitamin A measured in 1000 international units per gram, showed the following results:

$$\Sigma x = 187, \qquad \Sigma x^2 = 5009.$$

Find the mean and the standard deviation.

42. The diastolic blood pressures of 50 adult males were taken by means of two different types of instruments, and the difference, d, between the readings for each individual recorded. It was found that $\Sigma d = 314$ and $\Sigma d^2 = 2336$. Find the mean and the standard deviation of these differences.

43. The anesthetic indexes for ten dogs were as follows:

2.64, 2.27, 2.63, 2.30, 2.25, 2.25, 2.00, 2.00, 2.40, 2.79.

Show that $\bar{x} = 2.35$ and $s = 0.27$. (The anesthetic index is defined as the volume of the agent required to produce respiratory arrest divided by the volume required to produce surgical anesthesia.)

44. The temperature of a thermostat was read at two-minute intervals for a period of 20 minutes, with the following results:

Time	0	1	2	3	4	5
Temperature	3.161	3.158	3.159	3.160	3.152	3.162

Time	6	7	8	9	10
Temperature	3.152	3.158	3.162	3.162	3.155

Find the mean temperature and the mean deviation. (From *Journal of Chemical Education*, Feb. 1935.)

45. Fifteen persons made the following contributions to the Red Cross:

$5, 7, 2, 15, 2, 6, 12, 150, 5, 5, 20, 10, 12, 10, 8.

(a) Arrange these contributions in order of size and select the middle one. This is the *median* contribution.
(b) Find the mean contribution.
(c) Which average do you prefer? Why?

46. The salaries of ten vice-presidents in an insurance company were as follows:

$12,000, 18,000, 15,000, 13,000, 13,000, 14,000, 16,000, 12,000, 10,000, 14,000.

Find the median salary of this *even* number of salaries as that salary halfway between the two middle salaries when the salaries are arranged in order of magnitude.

47. Of a graduating class in a certain college, 40% concentrated in literature or the arts with a mean grade quotient of 3.12; 25% concentrated in the natural sciences or mathematics with a mean grade quotient of 1.85, and 35% concentrated in the social studies with a mean grade quotient of 2.67. What was the mean grade quotient for the entire class?

48. In computing the grade quotient of a student at a certain college, A = 4, B = 3, C = 2, D = 1, F = 0. A plus sign adds 0.3, and a minus sign subtracts 0.3. The numerical equivalents of the grades are weighted according to the number of hours' credit. Compared according to grade quotients, which of the following two records is the better one?

(a) B, 3 hrs; B−, 2 hrs; C+, 3 hrs; D, 3 hrs; F, 4 hrs

(b) B−, 3 hrs; C+, 3 hrs; C−, 4 hrs; D+, 4 hrs; D−, 1 hr

49. The following data were taken from the *Statistical Abstract of the United States* for 1959.

Grain	Average price (cents per bushel)	Production (1000 bushels)
Wheat	193	950,662
Corn	112	3,422,331
Oats	61	1,300,954
Rye	108	27,243
Barley	88	437,170
Sorghums	97	564,324

Find the average price of grain per bushel according to the following method. Let the price be weighted according to the production; assign a weight of 1 to rye, and compute the corresponding weights for the other grains to the nearest integer.

50. The mean hourly rate of pay for each of four industries and the number employed in each are given below. Compute the over-all mean hourly rate.

No. employed	Rate in dollars
463,000	1.30
1,328,000	1.42
217,000	2.68
97,000	2.11

7

Frequency Distributions and
Probability Functions;
The Discrete Case

There is nothing so fertile in utilities as
abstractions.

Anonymous

7.1. INTRODUCTION

In what follows, it is necessary to distinguish between patterns of behavior of data arising from actual experiments involving observations, records, interviews, questionnaires, etc., and patterns of behavior of random variables governed by assumed probability laws. The latter comprise distribution models or *probability distributions* which may or may not be compared with appropriate models. Thus, in analyzing data derived from an actual statistical experiment, we may frequently hypothesize that the data arise as values of a random variable, following more or less closely a probabilistic model defined by a *probability function*. We shall first give an example of a frequency distribution stemming from an actual experiment, and then define the probability function that might serve as a model for it.

Suppose that we toss two pennies 20 times and record the number of heads appearing on each of the 20 throws. Let the actual outcomes be represented by the *frequency table* or *distribution* (Table 7-1).

Next let us consider what, theoretically, should happen on the assumption that both pennies are unbiased. To each element of the sample space

$$\{HH, HT, TH, TT\}$$

TABLE 7-1
A FREQUENCY TABLE

No. Heads x_i	Frequency f_i
0	3
1	9
2	8
Total	20

we attach a probability of $\frac{1}{4}$, so that we may construct the following probability function:

TABLE 7-2
A PROBABILITY FUNCTION

No. Heads x	Probability $f(x)$	Theoretical Frequency or Expected Number in 20 Tosses
0	$\frac{1}{4}$	5
1	$\frac{1}{2}$	10
2	$\frac{1}{4}$	5
Totals	1	20

This is our model for studying the results shown in Table 7-1. The actual frequencies obtained in Table 7-1 do not agree with the theoretical frequencies in Table 7-2. No heads appeared less frequently, and two heads appeared more frequently than expected. A question that one might properly ask is, "Are these actual frequencies sufficiently different from the theoretical to warrant the conclusion that bias exists—that heads tend to appear more often than tails?" We are not prepared to answer this question at this stage of our study, but it can be shown by means of the Chi-square test in Chapter 11 that the discrepancies are probably due solely to chance.

7.2. PROBABILITY FUNCTIONS

A probability function of a discrete random variable, X, is defined as the set of ordered pairs $\{x_i, f(x_i)\}$, where x_i is a real number, $i = 1, 2, , , n, f(x_i)$ is the probability that $X = x_i$, and $\sum_{i=1}^{n} f(x_i) = 1$. We may define such a function by means of a table.

TABLE 7-3
A PROBABILITY FUNCTION

x	x_1	x_2	$\cdots$	x_n
$f(x)$	$f(x_1)$	$f(x_2)$	$\cdots$	$f(x_n)$

Thus the first two columns of Table 7-2 define the probability function for the tossing of two unbiased pennies.

Another illustration is found in Table 7-4.

TABLE 7-4

x	0	2	3	5
$f(x)$	0,1	0.3	0.4	0.2

Note the important condition that $\Sigma f(x) = 0.1 + 0.3 + 0.4 + 0.2 = 1$.

The graph of a probability function is shown in Fig. 7-1. The vertical lines have lengths proportional to the probabilities. The function defined

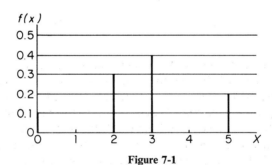

Figure 7-1

by Table 7-4 is represented in this figure. Another illustration, that of a binomial probability function, is given in Fig. 8-1.

7.3. CUMULATIVE PROBABILITIES; THE
CUMULATIVE DISTRIBUTION FUNCTION

In Table 7-3, we recall that $f(x_i) = P(X = x_i)$. If we now replace $f(x_i)$ by $F(x_i) = P(X \leq x_i)$, assume $x_1 \leq x_2 \leq x_3 \leq \cdots \leq x_n$, and construct a corresponding table (Table 7-5),

TABLE 7-5

x	x_1	x_2	$\cdots$	x_n
$F(x)$	$F(x_1)$	$F(x_2)$	$\cdots$	$F(x_n)$

where

$$F(x_1) = P(X \leq x_1) = f(x_1)$$
$$F(x_2) = P(X \leq x_2) = f(x_1) + f(x_2)$$
$$F(x_3) = P(X \leq x_3) = f(x_1) + f(x_2) + f(x_3)$$

$$\begin{array}{ccc} \cdot & \cdot & \cdot \\ \cdot & \cdot & \cdot \\ \cdot & \cdot & \cdot \end{array}$$

and

$$F(x_n) = P(X \leq x_n) = \sum_{i=1}^{n} f(x_i) = 1$$

we derive a *cumulative probability table* which defines a *cumulative distribution function* of the random variable X.[1] For example, from Table 7-4 we derive the cumulative distribution function, $F(X)$, which follows in Table 7-6.

TABLE 7-6

x	0	2	3	5
$F(x)$	0.1	0.4	0.8	1

Thus $P(X \leq 0) = 0.1$, $P(X \leq 2) = 0.4$, $P(X \leq 3) = 0.8$, and $P(X \leq 5) = 1$.

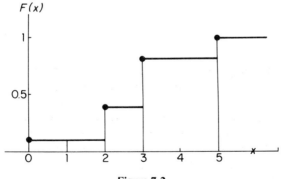

Figure 7-2

The corresponding cumulative probability diagram is shown in Fig. 7-2.

[1] Many statisticians prefer to call it merely a *distribution function*.

Its form reveals its name because it is called a *step function*. Note, from the diagram, that the probability for a value of X less than or equal to any value between 0 and 2, 2 and 3, or 3 and 5, is the same as that for 0, 2, or 3, respectively. For example, $F(\frac{1}{2}) = P(X \leq \frac{1}{2}) = P(X = 0)$ and $F(4.2) = P(X \leq 4.2) = P(X = 3)$. Also $P(X < 0) = 0$.

7.4. FREQUENCY DISTRIBUTIONS OF DISCRETE DATA

Empirical statistical data often come to us as large samples of observations and in a form unsuitable for immediate analysis until tabulated. The distribution, shown in the first two columns of Table 7-7, is discrete.

TABLE 7-7

NUMBERS OF QUESTIONS OUT OF TEN CORRECTLY ANSWERED BY A CLASS
OF NINETY PUPILS

(1) No. Correct x_i	(2) Frequency f_i	(3) Cum f_i	(4) $f_i x_i$	(5) $f_i x_i^2$
3	1	1	3	9
4	2	3	8	32
5	5	8	25	125
6	12	20	72	432
7	19	39	133	931
8	25	64	200	1600
9	18	82	162	1458
10	8	90	80	800
	90		683	5387

The frequency diagram for the data in Table 7-7 appears in Fig. 7-3. The lengths of the vertical lines are proportional to the frequencies.

It is common experience to hear questions of the following sort: How many pupils answered seven or fewer questions out of ten correctly? How many tons of shipping did the United States lose during the first six months of World War II? What per cent of American girls twenty years of age weigh less than 110 pounds? Such questions are designed to elicit information of a special and significant type and usually require for their answers certain partial sums obtained from a frequency table. In statistics, these modes of expressing important facts center about the concept of *cumulative frequency*.

The cumulative frequency (abbreviated cum f) of the mth class in a frequency

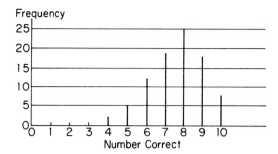

Fig. 7-3. Numbers of questions out of ten answered correctly in a class of 90 pupils.

distribution is the sum of the frequencies beginning with the first, f_1, and ending with the mth, f_m. Briefly,

$$cum\, f_m = \sum_{i=1}^{m} f_i.$$

From column 2 of Table 7-7, we construct column 3. Thus $cum\, f_1 = 1$; $cum\, f_2 = f_1 + f_2 = 1 + 2 = 3$; $cum\, f_3 = f_1 + f_2 + f_3 = 3 + 5 = 8$; and so on. When, for example, we say that $cum\, f_5 = 39$, we mean that 39 pupils had 7 or fewer questions correct. From the cumulative frequency table, a graph also of the step type has been constructed (Fig. 7-4). Recall, however, that the frequencies given are actual, not theoretical.

It is often desirable to calculate the mean, standard deviation, and other statistics from tables such as Table 7-7.

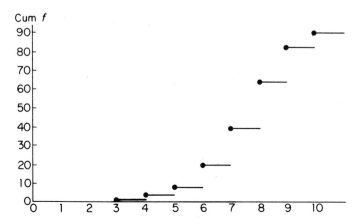

Fig. 7-4. Cumulative frequency diagram from Table 7.7.

7.5. THE ARITHMETIC MEAN OF A DISCRETE FREQUENCY DISTRIBUTION

The mean of a frequency distribution is conveniently conceived as a weighted mean (Section 6.9) where the weights are the frequencies. Formula (6.1) then becomes

$$\bar{x} = \frac{1}{N} \sum_{i=1}^{n} f_i x_i \tag{7.1}$$

where f_i is the frequency of the variate x_i, n is the number of different variates and the total frequency $N = \sum_{i=1}^{n} f_i$. Formulas (6.1) and (7.1) represent essentially the same thing, for the latter merely takes into account that certain variates occur repeatedly, the number of repetitions of x_i being designated as f_i. From Table 7-7, column 4,

$$\bar{x} = \frac{683}{90} = 7.59,$$

so that the mean number of correct answers is between 7 and 8.

7.6. EXPECTED VALUE OF A DISCRETE RANDOM VARIABLE

Formula (7.1) can be written:

$$\bar{x} = \sum_{i=1}^{n} \left(\frac{f_i}{N} \right) x_i.$$

Therefore, f_i/N can be interpreted as a *relative frequency* or probability. For example, from Table 7-7 we find that the probability that a pupil chosen at random from the class of 90 had just 8 answers correct is $\frac{25}{90} = 0.28$. From these ideas stems the definition of the *expected value* of a random variable X with the probability function $f(X)$.

If $\{x_i, f(x_i)\}$ defines a probability function, $i = 1, 2, , , n$, the theoretical mean or expected value of X

$$\mu = E(X) = \sum_{i=1}^{n} f(x_i) x_i. \tag{7.2}$$

EXAMPLE 1. From Table 7-4,

$$E(X) = (0.1)0 + (0.3)2 + (0.4)3 + (0.2)5 = 2.8.$$

EXAMPLE 2. Suppose that a box contains 20 small packages, all indistinguishable except for the contents. Assume that 10 of these packages contain a cent each, five packages contain a nickel each, three contain a dime each, and two contain a quarter each. If a package is drawn at random, what is the expected value of the coin contained in it?

Solution. The probability, p_1, of drawing a cent is $\frac{10}{20}$ or 0.50; of drawing a nickel, $p_2 = \frac{5}{20} = 0.25$; of a dime, $p_3 = \frac{3}{20} = 0.15$; and of a quarter, $p_4 = \frac{2}{20} = 0.10$. Note that $p_1 + p_2 + p_3 + p_4 = 1$ and that $x_1 = 1, x_2 = 5, x_3 = 10$, and $x_4 = 25$.

$$E(X) = \Sigma p_i x_i$$

$$= (0.50 \times 1) + (0.25 \times 5) + (0.15 \times 10) + (0.10 \times 25)$$

$$= 5.75.$$

The answer, 5.75 cents, may be interpreted as follows: If the selection of a package were repeated a large number of times under the same conditions, the mean value of the amounts obtained would approximate 5.75 cents.

7.7. THE VARIANCE AND STANDARD DEVIATION OF A DISCRETE FREQUENCY DISTRIBUTION

The computation of s^2 and s from a discrete frequency table follows the same general pattern as that for $\bar{x}$. We define

$$s^2 = \frac{1}{N} \sum_{i=1}^{n} f_i(x_i - \bar{x})^2 \tag{7.3}$$

which can easily be transformed to a formula better adapted to numerical calculation as in Section 6.11:

$$s^2 = \frac{1}{N} \sum_{i=1}^{n} f_i x_i^2 - \bar{x}^2. \tag{7.4}$$

From Table 7-7 we find that

$$s^2 = \frac{5387}{90} - (7.59)^2 = 2.25,$$

whence

$$s = 1.50.$$

Note that in computing $\Sigma f_i x_i^2$ (column 5), we use $x_i(f_i x_i) = f_i x_i^2$, that is, we find the product of the first column variates and their corresponding values in the fourth column.

7.8. THE VARIANCE AND STANDARD DEVIATION OF A DISCRETE RANDOM VARIABLE

Inasmuch as formula (7.3) can be written as

$$s^2 = \sum_{i=1}^{n} \left(\frac{f_i}{N}\right)(x_i - \bar{x})^2$$

and f_i/N interpreted as a probability, we are led, as in Section 7.6, to a useful definition.

The variance, σ^2, of a discrete random variable X with probability function $f(X)$ is defined as the expected value of the square of the deviation from the mean μ. That is,

$$\sigma^2 = E(X - \mu)^2 = \sum_{i=1}^{n} f(x_i)(x_i - \mu)^2 \qquad (7.5)$$

where $\mu = E(X)$.

EXAMPLE 1. From Table 7-2,

$$\mu = E(X) = \tfrac{1}{4} \cdot 0 + \tfrac{1}{2} \cdot 1 + \tfrac{1}{4} \cdot 2 = 1$$

$$\sigma^2 = E(X - 1)^2 = \sum_{x=0}^{2} f(x)(x - 1)^2$$

$$= \tfrac{1}{4}(0 - 1)^2 + \tfrac{1}{2}(1 - 1)^2 + \tfrac{1}{4}(2 - 1)^2 = \tfrac{1}{2},$$

whence

$$\sigma = \sqrt{0.5} = 0.707.$$

EXAMPLE 2. From Table 7-4, $\mu = 2.8$ (example 1, Section 7.6).

$$\sigma^2 = E(X - 2.8)^2$$

$$= (0.1)(0 - 2.8)^2 + 0.3(2 - 2.8)^2 + 0.4(3 - 2.8)^2$$

$$+ 0.2(5 - 2.8)^2 = 1.960.$$

It follows that $\sigma = 1.40$.

7.9. THEOREMS INVOLVING EXPECTED VALUE

The definition of the expected value of a random variable, X, given by formula (7.2) may be generalized to include functions of X. Thus, instead of

$$\mu_X = E(X) = \sum_{i=1}^{n} f(x_i)x_i,$$

we may write for the expected value of a function $h(X)$,

$$\mu_{h(X)} = E[h(X)] = \sum_{i=1}^{n} f(x_i)h(x_i). \tag{7.6}$$

In formula (7.5), $\sigma^2 = E(X - \mu)^2$ is the expected value of the function $(X - \mu)^2$. The following theorems are easily proved with the aid of Theorems 6.1–6.3. k and a are arbitrary constants, and the summations go from 1 to n.

Theorem 7.1.

$$E(kX) = kE(X), \quad \text{that is,} \quad \mu_{kX} = k\mu_X. \tag{7.7}$$

Here $h(X) = kX$.

Proof. $E(kX) = \Sigma f(x_i)(kx_i)$
$$= k \Sigma f(x_i)x_i$$
$$= kE(X).$$

Theorem 7.2.

$$E(X + k) = E(X) + k, \quad \text{that is,} \quad \mu_{X+k} = \mu_X + k. \tag{7.8}$$

Here $h(X) = X + k$.

Proof. $E(X + k) = \Sigma f(x_i)(x_i + k)$
$$= \Sigma f(x_i)x_i + \Sigma f(x_i)k$$
$$= E(X) + k \Sigma f(x_i).$$

But $\Sigma f(x_i) = 1$, hence,

$$E(X + k) = E(X) + k.$$

Theorem 7.3.

$$E(k) = k. \tag{7.9}$$

See exercise 39.

Theorem 7.4.

$$E(X - \mu) = 0. \tag{7.10}$$

Note the similarity to Theorem 6.4. See exercise 32.

Theorem 7.5.

$$\sigma_{kX}^2 = k^2 \sigma_X^2. \tag{7.11}$$

Proof.

$$\sigma_{kX}^2 = \Sigma f(x_i)(kx_i - \mu_{kX})^2.$$

By formula (7.7),

$$\mu_{kX} = k\mu_X,$$

hence,

$$\sigma_{kX}^2 = \Sigma\ f(x_i)(kx_i - k\mu_X)^2$$
$$= k^2\ \Sigma\ f(x_i)(x_i - \mu_X)^2$$
$$= k^2\sigma_X^2.$$

Theorem 7.6.

$$\boldsymbol{\sigma_{X+a}^2 = \sigma_X^2.} \tag{7.12}$$

Proof.

$$\sigma_{X+a}^2 = \Sigma\ f(x_i)[(x_i + a) - \mu_{X+a}]^2.$$
$$= \Sigma\ f(x_i)[(x_i + a) - (\mu_X + a)]^2 \qquad \text{By Eq. (7.8)}$$
$$= \Sigma\ f(x_i)(x_i - \mu_X)^2$$
$$= \sigma_X^2.$$

Note that the addition of a constant to the random variable does not affect the variance.

Theorem 7.7.

$$\sigma_{kX+a}^2 = k^2\sigma_X^2. \tag{7.13}$$

See exercise 33.

Theorem 7.8.

$$\sigma_X^2 = \Sigma\ f(x_i)x_i^2 - \mu_X^2 \tag{7.14a}$$
$$= E(X^2) - \mu_X^2 \tag{7.14b}$$

See exercise 34.

EXAMPLE 1. Let $Y = h(X) = 2X - 5$. Find μ_Y and σ_Y^2.

Solution. If we refer to exercises 31 and 33, we note that $k = 2$ and $a = -5$; hence, $\mu_Y = \mu_{2X-5} = 2\mu_X - 5$. From formula (7.12), we find that $\sigma_Y^2 = \sigma_{2X-5}^2 = 4\sigma_X^2$.

EXAMPLE 2. Table 7-4 defined a certain probability function. Let $Y = h(X) = X^2 + 1$. Then we may rewrite that table as follows:

TABLE 7-8

x	0	2	3	5
$y = x^2 + 1$	1	5	10	26
$f(x)$	0.1	0.3	0.4	0.2

$$\mu_y = (0.1)1 + (0.3)5 + (0.4)10 + (0.2)26 = 10.8.$$

By formula (7.14),

$$\sigma_y^2 = (0.1)1 + (0.3)5^2 + (0.4)10^2 + (0.2)26^2 - (10.8)^2$$
$$= 66.16.$$

EXERCISES

1. Use the table of random digits (Table 5-1) to make a frequency distribution for the digits 0 through 9, from those listed in the first five rows of the page. What frequencies would you expect to find?

2. From the distribution obtained in the previous exercise, make a frequency diagram as in Fig. 7-3.

Construct frequency diagrams for the data shown in exercises 3, 4, and 5.

3. Numbers of heads appearing when six pennies were tossed 128 times.

No. Heads	Frequency
0	2
1	10
2	28
3	44
4	30
5	13
6	1
Total	128

4. Numbers of mistakes in spelling noted on an episode dictated to 40 pupils.

No. Mistakes	Frequency
0	5
1	8
2	11
3	7
4	6
5	2
6	1

5. Sizes of shoes worn by 235 college girls.

Size	Number
$2\frac{1}{2}$	2
3	2
$3\frac{1}{2}$	15
4	21
$4\frac{1}{2}$	21
5	36
$5\frac{1}{2}$	48
6	42
$6\frac{1}{2}$	26
7	15
$7\frac{1}{2}$	5
8	1
$8\frac{1}{2}$	1

6. Construct a probability function for X, where X represents the number of heads appearing when three unbiased pennies are tossed.

7. Construct a probability function for the sum appearing when two honest dice are rolled.

8. A die has three faces numbered 1, two faces numbered 2, and one face numbered 3. A second die has four faces numbered 1 and two faces numbered 3. The two dice are to be rolled. Construct the probability function for the sum of the numbers appearing.

Find the mean, $\bar{x}$, and the standard deviation, s, for the distributions in the following two exercises:

9. Exercise 3.   10. Exercise 4.

11. Find the mean in exercise 5. Note that the mean is a nonexistent shoe size and, in this case, is not a useful average. The *mode* or most frequent size, $5\frac{1}{2}$, is more typical.

12. Assume that a college evaluates letter grades as follows: A $= 4$, B $= 3$, C $= 2$, D $= 1$, and F $= 0$. A group of 50 seniors received the following grades in a course in philosophy. Find their mean grade.

Grade	Number
A	7
B	16
C	22
D	4
F	1

13. Given the probability function:

x	-2	-1	0	1	2	3
$f(x)$	0.1	0.1	0.2	0.2	0.3	0.1

(a) Find μ and σ^2.
(b) Construct the cumulative distribution function $F(X)$, and its graph.

14. Given the probability function:

x	0	5	10	15	20
$f(x)$	0.1	0.2	0.3	0.3	0.1

(a) Find μ and σ^2.
(b) Construct the cumulative distribution function $F(X)$, and its graph.

Find μ and σ from the probability functions in the following two exercises.

15. Exercise 6.   16. Exercise 8.

17. A pair of dice is thrown and the thrower is to receive a number of dollars equal to the sum that appears. What is the expected value?

Construct a cumulative frequency table and diagram for the data in each of the following three exercises.

18. Exercise 3. How many times did two or fewer heads appear?

19. Exercise 4. How frequently were more than three mistakes made?

20. Exercise 5. How many girls wore shoes with sizes under $4\frac{1}{2}$?

Define the cumulative distribution function, $F(X)$, in each of the following three exercises and construct its graph.

21. Exercise 6. What is the probability that not more than two heads appear?

22. Exercise 7. What is the probability for a sum greater than 7?

23. Exercise 8. What is the probability for a sum less than or equal to 4?

24. A bag contains seven pennies, three nickels, two dimes, one quarter, and a half dollar; the coins are contained, one each, in uniform boxes. What is the sum expected by a person drawing a box at random?

25. A lottery has one prize of $1000, two prizes of $500, five of $100, and 50 of $5. If 1000 tickets are sold, what is the value of a ticket? Solve this problem by two methods.

26. Two dimes are tossed and the tosser is to receive the dimes showing heads. What is the expected sum?

27. Two pennies are tossed and the person tossing them is to receive $4 if two heads appear, to lose $2 if two tails appear, and to lose $1 if one penny shows head, the other tail. What is the expected gain or loss for this person?

28. A lottery has one prize of $500, two prizes of $300 each, and five prizes of $100 each. If 1000 tickets are sold, what is the real value of a ticket?

29. In an advertising game, a person entering has one chance in 10,000 of winning $1000, two chances in 10,000 of winning $500, two chances in 10,000 of winning $100, five chances in 10,000 of winning $50, and 9990 chances in 10,000 of winning nothing. What is the expected winning?

30. An urn contains eight balls alike in every respect except color. Four of the balls are red, three are white, and one is black. A ball is drawn at random. If it is red, the person drawing receives 10 cents; if it is white, he receives nothing; if it is black, he loses 50 cents. What is the player's expected value?

31. Prove that $E(kX + a) = k\mu_X + a$.

32. Prove that $E(X - \mu) = 0$.

33. Prove that $\sigma^2_{kX+a} = k^2\sigma^2_X$.

34. Prove that $\sigma^2_X = \sum_{i=1}^{n} f(x_i)x_i^2 - \mu^2_X$.

35. A random variable X has the following probability function:

x	0	1	2	3	4
$f(x)$	k	0.1	0.4	$2k$	$2k$

Find the value of k.

36. Given the probability function

x	-1	0	1	2
$f(x)$	0.1	0.4	0.3	0.2

Let $Y = X^3 - 2$; then find (a) the probability function of Y; (b) μ_Y; (c) σ_Y^2.

37. Given the probability function

x	0	1	2	3
$f(x)$	0.1	0.3	0.5	0.1

Let $Y = X^2 + 2X$; then find (a) the probability function of Y: (b) μ_Y; (c) σ_Y^2.

38. Given the probability function

x	0	1	2	3
$f(x)$	k	0.4	$3k$	0.2

Find (a) the value of k; (b) μ_X; (c) σ_X^2; (d) $E(X^2)$; (e) $P(X \geq 2)$.

39. Prove that $E(k) = k$.

8

The Binomial
Probability Function

And I believe that the Binomial Theorem
and a Bach Fugue are, in the long run,
more important than all the battles of
history.
I believe in the wisdom of often saying
"probably" and "perhaps."

JAMES HILTON
This Week Magazine[1]

8.1. BINOMIAL PROBABILITY

Assume that an operation, which we shall term a *trial*, can have only one of two possible outcomes; one outcome is called *success*, the other, *failure*. The toss of a coin, the planting of a seed, the testing of an electric circuit, and the inoculation of a patient are examples of trials. The coin may show a head or a tail; the seed may germinate or it may not; the circuit may be hot or cold; and the patient may recover or die. Let p be the probability for success, and q, the probability for failure, so that $p + q = 1$. Suppose that an experiment consists of N trials, each trial made under essentially the same conditions; we may then assume that the outcome of each trial is independent of the other outcomes.[2] What is the probability for exactly x successes? The probability that success results in each of the first x trials is, by the extension of the multiplication theorem (Section 4.4), p^x. The probability that failure results in each of the remaining $(N - x)$ trials is, by the same theorem, q^{N-x}. Hence the probability that the first x trials are successful

---

[1] Copyright, 1937, by the United Newspapers Magazine Corporation.
[2] More precise definitions of *independent trials* may be found, for example, on pages 113–115 of Reference 4.

and that the last $N - x$ trials are failures is $p^x q^{N-x}$. But this is the probability associated with one particular order of successes and failures, namely,

$$\underbrace{pp \cdots p}_{x \text{ factors}} \quad \underbrace{qq \cdots q}_{N - x \text{ factors}}.$$

Exactly x successes in N trials can happen in any one of $N!/[x!(N - x)!]$ different orders [formula (2.4)]; hence, by the addition theorem for mutually exclusive events [formula (4.2a)], the probability for x successes in N trials is

$$P(x) = \frac{N!}{x!(N - x)!} p^x q^{N-x}. \tag{8.1}$$

This formula defines a *binomial probability function* for reasons stated in Section 8.7.

> EXAMPLE 1. The probability that two heads appear when six pennies are tossed is:
>
> $$\frac{6!}{2!4!}\left(\frac{1}{2}\right)^2\left(\frac{1}{2}\right)^4 = \frac{15}{64},$$
>
> for $p = q = \frac{1}{2}$, $N = 6$, and $x = 2$. Note that the tossing of six pennies simultaneously is experimentally equivalent to the tossing of one penny six times in succession, provided p is the same for each penny.

> EXAMPLE 2. A box contains ten balls alike in every respect save color. Seven are white and three are black. A blindfolded person selects a ball at random and the color is then noted. Then the ball is replaced and all balls thoroughly mixed again. A second ball is withdrawn and followed by the same procedure, until five drawings have been made. What is the probability that three balls drawn were white and two black?
>
> The probability, p, for drawing a white ball is $\frac{7}{10}$; the probability, q, of drawing a black one is $\frac{3}{10}$. The number of trials, N, is 5, and $x = 3$. Then the desired probability is:
>
> $$\frac{5!}{3!2!}\left(\frac{7}{10}\right)^3\left(\frac{3}{10}\right)^2 = 0.3087.$$

8.2. A DECISION PROBLEM

Suppose that we possess a well-worn penny and wonder if it is biased, that is, if it tends to show heads more frequently than tails, or vice versa.

We may satisfy our curiosity in the following manner. Let us set up the hypothesis that the coin is a true one, that is, unbiased. In more precise mathematical language we may state our hypothesis, H_0, called the *null hypothesis*, as $p = \frac{1}{2}$, where p is the probability for head. Then let us toss this penny ten times and observe the number of times a head appears. If a head appears too often or too seldom we shall reject the hypothesis, H_0, and thus decide that the coin is biased; otherwise we shall decide that the penny is a fair one.

Before continuing this discussion, we must make clear that our decision is to be based on just one experiment consisting of ten tosses of the coin. Of course, we might increase the number of tosses to 50, or 100, or even more. This would be easy to do in the case of a coin, but in many practical problems the number of observations possible may be restricted. For example, suppose we are testing the hypothesis that Drug Q produces an undesirable aftereffect in 50 per cent of the patients to whom it is administered and we have only ten such patients available. Our procedure for the immediate future might be governed by the outcome from this sample of ten. Here we wish to decide what number of bad aftereffects will cause us to abandon the drug in favor of another. In all phases of human activity, decisions have to be made in the face of incomplete evidence.

Intuitively we feel that a well-behaved penny should show heads about half of the time, although we realize that results sometimes are erratic or unusual. Ordinarily, then, we expect somewhere near 5 heads to show; a deviation say, of two heads from the "expected" 5 should not cause us surprise. Therefore, 3, 4, 5, 6, or 7 heads might well be considered to be consistent with the hypothesis that the coin is a fair one. Where should we draw the line between results that cause us to accept our hypothesis and those that compel us to reject it, particularly when we realize that an unbiased coin may, at times give surprising results? These questions lead us to the fundamental problem of making a decision in the face of uncertainty. We cannot, positively, with *any* number of tosses of the coin make certain that our decision is the correct one; but we *can* calculate the probability of a decision being wrong. Our problem, restated, is to agree upon the numbers of heads appearing that seem abnormal to us and therefore cause us to reject the hypothesis that the coin is true. All other numbers of heads will be considered to be consistent with this hypothesis.

Let us agree that if 0, 1, 9, or 10 heads appear, we shall consider the null hypothesis, H_0, to be refuted. Zero or one head (i.e., 10 or 9 tails) will be interpreted as evidence that the probability for head, $p < \frac{1}{2}$, that is, that the penny is biased in favor of tails, and 9 or 10 heads (i.e., 1 or 0 tail) that $p > \frac{1}{2}$, or that the penny is biased in favor of heads. Any other number of heads 2, 3, 4, 5, 6, 7, or 8, will be construed as consistent with H_0.

8.3. REJECTION AND ACCEPTANCE
REGIONS

The probabilities for 0, 1, 2, ..., 10 heads for an unbiased penny may be found from formula (8.1) if we let $N = 10$, $p = q = \frac{1}{2}$, and $x = 0, 1, 2, ...$, 10, respectively. The 11 probabilities are computed to 4 decimal places as shown in Table 8-1, and are represented by the lengths of the vertical lines in Fig. 8-1.

TABLE 8-1

No. heads, x	Probability, P(x)
0	1/1024 = 0.0010
1	10/1024 = 0.0098
2	45/1024 = 0.0439
3	120/1024 = 0.1172
4	210/1024 = 0.2051
5	252/1024 = 0.2461
6	210/1024 = 0.2051
7	120/1024 = 0.1172
8	45/1024 = 0.0439
9	10/1024 = 0.0098
10	1/1024 = 0.0010

In Fig. 8-1, the 11 points on the x-axis corresponding to numbers of heads form a set of distinct points $\{0,1,2,3,4,5,6,7,8,9,10\}$ which we can

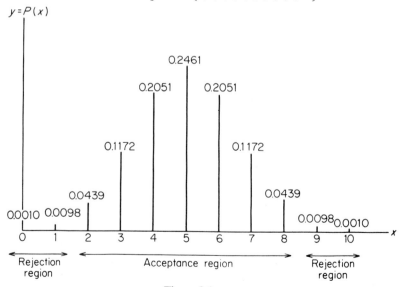

Figure 8-1

characterize geometrically as a one-dimensional sample space. The two points at each end of the set, that is, the subset $\{0,1,9,10\}$, form a *critical* or *rejection region* of the sample space for the hypothesis, $p = \frac{1}{2}$. Since these points constitute two ends or tails of the probability diagram of Fig. 8-1, we have a *two-tail critical region*, or we have a *two-tail test* of our hypothesis; either too many or too few heads cause us to reject H_0. The complementary subset $\{2,3,4,5,6,7,8\}$ constitutes the *acceptance region*. An outcome that yields a point in the latter region causes us to accept the hypothesis; an outcome in the former region causes us to reject it.

8.4. THE TYPE I ERROR

The probability of obtaining one or another of the four outcomes 0, 1, 9, 10 heads, when the coin is true is found from Table 8-1 or Fig. 8-1 to be the sum of their separate probabilities:

$$0.0010 + 0.0098 + 0.0098 + 0.0010 = 0.0216.$$

This may be interpreted to mean that in repeated experiments of throwing a true coin 10 times, 0, 1, 9, or 10 heads are expected to appear 2.16 per cent of the time. Thus, whenever we reject the hypothesis that the coin is true because 0, 1, 9, or 10 heads show, we have a probability of 0.0216 of being wrong; stated otherwise, about 2.16 per cent of the time that we make decisions on this basis, we shall be making the wrong decision. This is the risk that we run. On the other hand, $1 - 0.0216$ or 0.9784 is the probability of making the correct decision, "the coin is true," whenever we get 2, 3, 4, 5, 6, 7, or 8 heads, which correspond to points in the acceptance region of our sample space.

The probability of rejecting the null hypothesis when it is true is designated by the Greek letter alpha, α, and the error thus committed is called a type I error.

Above $\alpha = 0.0216$.

Example.[3] Suppose that past experience has shown that Drug Q produces an undesirable aftereffect in about 50 per cent of the patients to whom it is administered. A modification in the formula of the drug is expected to reduce the per cent of patients having bad aftereffects. To test this expectation, 20 patients are to be given the modified drug. Let p be the unknown probability for undesirable aftereffects from the modified drug, so that we test the hypothesis, H_0, that $p = \frac{1}{2}$ (or greater) against the alternative hypothesis, H_1, that $p < \frac{1}{2}$. Let us agree that if 5 or fewer patients have undesirable reactions, we shall reject H_0 in favor of H_1. By means of formula

---

[3] This example is taken from a paper by G. E. Noether, Boston University.

(8.1), where $N = 20$, $p = \frac{1}{2}$, and $x = 0, 1, 2, 3, 4$, and 5, we find that

$$P(0) + P(1) + P(2) + P(3) + P(4) + P(5)$$
$$= 0.0000 + 0.0000 + 0.0002 + 0.0011 + 0.0046 + 0.0148 = 0.0207.$$

Thus the type I error, $\alpha = 0.02$ (approximately). This means that if a large number of experiments with 20 patients were carried out with the new drug, and if it were no better or worse than the old drug ($p = \frac{1}{2}$), five or fewer patients would have adverse effects about 2 per cent of the time, and 2 per cent of the time we would be deciding that the modified drug is better, an incorrect decision. Note here that we are using a one-tail test, for only results that yield fewer aftereffects than expected would cause us to reject the hypothesis, $p \geq \frac{1}{2}$, in favor of the alternative $p < \frac{1}{2}$.

8.5. THE TYPE II ERROR

The consequence of rejecting a hypothesis when it is true may be costly in terms of dollars and cents, or perhaps, in terms of health or even life. Likewise, the acceptance of a hypothesis when it is false may have undesirable results.

The probability of accepting the null hypothesis when it is false is designated by the Greek letter beta, β, and the error thus committed is called a type II error.

Suppose that the true, but unknown probability of an aftereffect from the modified formula were 0.30. For this value of p, what is the probability that the number of aftereffects exceeds 5, so that we would accept the hypothesis, $p = \frac{1}{2}$, when it is false? Here $N = 20$, $p = 0.30$, and $x > 5$. Then

$$P(6) + P(7) + \cdots + P(20) = 1 - [P(0) + P(1) + \cdots + P(5)]$$
$$= 1 - (0.0008 + 0.0068 + 0.0278 + 0.0716 + 0.1304 + 0.1789)$$
$$= 1 - 0.4163 = 0.5837.$$

Thus, if $p = 0.30$, we would accept the hypothesis, $p = 0.50$, about 58 per cent of the time: our type II error, $\beta = 0.58$. Thus if we set $\alpha = 0.02$ (approximately), we run the risk 58 per cent of the time of not discovering that the modified drug is better if $p = 0.30$. Of course we should like to reduce the size of β, but we can only do this at the expense of α. The smaller α is, the larger β becomes and vice versa. In a practical problem, the experimenter must decide in advance what the consequences of a wrong decision are.

The possible decisions and the nature of the errors are shown in Table 8-2.

TABLE 8-2

		Hypothesis is correct	false
Hypothesis	accepted	Decision is correct	Type II error
	rejected	Type I error	Decision is correct

8.6. REMARKS

(1) In the drug experiment it should be noted that although the hypothesis to be tested was $p \geq \frac{1}{2}$, we used only the value $p = \frac{1}{2}$ to determine the probability associated with the rejection region. If $p > \frac{1}{2}$, the chance for the number of bad effects to be 5 or fewer would be even smaller than if p equalled $\frac{1}{2}$, hence, the rejection of the hypothesis would be more emphatic, or, to state the fact in a different way, the type I error would be even smaller than 0.02.

(2) In the coin-tossing experiment we were testing to see if the coin was biased—in what direction, we did not know, so we used a two-tail test. Either an excessively small number of heads or an excessively large number was taken as an indication of bias. In the drug experiment we hoped for a reduction in the customary number of bad effects so that only an abnormally small number of them would cause us to reject the hypothesis, $p \geq \frac{1}{2}$, in favor of $p < \frac{1}{2}$. Here we have a one-tail test. The decision to use either a one-tail or a two-tail test is usually guided by the aim of the experimenter and, particularly, by the alternative to be accepted if the null hypothesis is rejected. The size of the type II error, β, depends on the acceptance region, whether it includes one-tail or no-tail. Other things being equal, we select the acceptance region that minimizes β for a given α.

(3) In Table 8-3, the probabilities of type II errors for different values of p are shown. This table shows, for example, that if the new formula really cuts down the frequency of aftereffects from 0.50 to 0.40, the experimenter

TABLE 8-3

True value of p	Probability of wrong decision
0.10	0.01
0.20	0.20
0.25	0.38
0.30	0.58
0.40	0.87

has a probability of 0.87 of not discovering it; and if the reduction was from 0.50 to 0.25, there still would be a chance of 0.38 of not finding it out. If α is to be kept at 0.02 then such large probabilities of a type II error should be avoided if possible. The experimenter has three quantities at his disposal: α, β, and N, the number of observations (patients), to be taken. The choice of any two determines the third. It would be possible for him to select α and β and then determine N. If this were done, it might happen that the required number of observations is larger than he is able to handle; and if this is so, the researcher could find this out before he wastes his time with fruitless observations.

(4) Tests of hypotheses are sometimes called *tests of significance*, and the probability, α, is termed the *significance level*. A probability value is said to be *significant* if it causes us to reject the null hypothesis. In many statistical experiments, such as those discussed in Chapter 13, the type I error, α, or its equivalent, the significance level (often expressed as a per cent), is selected in advance, and then the rejection region is determined from it. Of course the choice of a P value for significance is for the experimental statistician to decide. Sometimes it is quite arbitrary; more often it is guided by weighty considerations. See Section 13.11 for further remarks on this topic.

8.7. THE BINOMIAL PROBABILITY FUNCTION

The binomial theorem in its elementary form may be written as the equation:

$$(q + p)^N = q^N + \frac{N!}{1!(N-1)!} q^{N-1}p + \frac{N!}{2!(N-2)!} q^{N-2}p^2$$

$$+ \frac{N!}{3!(N-3)!} q^{N-3}p^3 + \cdots$$

$$+ \frac{N!}{x!(N-x)!} q^{N-x}p^x + \cdots + p^N, \tag{8.2}$$

where N is a positive integer. The $(x + 1)$th term, or general term of the expansion, is identical with formula (8.1), which represents the probability for exactly x successes in N trials. Therefore, the terms of the binomial expansion in the right member of Eq. (8.2) represent, in order, the probabilities for exactly 0, 1, 2, 3 , , , N successes in N trials.

Equation (8.2) can also be written as

$$(q + p)^N = \sum_{x=0}^{N} \frac{N!}{x!(N-x)!} p^x q^{N-x}$$

whence

$$1 = \sum_{x=0}^{N} P(x),$$

by virtue of formula (8.1) and because $p + q = 1$. Thus the probabilities $P(x)$ satisfy a necessary condition for the existence of a probability function.

The binomial probability function is defined as the set of ordered pairs, $\{(x,P(x))\}$, *where* $x = 0, 1, 2, , , N$, *and* $P(x)$ *is given by formula* (8.1).

If in Eq. (8.2), we let $q = p = \frac{1}{2}$ and $N = 10$, we obtain:

$$\left(\frac{1}{2} + \frac{1}{2}\right)^{10} = \left(\frac{1}{2}\right)^{10} + \frac{10!}{1!9!}\left(\frac{1}{2}\right)^{9}\left(\frac{1}{2}\right) + \frac{10!}{2!8!}\left(\frac{1}{2}\right)^{8}\left(\frac{1}{2}\right)^{2} + \cdots$$

$$+ \frac{10!}{9!1!}\left(\frac{1}{2}\right)\left(\frac{1}{2}\right)^{9} + \left(\frac{1}{2}\right)^{10}$$

$$= \frac{1}{1024} + \frac{10}{1024} + \frac{45}{1024} + \cdots + \frac{10}{1024} + \frac{1}{1024}.$$

These 11 fractions are those shown in Table 8-1, where they represented the probabilities for just 0, 1, 2, , , 10 heads to appear when a penny is tossed ten times.

The term *binomial distribution* is often used to describe the pattern of the probabilities $P(x)$, a pattern which yields frequencies proportional to the successive terms of the binomial expansion in Eq. (8.2). The name *Bernoulli distribution* is also employed, in honor of James Bernoulli (1654–1705), who first discovered it. The binomial distribution may be used as a model for certain distributions arising in practice. A graphical representation of such a model appears in Fig. 8-1.

8.8. THE MEAN OF A BINOMIAL DISTRIBUTION

The mean μ, of a binomial distribution is easily derived with the aid of formula (7.2).

$$\mu = E(x) = \sum_{i=1}^{n} f(x_i)x_i. \qquad (8.3)$$

In this formula, $f(x_i)$ becomes the binomial probability

$$P(x) = \frac{N!}{x!(N - x)!} p^{x}q^{N-x}, \qquad (8.4)$$

and the values x_i, become the values 0, 1, 2, . . . , N. Thus

$$\mu = \sum_{x=0}^{N} P(x)x$$

$$= \sum_{x=0}^{N} \frac{N!}{x!(N-x)!} p^x q^{N-x} x. \tag{8.5}$$

When $x = 0$, the first term of this sum is zero, so that

$$\mu = \sum_{x=1}^{N} \frac{N!}{x!(N-x)!} p^x q^{N-x} x$$

$$= Np \sum_{x=1}^{N} \frac{(N-1)!}{(x-1)!(N-x)!} p^{x-1} q^{N-x}$$

$$= Np(q+p)^{N-1}.$$

But $p + q = 1$; hence,

$$\mu = Np. \tag{8.6}$$

Thus, if an unbiased coin is tossed 100 times, the expected number of heads or theoretical mean is $100 \times \frac{1}{2}$ or 50. Although we really do not "expect" heads to appear just 50 times, we do expect, in repeated experiments of tossing this coin 100 times, that the number of heads will average about 50.

8.9. THE STANDARD DEVIATION OF A BINOMIAL DISTRIBUTION

The variance of a discrete distribution is defined in formula (7.5):

$$\sigma^2 = E(x-\mu)^2 = \sum_{x=0}^{N} P(x)(x-Np)^2.$$

The products following the summation sign may be obtained in a convenient form for summing if we write:

$$(x - Np)^2 = x^2 - 2xNp + N^2 p^2$$

$$= x + x(x-1) - 2Npx + N^2 p^2.$$

We have then four sums of products where $P(x)$ is given by formula (8.4):

(1) $\quad \sum_{x=0}^{N} P(x)x = Np,$ from the preceding section;

(2) $\quad \sum_{x=0}^{N} P(x)x(x-1) = N(N-1)p^2 \sum_{x=2}^{N} \frac{(N-2)!}{(x-2)!(N-x)!} p^{x-2} q^{N-x}$

$$= N(N-1)p^2(q+p)^{N-2}$$

$$= N^2 p^2 - Np^2;$$

(3) $$\sum_{x=0}^{N} P(x)(-2Npx) = -2Np \sum_{x=0}^{N} P(x)x$$

$$= -2N^2p^2;$$

(4) $$\sum_{x=0}^{N} P(x)N^2p^2 = N^2p^2 \sum_{x=0}^{N} P(x)$$

$$= N^2p^2(q + p)^N$$

$$= N^2p^2.$$

When we add these four results we obtain

$$Np + N^2p^2 - Np^2 - 2N^2p^2 + N^2p^2 = Np - Np^2$$

$$= Np(1 - p)$$

$$= Npq.$$

Thus the variance

$$\sigma^2 = Npq,$$ (8.7)

and the standard deviation

$$\sigma = \sqrt{Npq}.$$ (8.8)

If a penny is tossed 100 times, the standard deviation will be $\sqrt{100 \times \frac{1}{2} \times \frac{1}{2}}$, or 5. This means that when 100 pennies are tossed a large number of times, the average deviation of the number of heads from the expected value, 50, as measured by σ, will be 5.

8.10. OTHER PROPERTIES OF THE BINOMIAL DISTRIBUTION

The mean and the standard deviation of the distribution defined by $(q + p)^N$ are but two important measures associated with the binomial distribution. The *mode* or *most probable* number of successes is that value of x corresponding to the maximum probability. This means that this probability must be greater than or at least equal to the probabilities for the number of successes immediately preceding and immediately following x. That is,

$$P(x - 1) \leq P(x), \qquad P(x + 1) \leq P(x)$$

or

$$\frac{N!}{(x - 1)!(N - x - 1)!} p^{x-1}q^{N-x-1} \leq \frac{N!}{x!(N - x)!} p^x q^{N-x}$$

$$\frac{N!}{(x + 1)!(N - x + 1)!} p^{x+1}q^{N-x+1} \leq \frac{N!}{x!(N - x)!} p^x q^{N-x}.$$

The signs of equality are necessary since some binomial distributions have two adjacent modes. See the second illustration following this proof. If we divide each member of these inequalities by the right-hand member we obtain:

$$\frac{xq}{(N - x + 1)p} \leq 1$$

$$\frac{(N - x)p}{(x + 1)q} \leq 1. \tag{8.9}$$

From the first inequality it follows that:

$$xq \leq (N - x + 1)p$$

whence

$$x(p + q) \leq Np + p$$

or

$$x \leq Np + p. \tag{8.10}$$

From the second inequality,

$$(N - x)p \leq (x + 1)q$$

whence

$$x \geq Np - q. \tag{8.11}$$

Combining (8.10) and (8.11), it follows that for the number of successes, x, to be the mode, x must satisfy the double inequality

$$Np - q \leq x \leq Np + p. \tag{8.12}$$

Since p and q are positive fractions having a unit sum, the most probable value of x, to within a proper fraction, is Np. In case $Np - q$ and $Np + p$ are integers, the equality signs hold, and there will be two adjacent modal values with equal probability.

As one illustration, consider the most probable number of black balls drawn when 10 drawings with replacements are made from a box containing 2 black and 4 white balls. Here $N = 10$, $p = \frac{1}{3}$, $q = \frac{2}{3}$; x is the integer determined by the inequality:

$$\frac{10}{3} - \frac{2}{3} \leq x \leq \frac{10}{3} + \frac{1}{3}.$$

Hence, $x = 3$.

As a second illustration, we find the most probable number, when 20 drawings are made, to be the integer x such that:

$$\frac{20}{3} - \frac{2}{3} \leq x \leq \frac{20}{3} + \frac{1}{3},$$

so that x may be either 6 or 7.

The third and fourth *moments* of this important distribution are defined as follows:

$$\alpha_3 = \Sigma\, P(x)(x - Np)^3,$$

and

$$\alpha_4 = \Sigma\, P(x)(x - Np)^4.$$

By methods similar to the one used in Section 8.9, one can prove that

$$\alpha_3 = \frac{q - p}{(Npq)^{1/2}} \; ; \qquad\qquad (8.13)$$

$$\alpha_4 = \frac{1}{Npq} - \frac{6}{N} + 3. \qquad\qquad (8.14)$$

8.11. BINOMIAL PROBABILITY CALCULATIONS

Except for fairly small N, say $N \le 10$, and simple probability values such as $p = 0.3, 0.5$, etc., the calculation of binomial probabilities can be wearisome if not practically impossible. For this reason, useful tables have been prepared which eliminate the need for troublesome computation. Table B of the Appendix is an abbreviated table of cumulative binomial probabilities. The method of use is explained on the page preceding the table.

The two most complete tables in the United States are *Tables of the Binomial Probability Distribution* published by the National Bureau of Standards (Reference 21) and the *Tables of the Cumulative Binomial Probability Distribution* published by the Harvard University Computation Laboratory (Reference 17). The former give both individual terms and cumulated terms for values of p ranging from 0.01 to 0.50 (by increments of 0.01) and for N ranging from 2 to 49. The latter give cumulated terms for similar values of p and for values of N up to 1000 (by varying increments). The individual terms can be derived from the cumulated terms by simple subtraction.

An effective method of approximating binomial probabilities is discussed in Section 10.10.

It is often desirable to estimate the "true" value of p from a sample of N trials. For a discussion of this problem, see Section 16.9.

8.12. BINOMIAL PROBABILITY PAPER

Besides the tables mentioned before, attention is also called to the possibilities of the type of graph paper known as binomial probability paper.

It is described in a paper by J. W. Tukey and F. Mosteller, "The Use and Usefulness of Binomial Probability Paper," in the *Journal of the American Statistical Association*, Vol. 44 (1949), p. 174.

8.13. THE TCHEBYCHEFF INEQUALITY

An important relation discovered by the French mathematician, Bienaymé (1796–1878), and later by the Russian mathematician, Tchebycheff (1832–1894), is important because it does not depend upon the form of the probability function. The proof is brief.

Let X be a discrete chance variable that assumes the mutually exclusive values $x_1, x_2, \ldots, x_N$, with probabilities $f(x_1), f(x_2), \ldots, f(x_N)$, respectively, where $\sum_{i=1}^{N} f(x_i) = 1$. By formula (7.5),

$$\sum_{i=1}^{N} f(x_i)(x_i - \mu)^2 = \sigma^2. \tag{8.15}$$

Let x_i' represent the values of x_i for which $|x_i - \mu| \geq k\sigma$, where $k > 1$. Then

$$\Sigma f(x_i')(x_i' - \mu)^2 \leq \sigma^2.$$

Since $(x_i' - \mu)^2 \geq k^2\sigma^2$, it follows that

$$k^2\sigma^2 \, \Sigma f(x_i') \leq \sigma^2$$

whence

$$\Sigma f(x_i') \leq \frac{1}{k^2}$$

Thus we have the following theorem bearing the name of Tchebycheff:

The fraction of observations in a population deviating numerically from the mean μ, by more than k times the standard deviation σ, cannot exceed $1/k^2$.

For example, in any population, the probability that a random variable deviates from the mean by as much as 5σ is less than or equal to $\frac{1}{25}$. Stated differently, this means that not more than $\frac{1}{25}$ of the variates can deviate from the mean by as much as 5σ.

8.14. THE LAW OF LARGE NUMBERS

In Chapter 8, we proved that when X is the number of successes in N binomial trials, $\mu_X = Np$ and $\sigma_X = \sqrt{Npq}$. If we change the variable X to the relative number of successes X/N, then by formula (7.7), where $k = 1/N$,

$$\mu_{X/N} = \frac{\mu_X}{N} = p. \tag{8.16}$$

Also by formula (7.11),

$$\sigma_{X/N} = \frac{1}{N}\,\sigma_X = \frac{1}{N}\sqrt{Npq}$$

or

$$\sigma_{X/N} = \sqrt{\frac{pq}{N}}\,. \tag{8.17}$$

Applying Tchebycheff's inequality to the relative number of successes, X/N, in N binomial trials with probability p, we may say that the probability that X/N deviates from $\mu_{X/N} = p$ by more than $k\sigma$, or its equivalent $k\sqrt{pq/N}$ is less than $1/k^2$. If we let $d = k\sqrt{pq/N}$ so that $k = d\sqrt{N/pq}$, this probability is less than pq/d^2N. As N becomes infinite this maximum probability approaches zero. This gives us the following:

Law of large numbers (**weak form**). *In N trials the probability that the relative number of successes X/N, deviates numerically from p by more than $d(d > 0)$, approaches zero as N becomes infinite.*

Note that this law holds for any positive d, no matter how small it may be.

The law states that if N is large and the trials are of the binomial type, the relative number of successes obtained, X/N, is probably a good approximation to the true probability, p, and that this approximation improves with increased N. For example, suppose that a factory begins to produce lamp filaments of a certain type. It is desirable to know what per cent of these are expected to be defective. If, after production is well under way, a sample of 1000 filaments shows 108 defective, a first estimate of the fraction p expected to be defective is $\frac{108}{1000}$, corresponding to 10.8 per cent. This estimate is derived from the premise that each filament is produced under the same conditions as every other filament. Later estimates based on more extensive experience, that is, on larger and larger samples produced under more careful control, will be even closer to the true value of p.

8.15. THE SIGN TEST

Consider the following systolic blood pressure readings made on a sample of 15 college men by means of two different types of sphygmomanometers. A reading from each instrument was made on the left arm when the subject was in a sitting position. The readings are shown on top of p. 116.

Test the hypothesis that the two instruments do not differ materially in their reading. Let $\alpha = 0.05$.

If the instruments read essentially the same, there would be only chance differences between any pair of readings, and one instrument would be as likely to read higher in a given pair of observations as the other. Thus the

Pair	1	2	3	4	5	6	7	8
Sphyg. $C(x)$:	136	138	129	145	158	170	111	125
Sphyg. $W(y)$:	138	145	130	148	166	173	117	120

Pair	9	10	11	12	13	14	15
Sphyg. $C(x)$:	129	144	115	132	141	126	132
Sphyg. $W(y)$:	135	144	120	140	143	132	137

probability for instrument C to read higher (or lower) than instrument W would be $\frac{1}{2}$. Too many higher (or lower) readings on the part of C will cause us to reject the hypothesis $p = \frac{1}{2}$.

Consider N pairs of observations (x_i, y_i), $i = 1, 2, \ldots, N$, and their corresponding differences $d_i = x_i - y_i$, obtained under similar conditions. If we delete any pair of observations for which $d_i = 0$, and change N to the number of d's remaining, then the sign of d_i will be either positive or negative. We may test the hypothesis that the probability, p, of getting a plus sign equals the probability of getting a minus sign. Let x be the number of occurrences of the less frequent sign. Then for $p = \frac{1}{2}$ we have the binomial probability,

$$P(x) = \frac{N!}{x!(N-x)!}\left(\frac{1}{2}\right)^x\left(\frac{1}{2}\right)^{N-x}$$

of obtaining the less frequent sign just x times in N trials or a probability

$$\sum_{x=0}^{r} \frac{N!}{x!(N-x)!}\left(\frac{1}{2}\right)^N$$

of obtaining that sign not more than r times.

Consider the foregoing data. The 15 d's in order, are

$$-2, -7, -1, -3, -8, -3, -6, +5, -6, 0, -5, -8, -2, -6, -5.$$

Eliminating the zero difference we have 14 signs of which only one is positive; thus $N = 14$ and $r = 1$. Then the probability for zero or one plus sign is

$$\left(\frac{1}{2}\right)^{14} + \frac{14!}{13!1!}\left(\frac{1}{2}\right)^{14} = 0.000916.$$

If the expectation is that, if the two instruments do yield different readings, sphygmomanometer C will read generally lower, then the one-tail probability just found emphatically refutes the hypothesis that $p = \frac{1}{2}$. That is, instrument C is judged to read lower than W. Otherwise the two-tail probability 2×0.000916 is calculated. This also refutes the hypothesis $p = \frac{1}{2}$ in favor of $p \neq \frac{1}{2}$.

Table C in the Appendix eliminates the necessity for the tedious calculation of probabilities. For our example where $N = 14$ and $r = 1$, if we desire a two-tail test, we find that for $\alpha = 0.05$, r must be at least as small as 2. Since our $r = 1$, we reject the hypothesis $p = \frac{1}{2}$. For a one-tail test, we halve α.

Often an answer to a question like the following is desired: Does sphygmomanometer W read higher than C by an average of 4 millimeters of mercury? In such a case d_i becomes $x_i - (y_i - 4)$ and a two-tail test is used for the alternative that the average may be more or less than 4.

The sign test and the Tchebycheff inequality are examples of *non-parametric* statistics characterized thus because the relations derived are independent of the form of the probability function. The *parameters* of a probability function are constants such as μ, σ, N, p, etc. which determine the shape of the distribution of the random variable. The Chi-square test described in Chapter 11 is nonparametric also.

EXERCISES

Exercises 1–8 should be done without the use of tables.

1. What is the probability that four heads appear when an unbiased coin is tossed seven times?

2. If, in general, 30% of patients afflicted with a certain disease die from it, what is the probability that just two die in a group of five?

3. About $\frac{2}{5}$ of persons in the United States belong to blood group A. What is the probability that in a randomly selected sample of five persons, just three belong to group A?

4. What is the probability of obtaining the sum 7 just twice in four rolls of a pair of dice?

5. A die has four black and two white faces; a second die has three black and three white faces. If this pair of dice is tossed five times, what is the probability that the first die shows a white face just three times and the second die shows a white face just four times?

6. A penny suspected of bias is to be tossed eight times. The hypothesis $p = \frac{1}{2}$ is to be rejected if seven or eight heads appear. What is the value of α?

7. A nickel suspected of bias is to be tossed ten times for the purpose of testing $H_0: p = \frac{1}{2}$ against $H_1: p \neq \frac{1}{2}$. If α is to be 0.10 and the tosses show just two heads, should we conclude that the coin is biased? Note that H_1 requires a two-tail test.

8. Would it be possible to conclude that a penny is biased with exactly five tosses when (a) $H_1: p < \frac{1}{2}$? (b) $H_1: p \neq \frac{1}{2}$? Let $\alpha = 0.05$ for both cases.

In exercises 9–17, Table B in the Appendix should be used.

9. On an average, 10% of the wooden rods used in a certain product are found to be too knotty. What is the probability that in a bundle of 20 rods, five or more are too knotty?

10. About 45% of New Englanders belong to blood group O. What is the probability that a random sample of 12 of them show at least eight belonging to this group?

11. As a rule, 25% of candidates fail a certain screening test. What is the probability that in a sample of 15 (a) at least eight fail? (b) not more than four fail?

12. Refer to the preceding exercise. What is the probability that just four fail?

13. The hypothesis H_0: $p = 0.70$ is to be tested with a sample of nine and rejected if the number of successes is fewer than three. What is the value of α?

14 Suppose that Drug X is effective in 60% of the cases in which it is used. A modified form of the drug is tried in the hope that a larger per cent of the cases will be improved. If the trial involves ten patients and we decide to reject H_0: $p = 0.6$ in favor of H_1: $p > 0.6$ provided nine or ten patients improve, what is the size of the type I error? What does your answer mean?

15. The hypothesis $p = 0.1$ is to be tested by means of a sample of ten and rejected if the number of successes is three or more. If $p = 0.2$ what is the value of β?

16. In a town election, the Republican candidate for mayor claims that at least 75% of the Independent voters will vote Republican. A random sample of 20 Independent voters are polled to test this claim, namely, that $p \geq 0.75$. α is to equal 0.05. (a) What is the rejection region for this claim? (b) Ten voters stated that they would vote Republican. Assuming that they were telling the truth, should the claim be accepted or rejected?

17. In the manufacture of two-way electric plugs, the ABC Company finds that, on an average, 5% are defective. The company tests its manufacture from time to time with samples of 20, and the hypothesis H_0: $p = 0.05$ is rejected whenever the sample shows more than three defective; then the company seeks to find the reason for the apparently larger per cent defective. (a) What is the value of α? (b) If the per cent of defectives, unknown to the company, had risen to ten, what would be the size of β? Recall that H_0 would be accepted erroneously whenever the number of defectives was less than four.

18. In the game of craps, the probability of winning is very close to $\frac{1}{2}$. A man enters a crap game in which he suspects that the dice are loaded and resolves to quit if and when he wins only two games or fewer out of the first ten. If the dice are not loaded, what is the probability that he quits after (a) the eighth game? (b) the ninth game? (c) the tenth game? (d) What is the probability that he quits the game?

19. William Shanks (1812–1882) computed the number π to 707 decimal places. How many times would you expect him to have found the digit 0?

20. A penny is tossed 64 times. Find (a) the expected number of heads; (b) the standard deviation.

21. One hundred cuts are made of a well-shuffled deck of 52 playing cards. What is the expected number of spades appearing? What is the standard deviation?

22. A pair of dice is thrown 100 times. What is the expected number of times that the sum 5 appears? What is the standard deviation?

23. If a coin is tossed 15 times, what is the most probable number of heads?

24. Find the most probable number of 7's obtained when a pair of dice is thrown five times.

25. A pair of dice is tossed 50 times. (a) What is the mean number of times that the sum 8 appears? (b) What is the expected value of the square of the deviation from the mean? (c) What is the most probable number of times that the sum 8 appears.

26. A small, regular tetrahedron has three faces painted white and one face, black. (a) What is the probability that in five tosses it lands on a white face just three times? If this tetrahedron is tossed 64 times, what is (b) the expected number of times that it lands on a white face? (c) the standard deviation for the number of times it lands on a white face?

27. A multiple-choice examination in statistics consisted of 20 questions, each had five answers listed. If a student knew none of the correct answers and resorted to guessing, (a) what is the expected number correct and what is the standard deviation? (b) If a student passes the examination when he answers at least 12 questions correctly, what is the probability that he passes by guessing? (c) What is the probability that he guesses all correctly? (d) none correctly?

28. A random variable X has a probability function with $\sigma = 5$. Use the Tchebycheff inequality to answer the following: What can you say about the probability that X deviates from the mean by as much as (a) 15? (b) 10? (c) 5?

29. A random variable X has a probability function with $\mu = 80$ and $\sigma = 10$. Use the Tchebycheff inequality to answer the following: What can you say about the probability that X lies between (a) 60 and 100? (b) 65 and 95?

30. Twenty pigs were paired according to equal weight. The two pigs of each pair were then fed different rations for a period of time. The following data show the daily gain in weight in ounces per day. Do the rations produce significantly different mean gains in weight? Apply the sign test.

Pair	1	2	3	4	5	6	7	8	9	10
Ration X	21	21	19	16	26	19	18	29	22	19
Ration Y	30	25	25	16	29	18	18	19	24	22

31. An attempt is made to compare the effectiveness of two teachers in a certain course. Pairs of pupils are selected who are as nearly alike as possible in

previous preparation and in other pertinent attributes. Thus any difference in the test scores of a matched pair will probably not be due to a difference in native ability or to a difference in quality of work done prior to the work to be tested. The data that follow arise from a test given after completion of the course. By means of the sign test, accept or reject the hypothesis that the teachers are essentially of the same effectiveness.

Pair	1	2	3	4	5	6	7	8	9	10	11	12
Teacher A	41	35	28	39	40	24	26	32	29	41	36	34
Teacher B	36	37	32	38	43	20	22	32	25	42	30	35

32. Two samples of 24 observations each were paired and the signs of the corresponding differences, d, were counted. There were five plus signs, 17 minus signs, and two zeros. Is there indication, say at the 10% level, that one population is different from the other?

33. A comparison of magnesium (gm per mm) was made by two methods, the U.S.P. XIV and the E.D.T.A. Apply the sign test to see if there is a significant difference (5%) between the two.

Sample No.	1	2	3	4	5	6	7	8
U.S.P. XIV	1.100	1.048	1.056	1.033	1.045	1.098	1.053	1.039
E.D.T.A.	1.094	1.045	1.049	1.034	1.044	1.093	1.048	1.045

9

Frequency Distributions and Probability Density Functions; The Continuous Case

9.1. AN EXAMPLE

Table 9-1 shows a frequency distribution of head lengths of criminals. The head lengths were measured to the nearest millimeter, so that any reading—184 mm, for example—is an approximate number and represents a true length not less than 183.5 mm and not more than 184.5 mm. An arbitrary class of head lengths may be defined by its *class limits*, *class boundaries*, or *class mark*, the last usually taken as the mid-value of the class interval. These are shown in Table 9-1. Realize that (i) head lengths represent values of a continuous variable, and (ii) the table may be considered as a partition of the set of 462 criminals by means of their head lengths. The criminals have been partitioned but not their head lengths, for the totality of head lengths include many duplicate measurements and, as such, do not constitute a set.

The frequency distribution of Table 9-1 may be pictured by means of a *histogram* (Fig. 9-1). This is constructed as follows. The 12 class intervals of four millimeters each are laid off to a convenient scale on a horizontal line. The end-points of these intervals correspond to the class boundaries. The corresponding class frequencies are measured to a convenient scale on a vertical line, and a rectangle is constructed for each class. Thus, the histogram consists of a set of adjacent rectangles whose bases equal the class width and whose altitudes equal the corresponding class frequencies. The total area of the histogram equals the sum of the areas of the rectangles; and in the usual case, where the class interval or width is the same, this total

TABLE 9-1

HEAD LENGTHS IN MILLIMETERS OF 462 ENGLISH
CRIMINALS, AGE 25–30[1]

(1) Class Limits	(2) Class Boundaries	(3) Class Mark (Mid-value) x_i	(4) Frequency f_i
172–175	171.5–175.5	173.5	3
176–179	175.5–179.5	177.5	9
180–183	179.5–183.5	181.5	29
184–187	183.5–187.5	185.5	76
188–191	187.5–191.5	189.5	104
192–195	191.5–195.5	193.5	110
196–199	195.5–199.5	197.5	88
200–203	199.5–203.5	201.5	30
204–207	203.5–207.5	205.5	6
208–211	207.5–211.5	209.5	4
212–215	211.5–215.5	213.5	2
216–219	215.5–219.5	217.5	1

Total $N = \Sigma f_i = 462$

[1] Data from Charles Goring, *The English Convict*, H.M.S. Office, 1913, p. 54. By permission of The Controller of Her Britannic Majesty's Stationery Office.

area equals the product of the common width and the sum of the frequencies (the heights). If we call the class width k, and the sum of the frequencies N, the area of the histogram will be $\Sigma kf_i = Nk$.

By joining the adjacent midpoints of the upper bases with line segments, as indicated in Fig. 9-1, we obtain a *frequency polygon*. When the polygon is continued to the horizontal axis just outside the range of lengths, as in the figure, the total area under the polygon will be equal to that of the histogram. For each triangular portion of a rectangle cut off by the polygon, an equivalent triangular portion above the lower adjacent rectangle is added. Sometimes it is convenient to consider each rectangle to have a width of unity and a height equal to the relative frequency. Such a choice makes the area of the frequency polygon unity. Its advantages will be apparent later.

The rectangular histogram suggests to the reader that each class frequency

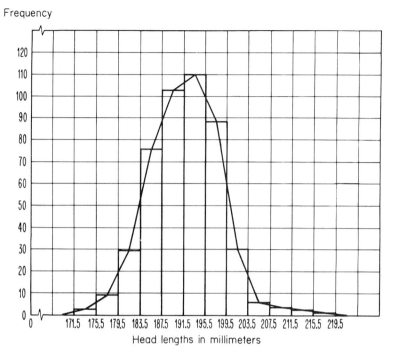

Fig. 9-1. Histogram and frequency polygon for the head lengths of 462 English criminals.

is associated, not with a single value, but with a whole range of values, represented by the width of a rectangle. The frequency polygon, with its line segments sloping upward and downward, gives a picture of the way in which frequency of occurrence varies over the complete gamut of values.

9.2. THE ARITHMETIC MEAN

The arithmetic mean of a frequency distribution of continuous data is again conveniently conceived as a weighted mean, where now the variates are the mid-values of the class intervals and the weights are the corresponding frequencies. Formula (7.1), which is repeated here, then becomes operative,

$$\bar{x} = \frac{1}{N} \sum_{i=1}^{n} f_i x_i \tag{9.1}$$

and the method outlined in Section 7.5 is used. In employing this formula, we replace the group of measurements comprising a given class by its mid-value. This procedure introduces no serious error into the calculation, provided the frequency distribution is roughly symmetrical.

TABLE 9-2

(1) No. of Trials	(2) f_i	(3) x_i	(4) $f_i x_i$	(5) $f_i x_i^2$
1–5	2	3	6	18
6–10	7	8	56	448
11–15	10	13	130	1,690
16–20	16	18	280	5,040
21–25	20	23	460	10,580
26–30	15	28	420	11,760
31–35	9	33	297	9,801
36–40	3	38	114	4,332
	82		1763	43,669

Example. The first two columns of Table 9-2 constitute a frequency distribution for the numbers of trials required by 82 boys in order to hit a given target in a game designed to test one's skill. Column 3 gives the mid-values of the class intervals, and column 4 gives the total used in computing $\bar{x}$. The mean number of trials is approximately 22, for

$$\bar{x} = \frac{1763}{82} = 21.5.$$

Because the arithmetical calculations are usually troublesome, the calculation of the mean from a frequency table is expedited by coding the mid-values x_i. A detailed description of this method is presented in Section 4.1 of Reference 8 but will not be treated in this book. By using formula (9.1) or an equivalent one derived by coding, we can show that the mean head length for the data of Table 9-1 is 191.8 mm.

9.3. THE VARIANCE AND STANDARD DEVIATION

The calculation of s^2 and s from a frequency table makes use of formula (7.4) repeated here.

$$s^2 = \frac{1}{N} \sum_{i=1}^{n} f_i x_i^2 - \bar{x}^2. \tag{9.2}$$

Column 5 of Table 9-2 is needed in order to compute s^2. The values $f_i x_i^2$ are obtained if we multiply the corresponding values x_i (column 3) and $f_i x_i$ (column 4). It follows from formula (9.2) that

$$s^2 = \frac{43,669}{82} - (21.5)^2 = 70.30,$$

hence

$$s = 8.38.$$

The troublesome arithmetical work may be simplified by coding as mentioned earlier. For the data of head lengths, it can be shown that $s^2 = 41.99$, whence $s = 6.48$ (see Section 4.3 of Reference 8).

9.4. CUMULATIVE FREQUENCY

From Table 9-1, we construct Table 9-3. The latter includes the boundary values of each class as well as the cumulative frequencies. When, for example, we say that $\operatorname{cum} f_5 = 221$, we mean that 221 head lengths were less than 191.5 millimeters.

TABLE 9-3

CUMULATIVE FREQUENCY TABLE OF HEAD
LENGTHS

Mid-value x_i	Frequency f_i	Boundary	Cum f_i
		171.5	0
173.5	3		
		175.5	3
177.5	9		
		179.5	12
181.5	29		
		183.5	41
185.5	76		
		187.5	117
189.5	104		
		191.5	221
193.5	110		
		195.5	331
197.5	88		
		199.5	419
201.5	30		
		203.5	449
205.5	6		
		207.5	455
209.5	4		
		211.5	459
213.5	2		
		215.5	461
217.5	1		
		219.5	462
Total	462		

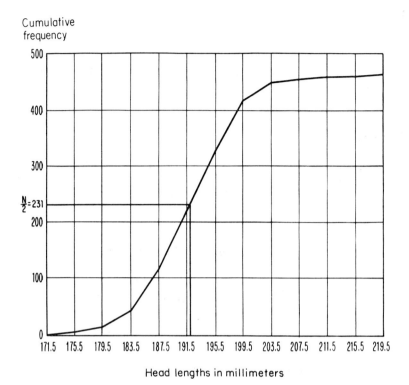

Head lengths in millimeters

Fig. 9-2. Cumulative frequency diagram illustrating the graphical determination of the median head length.[2]

The graph of the cumulative frequencies, sometimes called an *ogive*, is obtained when we plot the cumulative frequencies against the boundary values or end-points of the class intervals. The plotted points are connected by line segments or by a smooth curve. From Fig. 9-2, one can readily estimate the number of head lengths or the proportion or percentage of them less than any assigned value.

9.5. THE PERCENTILES, QUARTILES, AND MEDIAN

*The **mth** percentile, P_m, of a frequency distribution is the variate that corresponds to the cumulative frequency, **m** per cent of N. It is conceived as* that value for which *m* per cent of the variates are smaller and $(100 - m)$

[2] This is defined as the head length corresponding to the cumulative frequency $N/2$.

per cent are larger. Of major importance among the percentiles are the 50 percentile or median, the 25 percentile or first quartile, Q_1, and the 75 percentile or third quartile, Q_3. The method of calculating a percentile from a cumulative frequency table is demonstrated in Section 4.10 of Reference 8. However, percentiles may be estimated quite accurately from a cumulative frequency diagram. For example, to estimate the median head length from Fig. 9-2, we take 50 per cent of N or 231, since the median marks the halfway point in the ordered series of head lengths. From the intersection of a horizontal line through cum $f = 231$ and the cumulative frequency diagram, we drop a perpendicular to the base line. The foot of this perpendicular is estimated to be at 191.9. Thus the median head length is 191.9 mm. It may also be shown that $Q_1 = 187.4$ mm and that $Q_3 = 196.2$.

9.6. THE PROBABILITY DENSITY FUNCTION

The area of a histogram is equal to Nk (Section 9.1). If, for example, we considered each base of a rectangle to be of unit length instead of k units in length, and if we assumed each altitude to be equal to the appropriate relative frequency, f_i/N, instead of f_i, then the area of the entire histogram would be unity since $\Sigma f_i \cdot 1 = 1$ (Fig. 9-3). This change of units which reduces the histogram area to unity will enable us to appreciate more fully the manner in which the concept of a probability density function of a continuous variable has evolved. Under such a change of units the area f_i/N, of a rectangle can be interpreted as the probability that the value of a random variable lies within the corresponding base interval.

Since the area under the frequency polygon is always equal to the area of the histogram, we shall confine our attention to the first-named figure. Many frequency distributions yield polygons that are of the same general bell-shape as that of Figs. 9-1 and 9-4a. Some are partly bell-shaped but

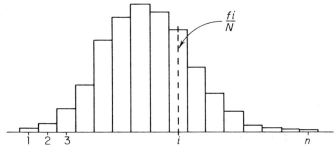

Figure 9-3

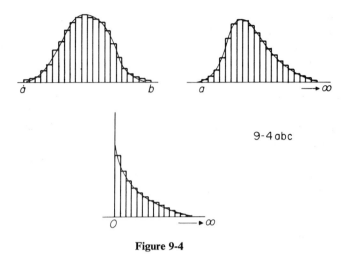

9-4 abc

Figure 9-4

asymmetrical with a longer tail on one side than on the other, as in Fig. 9-4b. Some are J-shaped (Fig. 9-4c), and some irregular in form. The "smoothing out" of such polygons suggests curves such as those shown. It would appear that the area under an arc of the curve corresponding to a given rectangle could also be interpreted as a probability, since the total area under such a frequency curve is always unity. These heuristic considerations lead us to an important definition.

The concept of a probability density function is dependent upon that of a *definite integral* as studied in calculus. For students unfamiliar with this concept, the following brief exposition is given.

Let $f(x)$ be a positive continuous function[3] on the interval $a \leq x \leq b$, and let the interval be subdivided into n parts, not necessarily equal, by the points $x_0 = a, x_1, x_2, , , x_{n-1}, x_n = b$, where $a < x_1 < x_2 < \cdots < x_{n-1} < b$ (Fig. 9-5). Let x_i' be any point of the interval (x_{i-1}, x_i), so that $x_{i-1} \leq x_i' \leq x_i$. Then the product $f(x_i')(x_i - x_{i-1})$ is the area of a rectangle with base of length $x_i - x_{i-1}$ and altitude $f(x_i')$. Throughout this discussion, i may have the values $1, 2, , , n$. If n is large and each subinterval is assumed to be very small, geometrical considerations suggest that the sum of the products $\sum_{i=1}^{n} f(x_i')(x_i - x_{i-1})$ is a close approximation to the area under the curve $y = f(x)$ between $x = a$ and $x = b$. Furthermore, the approximation becomes more and more accurate the larger n becomes, provided each

[3] For the purposes of this book, we may define $f(x)$ to be a continuous function of x over the interval $a \leq x \leq b$, if a small change in x produces a small change in $f(x)$ and if we can make the second change as small as we please by sufficiently reducing the change in x.

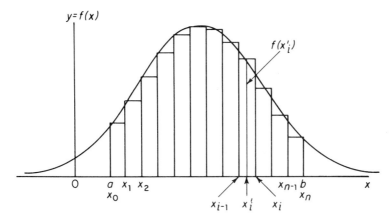

Figure 9-5

subinterval $x_i - x_{i-1}$ becomes correspondingly smaller. These considerations lead us to the following assumption and definition.

If $f(x)$ is a non-negative continuous function over the interval ($a \leq x \leq b$), the limit of the sum $\sum_{i=1}^{n} f(x_i')(x_i - x_{i-1})$ as n becomes infinite and $x_i - x_{i-1}$ approaches 0 exists, is designated as the definite integral of $f(x)$ from a to b, and is symbolized by $\int_a^b f(x)\, dx$. The area under the curve $y = f(x)$ from a to b is defined to be given by this integral.

Proofs of the existence of the limit of the sum above and extensions of this definition may be found in any good calculus text.

Following the preceding definition, we pass to that of a probability density function.

Consider the set of paired values $\{(x, f(x))\}$, where X is a random variable defined over the infinite sample space $\{a \leq x \leq b\}$. Let each value x_i in this space determine a non-negative number $f(x_i)$, where $f(x)$ is a continuous function of x. Furthermore, let the area under the curve $y = f(x)$ equal 1, that is, let $\int_a^b f(x)\, dx = 1$. Then the area under the curve between x_1 and x_2, where $a \leq x_1 < x_2 \leq b$, is defined as the probability $P(x_1 < x < x_2)$, and $f(x)$ is said to be the probability density function of the random variable X. In symbols,

$$P(x_1 < x < x_2) = \int_{x_1}^{x_2} f(x)\, dx, \qquad where \quad \int_a^b f(x)\, dx = 1.$$

Several remarks by way of clarification are in order.

(i) The definition may be extended to include cases where a or b or both may become infinite. For examples, in Fig. 9-4a, a and b are both finite; in Fig. 9-4b, a is finite but b has become infinite; in Fig. 9-4c, $a = 0$ but b has become infinite.

(ii) Since X is a continuous random variable, it has an infinite number of possible values between any two points x_1 and x_2; therefore, for $x_1 \leqq x_i \leqq x_2$, $P(x = x_i) = 0$. Thus, although x_i is a possible value, its probability is zero. (See the last paragraph of Section 3.4.)

(iii) In view of the preceding remark, $P(x_1 \leqq x \leqq x_2) = P(x_1 < x < x_2)$.

(iv) To any value x_i in the sample space, there corresponds one value of the function, $f(x_i)$; but this is not a probability [for $P(x = x_i) = 0$

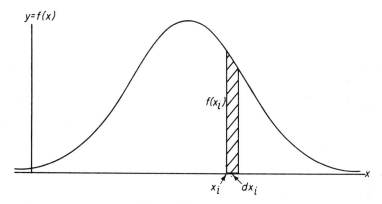

Figure 9-6

for all i] but a *probability density factor*. To clarify this statement, one may conceive of the x-axis as bearing a load which varies continuously from point to point. The magnitude of this density, conceived as a probability density, is measured by $f(x)$. The portion of the integral symbol "$f(x)\,dx$" suggests an area such as that shown in Fig. 9-6. The product of $f(x_i)$, the ordinate, and the length of the base, dx_i, is approximately equal to the shaded area if dx_i is small.

EXAMPLE 1. A rectangular density function.

Let $f(x) = 1/k$ for $0 \leq x \leq k$. Then $f(x)$ is constant throughout the given interval. Its graph is shown in Fig. 9-7. Note that $\int_a^b f(x)\,dx$ becomes, in this case, $\int_0^k (1/k)\,dx$. The area under this "curve," which is a horizontal line segment, is that of a rectangle of area 1.

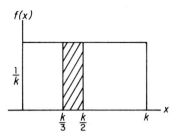

$$\int_{k/3}^{k/2} \frac{1}{k}\, dx = P\left(\frac{k}{3} \leq x \leq \frac{k}{2}\right)$$

$$= \left(\frac{k}{2} - \frac{k}{3}\right)\frac{1}{k} = \frac{1}{6}.$$

This probability is easily found as the area of the shaded rectangle in Fig. 9-7.

Figure 9-7

EXAMPLE 2. A semicircular density function.

Let $f(x) = \sqrt{2/\pi - x^2}$ for $-\sqrt{2/\pi} \leq x \leq$ $\sqrt{2/\pi}$. The graph appears in Fig. 9-8. Note that the radius of the semicircle equals $\sqrt{2/\pi}$ and that the area is unity. The shaded area represents

$$P\left(0 < x < \frac{1}{2}\sqrt{\frac{2}{\pi}}\right) - \int_0^{1/2\sqrt{2/\pi}} \sqrt{\frac{2}{\pi} - x^2}\, dx.$$

With the aid of calculus, it can be shown that the value of this integral which is the probability that x lies between 0 and $\frac{1}{2}\sqrt{2/\pi}$, is 0.305.

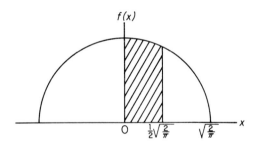

Figure 9-8

9.7. REMARKS ON THE USAGE
OF TERMS

There is no uniformity among writers concerning the usage of the terms connected with probability and density functions. Some prefer to reserve the phrase "distribution function" for cumulative probability functions. Often, some employ "distribution function," "frequency function," or merely "distribution" alternately with probability density function when no confusion is likely to result. This will be the practice in much of the work that follows.

Some of the more important density functions to be treated later are the normal distribution, the Student-Fisher t-distribution, and the Chi-square distribution.

9.8. MEAN AND VARIANCE

The mean μ, and the variance σ^2, of a continuous random variable. are defined in a manner analogous to that used in the discrete case. It is necessary, however, to employ concepts of calculus. For those unfamiliar with this subject, we may say that the summation signs of Sections 7.6 and 7.7 are replaced by integral signs. Thus we define:

$$\mu = E(x) = \int_a^b f(x)x \, dx$$

and

$$\sigma^2 = E(x - \mu)^2 = \int_a^b f(x)(x - \mu)^2 \, dx$$

where, of course, $\int_a^b f(x) \, dx = 1$. However, we shall not require the use of these formulas in this text.

EXERCISES

1. The salaries of a group of junior executives in the PDQ Corporation are shown below. Construct a histogram and frequency polygon for these data.

Salaries	Number
$6,000–8,000	7
8,000–10,000	10
10,000–12,000	28
12,000–14,000	15
14,000–16,000	4
16,000–18,000	1
	65

2. The systolic blood pressures in millimeters of 278 healthy adult males are tabulated below. Replace the class limits by class boundaries and construct a histogram. Label the class intervals by means of the boundary values, e.g., 99.5–104.5, 104.5–109.5, etc.

Blood Pressures	Frequency
100–104	2
105–109	6
110–114	13
115–119	25
120–124	31
125–129	47
130–134	53
135–139	42
140–144	30
145–149	17
150–154	8
155–159	4

3. Construct a histogram and frequency polygon for the weights of 100 aspirin tablets tabulated below. Note that the mid-values of the class intervals are given. Use these as labels for the mid-points of the bases of the rectangles comprising the histogram.

Weights	Frequencies
4.5	1
4.6	2
4.7	10
4.8	21
4.9	33
5.0	18
5.1	9
5.2	4
5.3	2

4. Construct a histogram and frequency polygon for the thicknesses of washers shown below. Read the note in the previous exercise.

Thickness	Frequency
0.095	1
0.096	4
0.097	9
0.098	15
0.099	20
0.100	24
0.101	21
0.102	16
0.103	7
0.104	3
0.105	2

5. Construct a histogram for the ages of admirals of the line of the United States Navy on active duty May 1, 1945, shown below. Replace class limits by

boundaries. The age is that at the last birthday; hence, the boundaries are 40–45, 45–50, etc.

Age	Number
40–44	1
45–49	37
50–54	75
55–59	87
60–64	44
65–69	22
70–74	6
75–79	1

6. By means of formula (9.1), compute the mean salary for the data of exercise 1. Let the mid-values be 7000, 9000, etc.

7. In exercise 3, compute the arithmetic mean weight by means of formula (9.1).

8. By means of formula (9.1), calculate the mean thickness of the washers in exercise 4.

By means of formula (9.2), compute the standard deviation for each of the following:

9. Exercise 1. The zeros may be omitted in the calculation but should be replaced in the answer.

10. Exercise 3. Use Table A in the Appendix.

Construct a cumulative frequency table and diagram for each of the following. Note that boundary values must be used.

11. Exercise 1.   12. Exercise 3.   13. Exercise 5.

14. In what salary class is the median of exercise 1 found? Estimate it by interpolating within this class interval.

15. Answer the question of the previous exercise for exercise 5.

16. From the data of exercise 3, find the probability that an aspirin tablet weighs (a) at least 4.9 grains; (b) less than 4.8 grains.

17. From the data of exercise 2 find the probability that the blood pressure of a man selected at random from this group is (a) between 115 and 134 inclusive; (b) greater than 144.

18. What information does each of the following statements yield?
(a) The median age of readers of College Board Examinations should be about 40 years.
(b) Chris Black's score on the intelligence test corresponded to the 86th percentile.
(c) The 35th percentile wage was $76.46.
(d) The third quartile I.Q. was 112.

19. Given the probability density function

$$y = bx \text{ where } 0 \leq x \leq 2,$$

(a) Evaluate b. (b) Draw the graph of this function.

20. If $y = bx$ is a probability density function defined for $0 \leq x \leq 4$, what must the value of b be? Find, from geometrical considerations, $P(0.5 < x < 1)$.

21. Given the parabolic density function $y = \frac{3}{4}(1 - x^2)$ defined for $-1 \leq x \leq 1$, plot its curve.

10

The Normal Probability
Density Function

You boil it in sawdust: you salt it in
glue:
You condense it with locusts and tape:
Still keeping one principal object in
view—
To preserve its symmetrical shape.

LEWIS CARROLL
The Hunting of the Snark

10.1. INTRODUCTION

In the preceding chapter, we defined a probability density function in terms of a function, $f(x)$, of a continuous random variable defined over the sample space $\{a \leq x \leq b\}$. Perhaps the most basic function in the entire field of statistics is the one that forms the title of this chapter. Here we shall find that the possible values of the random variable constitute the set $\{-\infty \leq x \leq \infty\}$, namely, the set of all the real numbers. We shall begin by showing briefly how the normal density function may be conceived to stem from the binomial probability function.

10.2. THE NORMAL DENSITY FUNCTION

From formula (8.1), we find that the binomial probability function yielding the probability of obtaining x heads when an unbiased coin is tossed ten times is

$$P(x) = \frac{10!}{x!(10-x)!}\left(\frac{1}{2}\right)^x\left(\frac{1}{2}\right)^{10-x}. \tag{10.1}$$

The probability diagram corresponding to this formula is shown as Fig. 8-1. We now reproduce this graph in a slightly different form by using artificial class boundaries $-\frac{1}{2}$ to $\frac{1}{2}$, $\frac{1}{2}$ to $1\frac{1}{2}$, $1\frac{1}{2}$ to $2\frac{1}{2}$, ..., $9\frac{1}{2}$ to $10\frac{1}{2}$, in place of the class marks 0, 1, 2, ..., 10 respectively, and by using rectangles instead of vertical lines. (See Fig. 10-1.) Since the base of each rectangle is of unit length, the area of each rectangle is numerically equal to its height. These changes give us a histogram that has the desirable property of permitting the areas of the rectangles, rather than the heights, to represent the probabilities.

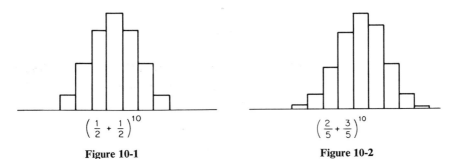

$$\left(\tfrac{1}{2}+\tfrac{1}{2}\right)^{10} \qquad\qquad\qquad \left(\tfrac{2}{5}+\tfrac{3}{5}\right)^{10}$$

Figure 10-1   **Figure 10-2**

Note that Fig. 10-1 is symmetrical and somewhat bell-shaped. This symmetry is due to the fact that $p = q$. Figure 10-2 represents the probability diagram for $N = 10$ as before, but with $p = \frac{3}{5}$, $q = \frac{2}{5}$. Note that the figure is very nearly symmetrical and bell-shaped. In Figs. 10-3, 4, and 5, $p = \frac{9}{10}$ and $q = \frac{1}{10}$, but N is 10 for the first named figure, 20 for the second, and 50 for the third. The extremely asymmetrical histogram of Fig. 10-3 becomes more symmetrical and bell-shaped in Figs. 10-4 and 5, although the last two named have long tails extending to the left. There the heights of the rectangles are so small as to be not reproducible in the text. If we refer to Fig. 10-10 where $N = 400$, $p = q = \frac{1}{2}$, there is clearly suggested a symmetrical bell-shaped curve with extremely long tails (not shown) to left and right that cover the intervals, 0 to 170 heads and 230 to 400 heads, all corresponding to very unlikely outcomes. These facts suggest that for large N, the area of the binomial histogram can be approximated by the area under a certain bell-shaped curve and this approximation improves the more nearly equal p and q are. This leads to a very important theorem which we shall state presently.

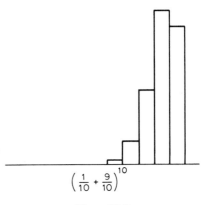

$$\left(\tfrac{1}{10}+\tfrac{9}{10}\right)^{10}$$

Figure 10-3

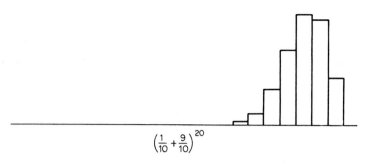

$$\left(\tfrac{1}{10}+\tfrac{9}{10}\right)^{20}$$

Figure 10-4

First, we recall that for a binomial distribution the mean $\mu = Np$ and the standard deviation $\sigma = \sqrt{Npq}$. Second, we introduce the standardized random variable Z, defined as follows:

$$Z = \frac{X - Np}{\sqrt{Npq}}$$

$$= \frac{X - \mu}{\sigma}.$$ **(10.2)**

Thus any value, z, of the standard variable represents the number of σ's by which x deviates from μ and is, therefore, a pure number. For example, if we refer to the experiment of tossing an unbiased penny ten times and let x denote the number of times heads appear, so that $\mu = 5$ and $\sigma = \sqrt{2.5} = 1.58$, then an outcome such as $x = 7$ corresponds to

$$z = \frac{7 - 5}{1.58} = 1.31.$$

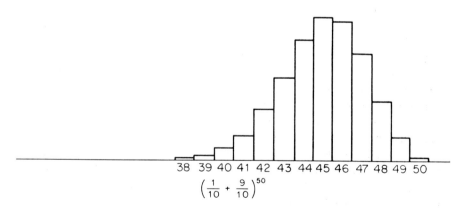

$$\left(\tfrac{1}{10}+\tfrac{9}{10}\right)^{50}$$

Figure 10-5

This means that seven heads exceeds the expected number by 1.31 σ's. Similarly, if $x = 2$, then

$$z = \frac{2 - 5}{1.58} = -1.90,$$

and two heads falls short of the expected number by 1.90 σ's. In particular, when $x = Np$, $z = 0$.

By the methods of mathematical statistics it is possible to prove this important theorem.

As the number of trials, N, increases indefinitely, the distribution of the standardized binomial variable, $(X - Np)/\sqrt{Npq}$, approaches the so-called standard normal distribution whose density function is defined by the equation

$$\phi(z) = \frac{1}{\sqrt{2\pi}} e^{-\frac{1}{2}z^2} . \tag{10.3}$$

The graph of Eq. (10.3) is called the *normal curve in standard form.* When N is large and p and q are not too small, the probabilities associated with a binomial distribution can be approximated with considerable accuracy by means of the corresponding areas under the normal curve. The method of approximation will be explained fully in Section 10.10.

Figure 10-6 shows the histograms for $p = q = \frac{1}{2}$, $N = 10$ (Fig. 10-1) and for $p = \frac{9}{10}$, $q = \frac{1}{10}$, $N = 50$ (Fig. 10-5) in terms of the standard variable. The former is shown with solid lines and the latter with dotted lines in Fig. 10-6. The graph of Eq. (10.3) is also plotted in Fig. 10-6. This normal curve "fits" the solid line histogram very well and the dotted line histogram only fairly well. The latter statement is true because of the great inequality

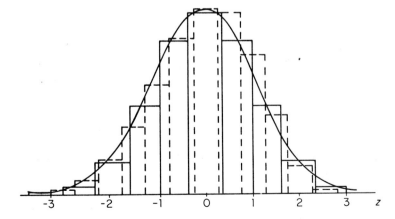

Figure 10-6

of $p = \frac{9}{10}$ and $q = \frac{1}{10}$. If we were to increase N beyond 50, the fit would improve.

For the present, we shall confine the discussion to the normal density function defined by Eq. (10.3). It can be shown that this function can be expressed in terms of the random variable as follows:

$$f(x) = \frac{1}{\sqrt{2\pi N pq}} e^{-\frac{(x-Np)^2}{2Npq}}$$

or, alternatively,

$$f(x) = \frac{1}{\sqrt{2\pi\sigma}} e^{-\frac{1}{2}\left(\frac{x-\mu}{\sigma}\right)^2}. \tag{10.4}$$

In formula (10.4), π is the familiar constant whose approximate value is 3.14159; e stands for another important constant, the base of the natural system of logarithms whose approximate value is 2.71828. In addition to these constants, there are two *parameters*, μ and σ, which determine the

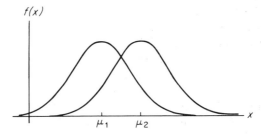

Figure 10-7

position and relative proportions of the normal curve. Thus, if two populations defined by normal density functions had different means, μ_1 and μ_2, but identical standard deviations, $\sigma_1 = \sigma_2$, their graphs would appear like those in Fig. 10-7. If the populations had identical means, $\mu_1 = \mu_2$, but different standard deviations, $\sigma_1 \neq \sigma_2$, their graphs would appear as shown in Fig. 10-8. If both the means and the standard deviations were different, we would have curves like those in Fig. 10-9. In all three diagrams, the areas under the curves are equal to one unit. In Figs. 10-8 and 9, there is a difference in the spread of the curves due to the difference in the σ's. Thus a normal distribution is completely characterized by the two parameters, μ and σ. These parameters bear to a normal population the same relation that the statistics $\bar{x}$ and s bear to a sample drawn from such a population.

The normal density function is used as a model by means of which many frequency distributions arising in practical work may be described and

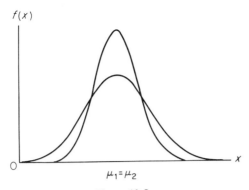

Figure 10-8

analyzed. Thus the graph of Fig. 9-1 suggests that the sample of 462 head lengths might reasonably be assumed to have been drawn from an infinite population of head lengths, the distribution of which is governed by a normal frequency function. Various tests exist for determining the validity of such an assumption.

The normal curve extends to infinity in both directions and, in so doing, approaches infinitely close to the *x*-axis without ever actually touching it. This property is described by stating that the curve is *asymptotic* to the *x*-axis.

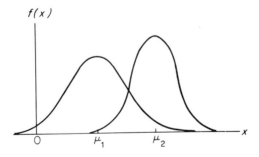

Figure 10-9

10.3. AREA AND PROBABILITY

The total area of a binomial histogram equals unity since the area of each rectangle represents a probability and the sum of these areas,

$$\sum_{x=0}^{N} P(x) = 1.$$

We note that because x can have only integral values from 0 to N, the binomial function is a function of a discrete variable. The normal density function, however, is a function of a continuous variable which may assume *any* real value.

By the methods of calculus, it can be shown formally that the area under the normal curve equals unity. Because of this fact, any partial area under the curve is interpreted as a probability. (See Section 9.6.) In order to clarify this last statement, let us refer to Fig. 10-10 where the probability, for

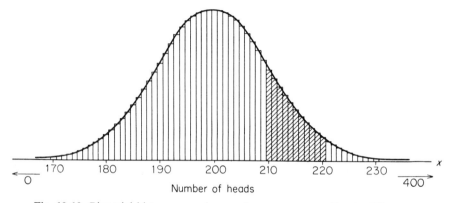

Fig. 10-10. Binomial histogram and normal curve corresponding to 400 tosses of a penny.

example, of getting anywhere from 210 to 220 heads inclusive in 400 tosses of a true coin is given by the sum of the areas of the rectangles from 210 to 220 inclusive. Since N is a large number, the form of the histogram is nearly that of a normal curve, so we should obtain an excellent approximation to the desired probability by taking the area under the corresponding normal curve from 210 to 220. Since $N = 400$, $p = q = \frac{1}{2}$, it follows that $\mu = 400 \times \frac{1}{2} = 200$, $\sigma = \sqrt{400 \times \frac{1}{2} \times \frac{1}{2}} = 10$, and the equation of the approximating normal curve becomes:

$$f(x) = \frac{1}{\sqrt{2\pi}10} e^{-\frac{1}{2}\left(\frac{x-200}{10}\right)^2}$$

The problem of finding the exact area under any portion of the normal curve is readily solved by calculus methods, but in order to eliminate unnecessary calculations, tables exist which enable one to find readily any desired area under the normal curve. The use of these tables is discussed in Section 10.6. The task of calculating directly from the binomial formula the probability of 210 to 220 heads inclusive;

$$P(210) + P(211) + \cdots + P(220) = \frac{400!}{210!\,190!}\left(\frac{1}{2}\right)^{210}\left(\frac{1}{2}\right)^{190}$$

$$+ \frac{400!}{211!\,189!}\left(\frac{1}{2}\right)^{211}\left(\frac{1}{2}\right)^{189} + \cdots + \frac{400!}{220!\,180!}\left(\frac{1}{2}\right)^{220}\left(\frac{1}{2}\right)^{180}. \quad \textbf{(10.5)}$$

would be very laborious.[1]

10.4. THE STANDARD FORM

The parameters μ and σ, characterize a given normal distribution as we have already noted. Thus if the statures of adult American males were

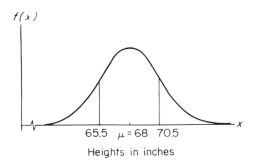

Heights in inches

Figure 10-11

assumed to be distributed normally with a mean, let us say, of 68 inches and a standard deviation of 2.5 inches, this population of statures would be characterized by the density function

$$f(x) = \frac{1}{\sqrt{2\pi}\,2.5}\,e^{-\frac{1}{2}\left(\frac{x-68}{2.5}\right)^2}$$

and represented graphically by Fig. 10-11. In this figure the unit of measure is one inch. The distance between the mean, 68, and the two statures, 65.5 and 70.5 inches, is 2.5 inches in each case—the value of σ.

If the population of English head lengths, assumed to be normal, had $\mu = 192$ millimeters and $\sigma = 6.5$ millimeters, its frequency function would be

$$f(x) = \frac{1}{\sqrt{2\pi}6.5}\,e^{-\frac{1}{2}\left(\frac{x-192}{6.5}\right)^2},$$

[1] If one has available *Tables of the Cumulative Binomial Probability Distribution* (see Reference 17), one can quickly find the above sum to be 0.15094.

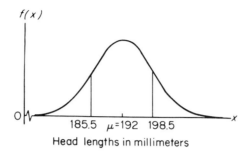

Figure 10-12

and its graph, that shown in Fig. 10-12. Here the unit of measure is one millimeter.

In order to make use of probability tables, it is desirable to employ a density function that is independent of the units used. To this end we use the *standard variable* or *standard deviate*, z,

$$z = \frac{x - \mu}{\sigma}. \tag{10.6}$$

As an example, let the head length, x, of an English criminal be 205 mm. Then $x - \mu = 205 - 192 = 13$ mm; $\sigma = 6.5$ mm; hence $z = 13/6.5 = 2$, a pure number. When the standard variable is used in place of x, the effect, graphically, is to place the origin (zero point) of z at the mean, μ_x, and to use σ as a horizontal unit of measure. It can be proved that the area under this transformed curve remains equal to unity. The function, $f(x)$, defined in formula (10.4) now is transformed into the *standard form* of the normal density function Eq. (10.3). The relations just described between the curves of $f(x)$ and $\phi(z)$ are illustrated in Fig. 10-13. The two points, $\mu_x + \sigma$ and $\mu_x - \sigma$, each at a σ's distance from μ_x in the upper graph correspond to the two points $+1$ and -1 each at a unit distance from the mean, $\mu_z = 0$. It can be proved easily by the methods of the calculus that the two *points of inflection* on the curve, that is, points at which the curve changes from one that is concave downward to one that is concave upward, are exactly at a distance of σ_x from μ_x (upper curve) and at a distance $\sigma_z = 1$ from $\mu_z = 0$ (lower curve).

10.5. ORDINATES OF THE
NORMAL CURVE

The values of the ordinate, $\phi(z)$, the height of the curve, corresponding to the variable z, are tabulated for values of z ranging numerically from $z = 0$ to $z = 4.00$ in Table D, of the Appendix.

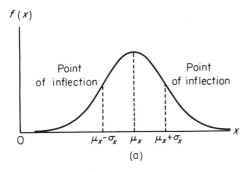

$f(x)$

Point
of inflection

Point
of inflection

0 $\mu_x - \sigma_x$ μ_x $\mu_x + \sigma_x$ x

(a)

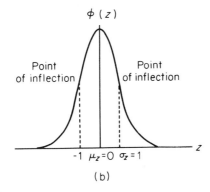

$\phi(z)$

Point
of inflection

Point
of inflection

-1 $\mu_z = 0$ $\sigma_z = 1$ z

(b)

Figure 10-13

Thus,
$$\text{for } z = 0, \qquad \phi(z) = 0.3989,$$
$$\text{for } z = 1.00, \qquad \phi(z) = 0.2420,$$
$$\text{for } z = 2.78, \qquad \phi(z) = 0.0084,$$

and
$$\text{for } z = -0.84, \qquad \phi(z) = 0.2803.$$

Here, because of symmetry $\phi(z) = \phi(-z)$. By making use of such values, one can plot very accurately the standard normal curve. (See exercise 11.)

Sometimes it is desirable to fit a normal curve to a frequency distribution arising from given data. In such a case for one method of fitting, a table of ordinates is necessary. (See Section 10.11.)

10.6. AREAS UNDER THE
NORMAL CURVE

The area under the curve [Eq. (10.3)] between two values of z, say $z = z_1$, and $z = z_2$ (Fig. 10-14), is designated in mathematics by the symbol:

$$\int_{z_1}^{z_2} \phi(z)\, dz,$$

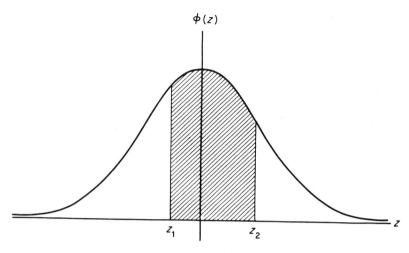

Figure 10-14

which may be read "the area under $\phi(z)$ from z_1 to z_2." (See Section 9.6.) For example, $\int_0^{z_1} \phi(z)\ dz$ represents the area from the origin to z_1, $\int_{-2}^{3} \phi(z)\ dz$ represents the area from $z = -2$ to $z = +3$, and $\int_{1.50}^{\infty} \phi(z)\ dz$ represents the area from $z = 1.50$ to infinity, that is, it represents the entire area to the right of 1.50.

Table E of the Appendix gives values of the areas under the standard normal curve to the right of any non-negative value of z, say z_1, that is, it gives values of $\int_{z_1}^{\infty} \phi(z)\ dz$. Because of the symmetry of the curve with respect to the vertical or $\phi(z)$-axis, the area from any z, say z_1, to $+\infty$, equals the area from $-\infty$ to $-z_1$. (Fig. 10-15.) Thus $\int_{z_1}^{\infty} \phi(z)\ dz = \int_{-\infty}^{-z_1} \phi(z)\ dz$.

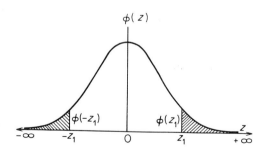

Figure 10-15

Note that we always express the interval for the area, from the left end-point to the right end-point. If we do this, the area under $\phi(z)$ can be shown always to be a positive number. From Table E one can easily verify that

$$\int_{0.50}^{\infty} \phi(z)\, dz = 0.3085, \qquad \int_{2.17}^{\infty} \phi(z)\, dz = 0.0150,$$

and so on.

All areas under the curve other than those given in the table can be easily derived from them. Thus,

$$\int_{1.50}^{2.00} \phi(z)\, dz = \int_{1.50}^{\infty} \phi(z)\, dz - \int_{2.00}^{\infty} \phi(z)\, dz$$
$$= 0.0668 - 0.0228 = 0.0440.$$

$$\int_{-1.50}^{\infty} \phi(z)\, dz = 1 - \int_{-\infty}^{-1.50} \phi(z)\, dz$$
$$= 1 - \int_{1.50}^{\infty} \phi(z)\, dz = 1 - 0.0668 = 0.9332$$

$$\int_{-1.32}^{2.13} \phi(z)\, dz = 1 - \left[\int_{-\infty}^{-1.32} \phi(z)\, dz + \int_{2.13}^{\infty} \phi(z)\, dz \right]$$
$$= 1 - \left[\int_{1.32}^{\infty} \phi(z)\, dz + \int_{2.13}^{\infty} \phi(z)\, dz \right]$$
$$= 1 - (0.0934 + 0.0166) = 0.8900.$$

The total area under the curve may be expressed as:

$$\int_{-\infty}^{\infty} \phi(z)\, dz = 2 \int_{0}^{\infty} \phi(z)\, dz = 1.$$

The symbol for *infinity*, ∞, indicates that the limit has become infinitely great.

10.7. PROPERTIES OF THE STANDARD CURVE

Let us set down again for convenient reference the equation of the normal frequency curve in standard form:

$$\phi(z) = \frac{1}{\sqrt{2\pi}}\, e^{-z^2/2}. \tag{10.7}$$

The following properties are of chief importance. Some of them have already been noted.

(1) *Symmetry.* The curve is symmetrical with respect to the $\phi(z)$-axis. This can be shown directly from Eq. (10.7). If z were replaced by $-z$,

$\phi(z)$ would remain unchanged. In other words, the ordinate $\phi(z)$ is the same at equal distances on either side of the origin. Statistically, this means that the arithmetic mean and the median of a normal frequency distribution coincide at the center of it. $\mu_z = 0$ corresponds to $x = \mu_x$.

(2) *Shape.* The exponent of e in $\phi(z)$ is negative, $-\frac{1}{2}z^2$. Hence, $\phi(z)$ is a maximum when $z = 0$; all other values of z make $\phi(z)$ smaller, since $e^{-z^2/2} = 1/e^{z^2/2}$. The maximum value of $\phi(z)$ is, therefore,

$$\phi(0) = \frac{1}{\sqrt{2\pi}} = 0.3989.$$

As z increases numerically, $e^{-z^2/2}$ decreases; and when z becomes infinite, $\phi(z)$ approaches zero. Thus, the curve is asymptotic to the z-axis in both the positive and negative directions.

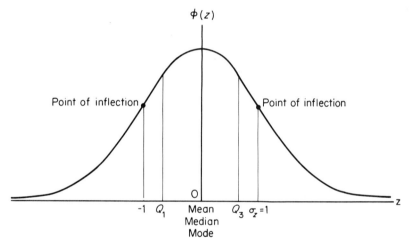

Fig. 10-16. Important values associated with the normal frequency curve in standard form.

It has already been shown that the *points of inflection* of the curve are situated at a unit's distance from the $\phi(z)$-axis and that $\sigma_z = 1$. (Fig. 10-16.) It is clear, then, from the preceding paragraphs that the standard curve has its maximum value $1/\sqrt{2\pi}$ units above the origin, that it is concave downward until $z = \pm1$, when it becomes concave upward, and that it rapidly approaches, but never quite reaches, the z-axis. These properties determine its bell-shaped form.

(3) *Areas.* The total area under the curve has already been shown to be exactly one.

The area under the curve from $z = 1$ to $z = \infty$ is 0.1587, so that the area comprised within the interval -1 to $+1$,

$$\int_{-1}^{1} \phi(z)\, dz = 1 - 2(0.1587) = 0.6826.$$

Statistically, this means that about 68 per cent of normal variates deviate from their mean by less than one standard deviation. (Fig. 10-17.) Similarly,

$$\int_{-2}^{2} \phi(z)\, dz = 0.9544 \quad \text{and} \quad \int_{-3}^{3} \phi(z)\, dz = 0.9974.$$

The preceding values show that, although the curve extends indefinitely to the left and to the right, it approaches the z-axis so closely that over 95 per cent of the area is included between the limits -2 and $+2$, and over 99.7 per cent of the area is included between -3 and $+3$. (Fig. 10-18.)

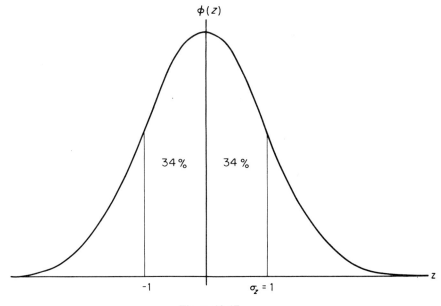

Figure 10-17

(4) *Quartiles.* The quartiles Q_1 and Q_3 of the curve are the values of z whose ordinates together with the $\phi(z)$-axis divide the area under the curve into four equal areas. From the equation

$$\int_{z_1}^{\infty} \phi(z)\, dz = 0.2500$$

we can, by inverse interpolation in Table E, find the value of z_1 corresponding

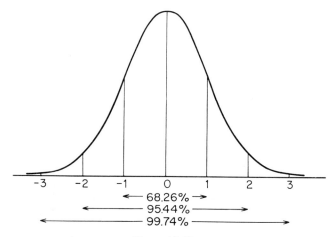

Figure 10-18

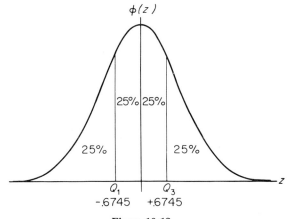

Figure 10-19

to one-fourth the area. This value of z is found to be 0.6745, and represents Q_3. Hence, $Q_1 = -0.6745$ and $Q_3 = +0.6745$. (Fig. 10-19.)

The *semi-interquartile range* or *quartile deviation* is 0.6745. Fifty per cent of the area lies between -0.6745 and $+0.6745$.

10.8. $\phi(z)$ AND $f(x)$

We have seen that the unit of measure along the x-axis is σ_x times as great as that along the z-axis. In other words, σ_x itself is the unit when we employ the variable z. That is why $\sigma_z = 1$. This is a very useful device and enables us to express easily many of the properties just enumerated, in terms of the original variable, x. For example, abscissas of the points of inflection of the curve (10.4) are $\mu \pm \sigma_x$. Therefore, 68 per cent of the variates have values lying between the limits $\mu + \sigma_x$ and $\mu - \sigma_x$. Less than 0.3 per cent of the variates deviate from the mean by more than $3\sigma_x$. Fifty per cent of the variates lie within the limits $\mu \pm 0.6745\sigma_x$.

10.9. SOME APPLICATIONS

EXAMPLE 1. Referring to the data for head lengths, Table 9-1, let us assume that head lengths are normally distributed and find the probability that a criminal chosen at random has a head length between 190.0 and 195.0 millimeters. Let $x_1 = 190.0$ and $x_2 = 195.0$. We have found that $\bar{x} = 191.8$ and $s = 6.48$. Since the sample is large we assume $\bar{x} = \mu$ and $s = \sigma$. Hence, by virtue of (10.6)

$$z_1 = \frac{x_1 - \bar{x}}{s_x} \qquad\qquad z_2 = \frac{x_2 - \bar{x}}{s_x}$$

$$= \frac{190.0 - 191.8}{6.48} \qquad\qquad = \frac{195.0 - 191.8}{6.48}$$

$$= -0.28 \qquad\qquad\qquad = 0.49.$$

Fig. 10-20 shows the relation between the x- and z-curves.

$$\int_{-0.28}^{0.49} \phi(z)\, dz = 0.2982;$$

hence the probability sought is about 0.30.

EXAMPLE 2. In the manufacture of washers to be used in radio receivers, it has been found that the mean thickness $\mu = 2.20$ mm and $\sigma = 0.15$ mm. All washers exceeding a thickness of 2.50 mm are rejected. What percentage can be expected to be discarded?

Solution. Since $x_1 - \mu = 0.30$, $z_1 = 0.30/0.15 = 2.00$. The probability for deviations greater than 0.30 mm is:

$$\int_{2.00}^{\infty} \phi(z)\, dz = 0.0228.$$

The percentage to be discarded will be about 2.28. The probability just found is represented by the shaded area in Fig. 10-21.

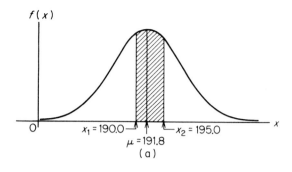

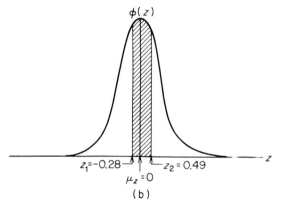

Figure 10-20

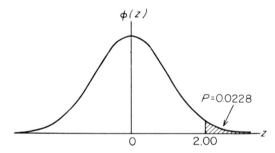

Figure 10-21

EXAMPLE 3. Assume that the scores in a Graduate Record Examination are normally distributed with $\mu = 500$ and $\sigma = 100$. Of 674 persons taking this examination, it is desired to pass 550 of them. What should be the lowest score permitted for passing?

Solution. $\frac{550}{674} = 0.8160$ so that 81.60 per cent are to pass. The fraction failing is represented by the left-tail area shown in Fig. 10-22a. z_1,

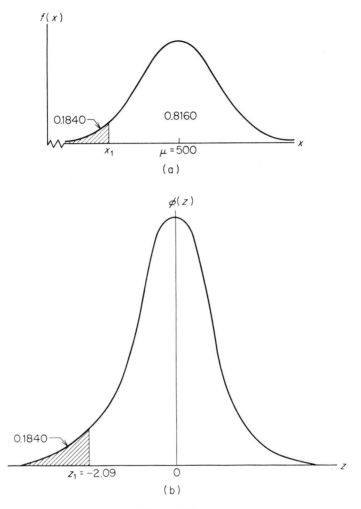

Figure 10-22

corresponding to the desired cut-off value, x_1, is a negative number
(see Fig. 10-22b) and is found from the relation:

$$\int_{-\infty}^{z_1} \phi(z)\, dz = \int_{-z_1}^{\infty} \phi(z)\, dz = 0.1840.$$

Note that $-z_1$ is a positive number. From Table E, we find by inverse
interpolation that $-z_1 = 0.91$, or $z_1 = -0.91$ approximately. Then

$$-0.91 = \frac{x_1 - 500}{100}$$

whence $x_1 = 409$. Thus all candidates having scores of 409 or above will pass.

10.10. APPLICATIONS TO BINOMIAL DISTRIBUTIONS

In Section 10.3, it was observed that probabilities associated with the binomial distribution for $N = 400$ and $p = \frac{1}{2}$, could be well approximated by means of the normal distribution. In general, when N is moderately large and p (or q) $\leq \frac{1}{2}$, but Np (or Nq) > 5, the normal approximation is valid. In this connection, it is important to bear in mind that binomial frequencies are functions of a *discrete* variable, whereas normal frequencies are functions of a *continuous* variable. For this reason, a *correction for continuity* should be used.

Figure 10-23 represents a binomial histogram. Suppose that we seek the probability that the number of successes, x, lies between x_1 and x_2 inclusive. Since each point representing a number of successes is the mid-point of the

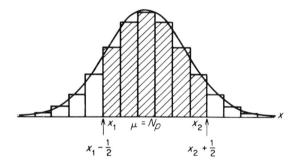

Figure 10-23

base of a rectangle, this probability is given by the sum of the areas of the rectangles within the interval from $x_1 - \frac{1}{2}$ to $x_2 + \frac{1}{2}$. The number $\frac{1}{2}$ is the *correction factor* for continuity. Then the sum of the probabilities for a number of successes from x_1 to x_2 inclusive is given by the integral

$$\int_{x_1-\frac{1}{2}}^{x_2+\frac{1}{2}} f(x)\, dx = \int_{z_1}^{z_2} \phi(z)\, dz$$

where z_1 and z_2 correspond to $x_1 - \frac{1}{2}$ and $x_2 + \frac{1}{2}$.

Thus $z_1 = \dfrac{x_1 - \frac{1}{2} - \mu}{\sigma}$ and $z_2 = \dfrac{x_2 + \frac{1}{2} - \mu}{\sigma}$ where $\mu = Np$ and $\sigma = \sqrt{Npq}$.

EXAMPLE 1. Let us calculate the sum of the probabilities $P(210) + P(211) + \cdots + P(220)$ of (10.5) by the method given before. $\mu = 200$, $\sigma = 10$,

$x_1 = 210$, and $x_2 = 220$. Then

$$z_1 = \frac{210 - \frac{1}{2} - 200}{10} = 0.95, \qquad z_2 = \frac{220 + \frac{1}{2} - 200}{10} = 2.05.$$

$$\int_{0.95}^{2.05} \phi(z)\, dz = 0.1711 - 0.0202 = 0.1509.$$

The probability that in 400 tosses there would be a number of heads from 210 to 220 inclusive, is 0.1509. This agrees with the value given in the footnote accompanying formula (10.5). The excellent agreement of the normal approximation (to four decimal places) with the exact binomial sum is due to the facts that N is a large number and $p = q$.

EXAMPLE 2. In Section 8.4, we calculated the probability for the number of heads in ten tosses of a true coin to be 0, 1, 9, or 10. There we used the binomial probability formula to find

$$P(0) + P(1) + P(9) + P(10) = 0.0216.$$

Using the normal approximation (Fig. 10-24), we find that $\mu = 5$, $\sigma = \sqrt{10 \times \frac{1}{2} \times \frac{1}{2}} = 1.58$. Let $x_1 = 1$ and $x_2 = 9$. Then

$$z_1 = \frac{1.5 - 5}{1.58} = -2.22, \qquad z_2 = \frac{8.5 - 5}{1.58} = 2.22.$$

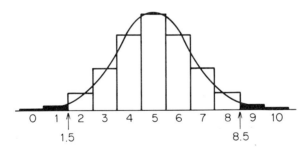

Figure 10-24

Hence,

$$P(x \leq 1) + P(x \geq 9) = \int_{-\infty}^{-2.22} \phi(z)\, dz + \int_{2.22}^{\infty} \phi(z)\, dz$$

$$= 2 \int_{2.22}^{\infty} \phi(z)\, dz = 0.0264.$$

The discrepancy between these two values, 0.0216 and 0.0264, is not important but is due to the small value of N and the use of the tail areas only.

EXAMPLE 3. In the manufacture of certain experimental light bulb filaments, 20% of them have been, as a rule, defective. A modification of the shape of the filament is to be tried out on a sample of 80, and if 10 or fewer are found defective, the hypothesis $H_0 : p_0 = 0.20$ will be rejected in favor of $H_1 : p_1 < 0.20$. On the other hand, if 11 or more are found to be defective, H_0 will be accepted, that is, the modification will be deemed to be no improvement. (a) What is the value of α? (b) If later extensive experience with the new filament showed that $p = 0.15$, what would be the size of β?

(a) Under H_0, $\mu_0 = 80 \times 0.20 = 16$, $\sigma_0 = \sqrt{80 \times 0.20 \times 0.80} = 3.58$;

$$z_1 = \frac{10.5 - 16}{3.58} = -1.54,$$

hence

$$P(x \leq 10) = P(z < -1.54) = 0.0618 = \alpha.$$

(b) Under H_1, $\mu_1 = 80 \times 0.15 = 12$, $\sigma_1 = \sqrt{80 \times 0.15 \times 0.85} = 3.19$;

$$z_1 = \frac{10.5 - 12}{3.19} = -0.470;$$

$$P(x \geq 11) = P(z > -0.47) = 0.6808 = \beta.$$

Thus there is a 6% chance of rejecting the hypothesis H_0, and deciding that the modification is better when it is not. On the other hand, there is a 68% chance of accepting H_0 and not adopting the modified filament, when actually it is an improvement. (See Fig. 10-25.)

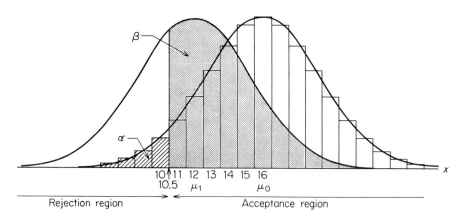

Figure 10-25

EXAMPLE 4. In the United States, 45% of the population belongs to blood group O. We are to test the hypothesis $H_0 : p_0 = 0.45$ against the alternative $H_1 : p_1 < 0.45$ on a sample of 200 persons of race R. If α is to be equal to 0.05, what is the critical number for the rejection of H_0? (b) What hypothesis should we accept if 80 such persons in the sample are found to belong to blood group O?

Here $\mu_0 = 200 \times 0.45 = 90$ and $\sigma_0 = \sqrt{200 \times 0.45 \times 0.55} = 7.04$. Then for a left-tail area of 0.05, $z = -1.645$. Since

$$-1.645 = \frac{x + \frac{1}{2} - 90}{7.04},$$

$x = 77.9$; hence, the critical number (integer) is 77.9 (say 78). Therefore, if the number in the sample of 200 equals or is less than 78, we reject H_0; otherwise we accept it. Since 80 exceeds 78 we accept H_0.

10.11. NORMAL CURVE FITTING

It is sometimes useful to fit a normal curve to a histogram constructed from a sample that appears to have arisen from a population that is reasonably normal. We assume that the population mean, μ, is very nearly equal to the mean, $\bar{x}$, of the sample, and that the population standard deviation, σ, is very nearly equal to the corresponding statistic, s, of the sample. These assumptions seem to be valid in view of the fact that, in order to have a histogram possible, the sample size, N, must be large.

The successive mid-points of the bases of the rectangles are labeled $x_1, x_2, \ldots, x_n$, and the latter are converted into standard variates, $z_1, z_2, \ldots,$

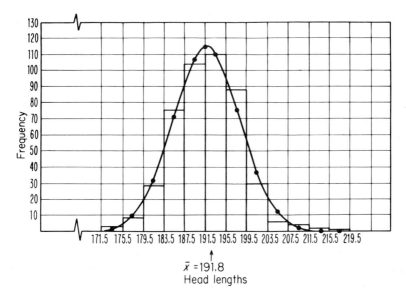

Fig. 10-26. Histogram and normal frequency curve for head lengths.

z_n. From Table D of the Appendix we can find the ordinates $\phi(z_1)$, $\phi(z_2)$, ..., $\phi(z_n)$ of these mid-points. These represent the heights of the normal curve in standard form, and must be multiplied by the scale factor, Nk/σ, in order to be plotted on the same scale as the histogram. Here k denotes the width of the class interval. It is good practice to plot also the maximum ordinate, obtained as $(Nk/\sigma)\phi(0)$.

Figure 10-26 shows the normal curve corresponding to the distribution of head lengths, Table 9-1 and Fig. 9-1.

10.12. TESTS OF NORMALITY

Whether a normal probability function can be used as a model for a given frequency distribution is commonly decided by visual estimation: the histogram looks fairly symmetrical and is bell-shaped. It is possible to reinforce this qualitative procedure by tests which yield numerical measures. The *third moment*, $\mathbf{a_3}$, known as the *skewness*, the *fourth moment*, $\mathbf{a_4}$, and the *mean deviation*, $\mathbf{a}$, are defined as follows:

$$a_3 = \frac{1}{N} \sum_{i=1}^{n} f_i z_i^3 \tag{10.8}$$

$$a_4 = \frac{1}{N} \sum_{i=1}^{n} f_i z_i^4 \tag{10.9}$$

and

$$a = \frac{1}{N} \sum_{i=1}^{n} |z_i| \tag{10.10}$$

where

$$z_i = \frac{x_i - \bar{x}}{s} . \tag{10.11}$$

It can be demonstrated mathematically that, for a normal density function, the parameters corresponding to the foregoing statistics have the following values:

$$\alpha_3 = 0$$
$$\alpha_4 = 3$$
$$\alpha = \sqrt{(2/\pi)} \text{ exactly}$$
$$= 0.798 \text{ approximately.}$$

The discrepancies between a_3 and α_3, a_4 and α_4, and a and α are used as tests for the normality of a given sample. Tables of probability points for a_3, a_4, and a are available, and the methods of Chapter 13 are used. (See E. S. Pearson and R. C. Geary; *Tests of Normality*, Biometrika Office, University College, London.)

The quantity *Chi-square* enables one to test for the "goodness of fit" of a normal curve to a given sample conjectured to be normal. (See Chapter 11.)

10.13. THE CUMULATIVE NORMAL CURVE

In Section 9.4, we plotted the cumulative frequency diagram (Fig. 9-2) corresponding to the frequency polygon (Fig. 9-1) of head lengths. These graphs are characteristic of large samples of normal type. In like manner,

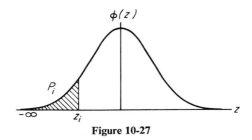

Figure 10-27

there exists a *cumulative* normal curve associated with a normal curve. The former is plotted on this wise. The cumulative probabilities, $P_1, P_2, \ldots, P_n$, corresponding to the standardized end-values, $z_1, z_2, \ldots, z_n$, are obtained from Table E of the Appendix. (See Fig. 10-27.)

$$P_i = \int_{-\infty}^{z_i} \phi(z) \, dz.$$

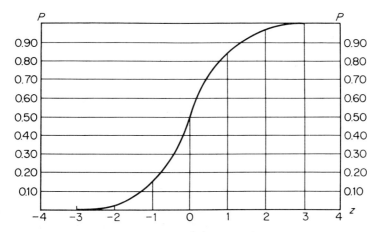

Fig. 10-28. A cumulative normal curve.

These become the ordinates of these z's. The resulting curve has the sigmoidal form shown in Fig. 10-28.

A useful device for making estimates of the parameters μ and σ and for studying other properties of a normal density function used as a model for a given frequency distribution is found in *arithmetic probability paper*. The scales or coordinate rulings of such paper are so chosen as to transform the fitted cumulative normal curve into a straight line. The paper may also be used as a quick test for normality. (See Reference 8.)

EXERCISES

By using Table D of the Appendix, find $\phi(z)$ for the values of z given in exercises 1–3.

1. (a) 0.50; (b) 0.25; (c) -1.18; (d) 2.57.

2. (a) 1.78; (b) 0.32; (c) -2.70; (d) -1.35.

3. (a) 3.12; (b) -1.04; (c) 0.66; (d) -2.86.

By using Table E of the Appendix, find the areas (probabilities) indicated in exercises 4–7.

4. (a) $\int_{0.40}^{\infty} \phi(z)\, dz$; (b) $\int_{-\infty}^{-1.38} \phi(z)\, dz$; (c) $\int_{0.25}^{0.92} \phi(z)\, dz$.

5. (a) $\int_{2.71}^{\infty} \phi(z)\, dz$; (b) $\int_{-\infty}^{-2.75} \phi(z)\, dz$; (c) $\int_{2.00}^{2.67} \phi(z)\, dz$.

6. (a) $\int_{0.35}^{1.09} \phi(z)\, dz$; (b) $\int_{1.23}^{2.36} \phi(z)\, dz$; (c) $\int_{-0.46}^{0.46} \phi(z)\, dz$.

7. (a) $\int_{2.10}^{3.06} \phi(z)\, dz$; (b) $\int_{-1.00}^{\infty} \phi(z)\, dz$; (c) $\int_{-2.65}^{-1.65} \phi(z)\, dz$.

By means of inverse interpolation in Table E of the Appendix, find the values of z_1 corresponding to the areas given in exercises 8–10.

8. (a) $\int_{z_1}^{\infty} \phi(z)\, dz = 0.2819$;   (b) $\int_{z_1}^{\infty} \phi(z)\, dz = 0.4625$.

9. (a) $\int_{-\infty}^{-z_1} \phi(z)\, dz = 0.2438$;   (b) $\int_{-z_1}^{z_1} \phi(z)\, dz = 0.9940$.

10. (a) $\int_{-z_1}^{0} \phi(z)\, dz = 0.2589$;   (b) $\int_{0}^{z_1} \phi(z)\, dz = 0.4692$.

11. With the aid of Table D (ordinates), plot carefully a normal curve on a full sheet of rectangular coordinate paper. Use values of z from -3 to 3 at intervals of 0.2.

12. With the aid of Table E (areas), plot on a full sheet of rectangular co-ordinate paper a cumulative normal curve by using intervals of 0.2 from $z = -3$ to $z = 3$.

In the following exercises, assume all distributions to be normal.

13. If the scores in a certain test have $\mu = 500$ and $\sigma = 100$, what per cent of the scores are between 400 and 600?

14. The mean systolic blood pressure of men 20–24 years of age is 123 with a standard deviation of 13.7. What is the probability that a man of this age group, selected at random, has a blood pressure (a) above 140? (b) below 110?

15. It is desired to form a company of soldiers 6 feet or more tall. If the mean height for the regiment is 68 inches with a standard deviation of 2.5 inches, how many such soldiers may be expected to be found in this regiment of 1200 men?

16. If the mean stature of college women was 5 feet 6 inches and the standard deviation, 2.40 inches, what percentage of college women would have statures between 5 feet 2 inches and 5 feet 8 inches?

17. If the thicknesses of a certain type of washer have $\mu = 1.95$ mm and $\sigma = 0.12$ mm, how many washers in 1000 should have thicknesses between 1.80 and 2.10 mm?

18. In a certain community, the mean per cent of income saved by families was 8.32 with a standard deviation of 1.94. What percentage of the families saved more than 10% of their income?

19. A man drives to work every day and finds that the time per trip from his home to his office shows $\mu = 35.5$ minutes and $\sigma = 3.11$ minutes. If he leaves his home each day at 8:20 and must be in his office at 9, how many times per year should he expect to be late? Assume 240 trips per year.

20. For cats, the mean lethal dose of a certain tincture of digitalis is 13.40 cc and $\sigma = 0.845$. What percentage of the cats would you estimate to die for a dose less than 12.00 cc?

21. What is the value of z corresponding to the 70 percentile? (Three decimal places.)

22. If the range (mean horizontal distance traveled) of a certain gun at a given elevation is 2560 yards with a standard deviation of 30 yards, how many shots in 100 should be "over" or "short" by more than 70 yards? If a burst within 10 yards of the target is considered a hit, how many hits should there be if the gun is "on the target?"

23. An examination has a mean score of 500 and $\sigma = 100$. The top 75% of candidates taking this examination are to be passed. What is the lowest passing score?

24. The tolerance (acceptance) limits for the diameters of ball bearings produced by a machine are $\mu \pm k\sigma$. What percentage of the bearings will be accepted if (a) $k = 2.0$? (b) $k = 2.5$? (c) the lower limit corresponds to $k = 2.0$ and the upper, to $k = 2.5$?

25. The diameters of tubes made by a machine show a mean of 9.80 mm and a standard deviation of 0.536 mm. All tubes less than 9.00 mm in diameter are rejected. What percentage are rejected?

26. The blood pressures of U.S. soldiers have $\mu = 127$ and $\sigma = 14.0$. It is desired to separate from a regiment those soldiers whose blood pressures belong to the highest 10%. At what blood pressure should the separation be made?

27. Problems of the following type arise in anthropology (matching bones) and in industry (assembling parts). A characteristic x has $\mu = 50$ and $\sigma = 10$. A characteristic y, independent of x, has $\mu = 20$ and $\sigma = 5$. In a random sample of one item from each population, what is the probability of obtaining a value of $x > 60$ at the same time that $y < 17$?

28. Extensive records of loss of weight by evaporation of a certain packaged product show a mean loss of 6.45 grams with a standard deviation of 1.30 grams. If two packages were selected at random from a lot, what is the probability that both of them would show a loss of more than 8.00 grams each?

29. From the data of the preceding problem, what is the probability that, if five packages were selected, at least one package would show a loss of weight of more than 8.00 grams?

In the following exercises use the normal approximation to the binomial distribution. If binomial probability tables are available (References 17 and 21), check your answers by them.

30. In a certain mathematics examination, the number of failures over a period of years constituted 10% of the candidates. In 1959, there were 60 failures in a group of 517 who took this examination. If we take $\alpha = 0.02$, should we attribute this result to chance?

31. In general, 80% of the patients inoculated with a certain serum recover. If only 45 out of 75 patients over 60 years of age recover after inoculation, could we accept the hypothesis that older persons react differently to this serum? Assume $\alpha = 0.02$.

32. If a pair of dice were tossed 720 times and showed the sum 6 just 80 times, would you consider the outcome unusual? At what significance level?

33. We are to test the hypothesis that thumb tacks, when dropped on the floor, land point up 60% of the time. One hundred of them are dropped and 53 land point up. If $\alpha = 0.05$, and we use a two-tail test, should we accept or reject the hypothesis?

34. In New England, 40% of the population has been found to belong to blood group A. (a) Write, but do not compute the probability that exactly 90 persons in a New England community of 200 belong to this group. (b) Compute this probability by means of the normal approximation.

35. If the sum 5 appeared 33 times when a pair of dice is tossed 450 times, would you consider the outcome unusual at the 5% level?

36. As a rule, 8% of the students in a certain college are elected to Phi Beta

Kappa. What is the probability that at least 15 of the 120 veterans graduating are elected?

37. In an unfair game of chance the probability that a certain man wins is $\frac{3}{5}$. If he makes 100 bets of one dollar each, what is the probability that his profit is at least ten dollars?

38. How many times must you toss a penny in order that the chance of getting a deviation of more than ten from the mean number of heads is $\frac{2}{5}$?

39. The chance of guessing a certain card correctly is $\frac{1}{5}$. In 800 trials there were 207 correct guesses. Was this an unusual result? Let $\alpha = 0.05$.

40. Compute to three decimal places the probability of obtaining less than four heads when a penny is tossed 10 times by means of (a) the binomial probability formula and (b) the normal approximation.

41. If two guinea pigs, one of pure black race and the other of pure white race are mated, the probability that an offspring of the second generation is pure white is $\frac{1}{4}$. What is the probability that among 400 such offspring more than 115 are pure white?

42. The probability of winning a game of craps is 0.495. If a player won 27 games out of 50, what could you say about this result?

43. Assume that when *macrosiphoniella sanborni* (the chrysanthemum aphis) are sprayed with a concentration of 4 milligrams per liter of rotenone, $\frac{1}{3}$ of the insects die. Find the mean and standard deviation for the number dying when samples of 50 of the same insects are sprayed. What conclusion would you draw if just half of a sample of 50 died?

44. In example 4 of Section 10.10, calculate β if $p = 0.42$ were true.

45. For the data of exercise 33 let us test $H_0 : p_0 = 0.60$ with $\alpha = 0.05$ and $N = 100$, against $H_1 : p_1 < 0.60$. (a) What is the critical rejection number of times for the thumb tacks to land point up? (b) If $H_1 : p_1 = 0.55$, what is the value of β?

46. Fit a normal curve to the data of exercise 9.2.

47. Fit a normal curve to the data of exercise 9.4.

The Multinomial and
Chi-Square Distributions

Come, let us see how the squares go.

Anonymous

11.1. THE MULTINOMIAL DISTRIBUTION

We recall that the binomial distribution is discrete with probabilities given by the successive terms of the expansion of $(q + p)^N$. It is concerned with two mutually exclusive categories, occurrence and nonoccurrence of an event. In certain problems, we can avoid the labor of computing a desired sum of binomial probabilities by approximating to it by means of the area under a continuous curve, that of the normal distribution.

A similar situation arises when more than two mutually exclusive categories exist. For example, in a toss of six pennies, any number of heads from 0 to 6 may occur; hence, there are seven mutually exclusive categories. It may be proved that, if $p_1, p_2, \ldots, p_k$ are the respective probabilities of obtaining the mutually exclusive values $x_1, x_2, \ldots, x_k$, then the probability P, of obtaining in N independent trials, x_1 just n_1 times, x_2 just n_2 times, $\ldots, x_k$ just n_k times, where $\sum_{i=1}^{k} n_i = N$ and $\sum_{i=1}^{k} p_i = 1$, is given by the formula

$$P = \frac{N!}{n_1! n_2! \cdots n_k!} p_1^{n_1} p_2^{n_2} \cdots p_k^{n_k} \qquad (11.1)$$

which is a general term derived from the multinomial expansion

$$(p_1 + p_2 + \cdots + p_k)^N. \tag{11.2}$$

Formula (11.1) defines the *multinomial probability function*. Its derivation is straightforward and resembles that of Section 8.1.

The particular sequence of events

$$\overbrace{x_1 x_1 \cdots x_1}^{n_1} \overbrace{x_2 x_2 \cdots x_2}^{n_2} \cdots \overbrace{x_k x_k \cdots x_k}^{n_k},$$

where x_i occurs n_i times in succession, has a probability

$$p_1^{n_1} p_2^{n_2} \cdots p_k^{n_k} \tag{11.3}$$

of occurring, since all N trials are independent of one another. Any other sequence has the same probability associated with it and there are

$$\frac{N!}{n_1! n_2! \cdots n_k!} \tag{11.4}$$

different sequences possible [see formula (2.3)]; hence, the probability for any one of these sequences is given as the product of (11.3) and (11.4), which is the multinomial formula (11.1).

Example. A community consists of 50% English, 30% Irish, and 20% Scottish persons. If a sample of six individuals is selected at random, what is the probability that two are English, three are Irish, and one is a Scot?

The probabilities for persons of these three races are respectively, 0.50, 0.30, and 0.20. Then

$$P = \frac{6!}{2!3!1!} (0.5)^2 (0.3)^3 (0.2) = 0.081.$$

11.2. AN EXAMPLE

Consider the data of Table 11-1, where the actual frequency distribution that resulted when six pennies were tossed 128 times is compared with the model binomial distribution. For a reason to be explained in Section 11.6, we have combined the two frequencies at each end of the table.

The probabilities listed in the second column were obtained from the binomial probability formula

$$\frac{6!}{x!(6-x)!} \left(\frac{1}{2}\right)^x \left(\frac{1}{2}\right)^{6-x}, \qquad x = 0, 1, 2, 3, 4, 5, 6.$$

TABLE 11-1

No. of Heads	Probability: p_i	Theoretical No. of Heads: Np_i	Actual No. of Heads: f_i	Difference: $f_i - Np_i$
0 or 1	7/64	14	12	−2
2	15/64	30	28	−2
3	20/64	40	44	4
4	15/64	30	30	0
5 or 6	7/64	14	14	0
Sum	1	128	128	0

By the multinomial formula, the probability for the complete set of five frequencies that actually occurred is:

$$P = \frac{128!}{12!28!44!30!14!}\left(\frac{7}{64}\right)^{12}\left(\frac{15}{64}\right)^{28}\left(\frac{20}{64}\right)^{44}\left(\frac{15}{64}\right)^{30}\left(\frac{7}{64}\right)^{14} \qquad (11.5)$$

If we were to ask, "What is the probability for a result as usual as this or less usual?" we would be faced with the task of calculating a sum of probabilities similar to that in Eq. (11.5), and this task we would not relish. Just as the (continuous) normal distribution enabled us to compute easily a sum of (discrete) binomial probabilities, so does the (continuous) *Chi-square* (Greek symbol, χ^2) distribution furnish us with a means of approximating a sum of (discrete) multinomial probabilities.

11.3. THE CHI-SQUARE FUNCTION

The distribution just referred to is very important and is defined by means of the function

$$y = Ce^{-(\chi^2/2)}(\chi^2)^{(n/2)-1} \qquad (11.6)$$

where C is a constant depending on n, called the *number of degrees of freedom*. (See the next section.) The curve for $n = 6$ is shown in Fig. 11-1. It is skew with a range of values from $\chi^2 = 0$ to $\chi^2 = \infty$. When $n = 1$ the curve for χ becomes the right half of a normal curve with doubled ordinate (Fig. 11-2). As n increases, the curve becomes more symmetrical. In fact, if we set $z = \sqrt{2\chi^2}$, the resulting distribution of z can be proved to approximate very well, for moderately large values of N, the normal curve with mean at $\sqrt{2n-1}$. For this reason when $n > 30$ one obtains good practical accuracy by using the normal curve with the standard deviate

$$z = \sqrt{2\chi^2} - \sqrt{2n-1}.$$

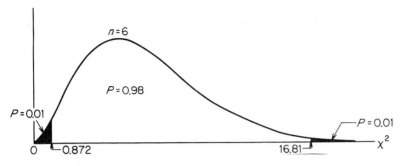

Figure 11-1

The values of χ^2 for degrees of freedom from $n = 1$ to $n = 30$ have been tabulated for various convenient probability values and may be found in Table G of the Appendix. This table yields the values for the probability, P, that χ^2 exceeds a given value. The shaded portion of the right tail in Fig. 11-1, where $n = 6$, represents the probability, 0.01, that χ^2 exceeds 16.81; the area to the right of the ordinate erected at $\chi^2 = 0.872$ represents the probability, 0.99, that $\chi^2 > 0.872$; hence, the shaded portion of the left tail corresponds to the probability 0.01, that $\chi^2 < 0.872$. We may combine these statements into the assertion,

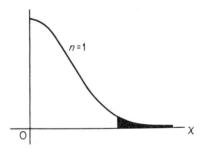

Figure 11-2

$$P(0.872 < \chi^2 < 16.81) = 0.98.$$

A convenient notation for probability statements such as the first two just made is illustrated by the following:

$$\chi^2_{0.01} = 16.81, \qquad \chi^2_{0.99} = 0.872.$$

The former may be read, "Chi-square at the one per cent level equals 16.81."

11.4. DEGREES OF FREEDOM

The data of Table 11-1 will illustrate the title of this section. In this table, the actual frequencies are to be compared with the theoretical, under the hypothesis that $p = \frac{1}{2}$ for each penny. The probability function is clearly multinomial. Are the experimental or actual outcomes consistent with this hypothesis?

If the experiment of tossing six pennies 128 times were repeated over and over again, each experiment would yield five actual frequencies such as those listed in the fourth column of Table 11-1. Any frequency could be an integer from 0 to 128 inclusive, provided that the total frequency equalled 128. Thus, there would be an exceedingly large, but not an infinite, number of ways in which the five frequencies could occur, but these frequencies would be subject to the restriction

$$\sum_{i=1}^{5} f_i = 128. \tag{11.7}$$

Once four frequencies are given, the fifth is determined from Eq. (11.7) which is linear in the f's. Thus there are four degrees of freedom for the f's. In many situations, we must take into account the number of variates (here the f's) and the restrictions imposed upon them by the conditions of the experiment.

11.5. TESTING A MULTINOMIAL DISTRIBUTION

At this point, we introduce the important fact that the quantity

$$\sum_{i=1}^{m} \frac{(f_i - Np_i)^2}{Np_i}, \tag{11.8}$$

although a discrete variable, has been shown to behave like χ^2 with n degrees of freedom. In (11.8), m is the number of frequencies, and in this problem $n = m - 1 = 4$. If we set χ^2 equal to the quantity in Eq. (11.8), then the number of possible values of χ^2 is finite, its distribution is discrete and representable by a histogram. Areas of this histogram can be well approximated by corresponding areas under the true χ^2 curve defined in Eq. (11.6). Note that the quantity (11.8) is a sort of pseudo-χ^2, a discrete variable, whereas the χ^2 of Eq. (11.6) is the genuine one, the continuous variable. The use of χ^2 in these two senses does not usually cause difficulty.

From the last column of Table 11-1 and from formula (11.8) we find that

$$\chi^2 = \frac{(-2)^2}{14} + \frac{(-2)^2}{30} + \frac{4^2}{40} + \frac{0^2}{30} + \frac{0^2}{14}$$
$$= 0.82.$$

It is clear that if $\chi^2 = 0$, the agreement between the theoretical and the actual frequencies is perfect. As χ^2 increases, the disparity between the two sets of values increases also. The question that then arises is the following: What is the probability that, in a given sample, the discrepancy between the actual values and the theoretical will lead to a value as large as or larger than 0.82?

The five *cell frequencies* were subject to the single restriction

$$\sum_{i=1}^{5} f_i = 128,$$

hence the number of degrees of freedom, $n = 5 - 1 = 4$. To find the probability, P, that $\chi^2 > 0.82$ for four degrees of freedom we note that

$$\chi^2_{0.95} = 0.711 \quad \text{and} \quad \chi^2_{0.90} = 1.064.$$

Since

$$0.711 < 0.82 < 1.064,$$

it follows that

$$0.90 < P < 0.95.$$

Thus, the probability for sample frequencies to deviate from the theoretical at least as much as these do is close to unity. We say, then, that the actual frequencies are in excellent agreement with the theoretical. There is no reason to doubt the validity of the hypothesis that the distribution is a multinomial one with $p = \frac{1}{2}$ for each penny.

11.6. REMARKS ON THE CHI-SQUARE TEST

Mathematical considerations involved in the derivation of the χ^2-function and experience with practical problems lie behind the formulation of the following general rules for the applications of χ^2.

(*a*) Each cell frequency, f, should exceed five at least, and should preferably be much larger. When cell frequencies are too small they may be grouped together. This was done in forming Table 11-1.

(*b*) The number, m, of classes or cells should be neither too large nor too small. If $5 \leq m \leq 20$, one is usually on the safe side. Smaller values of m than 5 may be compensated somewhat if we ensure that the f's are larger than 5.

(*c*) The restrictions imposed on the cell frequencies must be expressible as equations of the first degree in the f's. Thus, in the example,

$$f_1 + f_2 + f_3 + f_4 + f_5 = 128.$$

(*d*) Values of P near unity are sometimes suspect, as the character of the sample or the design of the experiment may be faulty.

11.7. 2 × 2 TABLES

An example. In a study of "College Affiliation and Political Attitudes," samples of students eligible to vote for the first time in a presidential election were taken from the College of Liberal Arts (CLA) and the College of Business Administration (CBA) of Boston University in 1956.[1] The numbers not in parentheses in Table 11-2 summarize the results of the study.

TABLE 11-2

	CLA	CBA	Totals
Eisenhower	30 (36.9)	38 (31.1)	68
Stevenson	34 (27.1)	16 (22.9)	50
Totals	64	54	118

Let us test the hypothesis that college affiliation and political attitude are independent of each other. More precisely, the null hypothesis may be stated thus, in words: "The fraction of students in the college population (eligible to vote for the first time) who voted for Eisenhower is essentially the same whether they were students enrolled in the CLA or the CBA."

A model for the analysis of these data is shown in Table 11-3 where

TABLE 11-3

	A	$\bar{A}$	
B	P_{AB}	$P_{\bar{A}B}$	P_B
$\bar{B}$	$P_{A\bar{B}}$	$P_{\bar{A}\bar{B}}$	$P_{\bar{B}}$
	P_A	$P_{\bar{A}}$	1

P_{AB} is the probability that A and B occur together, $P_{\bar{A}B}$, that $\bar{A}$ and B occur together, etc. $P_B = P_{AB} + P_{\bar{A}B}$, $P_{\bar{B}} = P_{A\bar{B}} + P_{\bar{A}\bar{B}}$, etc. For the data of Table 11-2, we do not know the basic probabilities; therefore, we estimate them under the hypothesis that college affiliations (A and $\bar{A}$) and political preferences (B and $\bar{B}$) are independent of each other. Thus, in Table 11-2, to estimate the probability, P_{AB}, that CLA students will vote for Eisenhower, assuming independence so that $P_{AB} = P_A P_B$, we compute $P'_{AB} = \frac{68}{118} \cdot \frac{64}{118} = 0.312$. Similarly, $P'_{\bar{A}B} = \frac{68}{118} \cdot \frac{54}{118} = 0.264$, and so on. From these estimated probabilities, we find the estimated or theoretical frequencies. For example, $NP'_{AB} = 0.312 \times 118 = 36.9$, $NP'_{\bar{A}B} = 0.264 \times 118 = 31.1$. In practice, these last estimates are more easily found as follows:

We estimate the theoretical frequencies by stating that $\frac{68}{118}$ or 57.7 per cent of the entire sample voted for Eisenhower and 42.3 per cent voted

[1] Levin, M. B. and P. Nogee, "College Affiliation and Political Attitudes," *Boston University Graduate Journal*, Vol. 6, 1958.

for Stevenson. If college affiliation and political attitude are independent of each other, then 57.7 per cent of the 64 CLA students, or about 37 of them, on the average, would have voted for Eisenhower. The remaining 27 CLA students would have voted for Stevenson. Likewise, 57.7 per cent of the 54 CBA students, or 31 of them would, on the average, vote for Eisenhower and the remaining 23, for Stevenson. These theoretical frequencies, computed to the nearest 0.1, appear in parentheses in the table. Denoting the actual frequencies by f_i and the theoretical, by f'_i and applying Formula (11.8), we have

$$\chi^2 = \Sigma \frac{(f_i - f'_i)^2}{f'_i} \tag{11.9}$$

$$= \frac{(-6.9)^2}{36.9} + \frac{(6.9)^2}{27.1} + \frac{(6.9)^2}{31.1} + \frac{(-6.9)^2}{22.9} = 6.66. \tag{11.10}$$

The number of degrees of freedom, as will be shown in the next paragraph is 1, and from Table G, $\chi^2_{0.01} = 6.64$ and $\chi^2_{0.05} = 3.84$. Thus it appears that the hypothesis of independence is just barely refuted for $\alpha = 0.01$ and more definitely refuted for $\alpha = 0.05$.

In this illustration, we are imagining that the experiment of sampling a total of 118 students is repeated an infinite number of times and that from these repetitions we select the samples that contain the same marginal frequencies, 64, 54, 68, and 50. Then we inquire, what is the probability that for fixed marginal frequencies, we would obtain the cell frequencies shown in Table 11-2? There are 2×2, or 4 cell frequencies given, subject to the restrictions set by the marginal totals. Each row and column of two cells each must have the appropriate marginal total; also, if we know three marginal totals, we know all four, for the complete total is the sum of two adjacent ones. Thus, there are only three restrictions, and $n = 4 - 3 = 1$. Another way of determining n is to note that any single cell frequency may be assigned at will, and then the remaining three are determined by the marginal totals.

11.8. THE YATES CORRECTION

When we approximated to a binomial distribution by means of the normal we found it desirable to add or subtract a correction of $\frac{1}{2}$ to the actual frequency being tested. For a similar reason, we make use of a correction due to Yates (1934) for 2×2 tables. The rule may be stated as follows: *Reduce the absolute value of each difference,* $|f_i - f'_i|$, *by $\frac{1}{2}$ before squaring.* Thus

$$\chi^2 = \Sigma \frac{[|f_i - f'_i| - \frac{1}{2}]^2}{f'_i} . \tag{11.11}$$

If we apply this correction in the previous example, the numerators in Eq. (11.10) become $(6.4)^2$ and $\chi^2 = 5.73$. Thus the hypothesis is *not* refuted at the one per cent level but is refuted for a level, say, of two per cent or higher.

Example. It is suspected that different combinations of temperature and humidity affect the number of defective articles produced in a certain workroom. Do the data in Table 11-4 confirm this suspicion?

TABLE 11-4

		Humidity		
		Low	High	
Temperature	Low	10	4	14
	High	3	17	20
		13	21	34

Let $f_1 = 10$, $f_2 = 4$, $f_3 = 3$, and $f_4 = 17$. Then $f_1' = \frac{13}{34} \times 14 = 5.4$, whence, because of the marginal totals, $f_2' = 8.6$, $f_3' = 7.6$, $f_4' = 12.4$. Each difference $f_i - f_i' = 4.6$; hence, each corrected difference is $4.6 - 0.5 = 4.1$. Then,

$$\chi^2 = (4.1)^2\left(\frac{1}{5.4} + \frac{1}{8.6} + \frac{1}{7.6} + \frac{1}{12.4}\right) = 8.63.$$

For $n = 1$, $P < 0.01$; hence, the null hypothesis that the proportion of defectives in the population when the humidity is low is the same whether the temperature is low or high is untenable. The data confirm our suspicion. It appears that a combination of low temperature with low humidity or high temperature with high humidity produces an excessive number of defectives.

11.9. AN ALTERNATIVE FORMULA

A 2×2 table may be symbolized as in Table 11-5.

TABLE 11-5

	A	$\bar{A}$	Row Totals
B	a	b	$a + b = r_1$
$\bar{B}$	c	d	$c + d = r_2$
Column totals	$a + c = c_1$	$b + d = c_2$	$N = a + b + c + d$

Here $\bar{A}$ means "not-A" and $\bar{B}$, "not -B".

It may be proved that

$$\chi^2(\text{uncorrected}) = \frac{N(ad - bc)^2}{r_1 r_2 c_1 c_2} \qquad \textbf{(11.12)}$$

$$\chi^2(\text{corrected}) = \frac{N[|ad - bc| - N/2]^2}{r_1 r_2 c_1 c_2}. \qquad \textbf{(11.13)}$$

Many statisticians prefer formulas (11.12) and (11.13) to formulas (11.9) and (11.11).

11.10. MATHEMATICAL MODELS FOR 2 × 2 TABLES

The discussions of Sections 11.7 and 11.8 were devoted to "approximate tests." However, for 2 × 2 tables with small cell frequencies, certain "exact tests" are available. The multinomial formula supplied one such test. Section 5.5 discusses another. The subject is quite an extensive one and presents many problems still under investigation. In particular, the mathematical model which forms a basis for the derivation of a test needs careful elucidation. A more detailed discussion of the 2 × 2 table in its theoretical aspects will be found in Chapter 14. The tables of References 15 and 19 are particularly useful in dealing with experimental data yielding small cell frequencies. A useful and suggestive contribution to 2 × 2 tables may be found in *Biometrika* (Reference 26), G. A. Barnard, "Significance Tests for 2 × 2 Tables," Vol. 34, 1947, pp. 123–138.

11.11. p × q TABLES

The method of χ^2 used in fourfold tables may be extended to tables having p rows and q columns. Such a *contingency table* is illustrated in Table 11-6, and the method of analysis follows it. Note that Yates' correction is not, in general, applicable to other than 2 × 2 tables.

TABLE 11-6

CLASSIFICATION OF CANDIDATES FOR ADMISSION TO COLLEGE
ON THE BASIS OF THE COLLEGE'S RATING OF CANDIDATES

	Rating I	*Rating II*	*Rating III*	*Total*
Veterans	19 (22.9)	88 (71.2)	175 (187)	282
Nonveterans	33 (29.1)	76 (91.8)	251 (239)	360
Total	52	164	426	642

The fraction of veterans is $\frac{282}{642}$ or 0.440, from which we estimate the theoretical frequencies shown in parentheses. As soon as two frequencies in any two different columns are known, the remaining ones are determined; hence, there are two degrees of freedom. In fact, it is easily proved that the number of degrees of freedom for a $p \times q$ table with marginal totals fixed is $(p - 1)(q - 1)$. Here $p = 2$ and $q = 3$, hence $n = 2$.

$$\chi^2 = \frac{(3.9)^2}{22.9} + \frac{(3.9)^2}{29.1} + \cdots + \frac{(12)^2}{239} = 8.30.$$

Since $\chi^2_{0.02} = 7.82$ and $\chi^2_{0.01} = 9.21$, there are clearly significant differences between veterans and nonveterans on the 2% level. If the percentage of veterans in each of the three ratings is computed, we obtain the values 36.5, 53.6, and 41.0. Apparently, there is less variation between ratings I and III than between any other two.

11.12. CHI-SQUARE AND VARIANCE

A well-known theorem of mathematical statistics is the following:
If s^2 is the variance of a sample of N drawn from a normal population with variance, σ^2, then Ns^2/σ^2 has a χ^2-distribution with $N - 1$ degrees of freedom.
By means of this theorem, one can test a hypothesis concerning σ^2 by means of a sample variance s^2.

Example. A certain time factor in a manufacturing operation has a standard deviation of 14 seconds. If a group of 12 workers show a standard deviation of 17 seconds, could we say that this difference in variability is significant on the 10% level?

First find the 90% acceptance region for χ^2. For $n = 11$, $\chi^2_{0.95} = 4.575$, and $\chi^2_{0.05} = 19.68$. Hence,

$$P(4.575 < \chi^2 < 19.68) = 0.90. \tag{11.14}$$

Let H_0: $\sigma = 14$ and assume the distribution of times to be normal. Set $\chi^2 = Ns^2/\sigma^2$ and substitute $N = 12$, $s = 17$, and $\sigma = 14$, so that

$$\chi^2 = \frac{12 \times 17^2}{14^2} = 17.7.$$

Since this sample value of χ^2, 17.7 lies within the acceptance interval shown in Eq. (11.14), we cannot reject H_0.

EXERCISES

1. As the result of a psychological test, candidates are rated as (1) superior; (2) average; (3) inferior. In general, the per cents falling into these categories are

20, 50, and 30, respectively. If the test is given to eight persons, what is the probability that two are rated superior, three average, and three inferior?

2. A package of candy contains 20 wafers of five different flavors and colors. The mixing apparatus in the candy factory uses wafers in the following proportions but mixes them randomly:

	Per Cent
White (peppermint)	30
Brown (chocolate)	20
Yellow (lemon)	35
Green (lime)	10
Black (licorice)	5

If a boy purchases a package of these wafers, what is the chance that he gets a package mixed exactly in these proportions? Do not attempt to evaluate your result.

3. A die has three faces colored red, two colored white, and one colored blue. If this die is thrown nine times, what is the probability that each color appears three times? Compute to three decimal places.

4. Refer to exercise 4.23. A random sample of 100 persons from a New England community showed the following blood groupings: O, 50; A, 35; B, 8; AB, 7. (a) Write, but do not attempt to evaluate, the probability for this particular result. (b) Using $\alpha = 0.10$, decide if this sample is unusual or not.

5. When four pennies were tossed 160 times, the actual frequencies of occurrence of 0, 1, 2, 3, and 4 heads were 7, 45, 53, 49, and 6, respectively. Discuss this outcome with the aid of the χ^2-test.

6. The Pasteur Drug Store found that of the last 160 patrons of its ice-cream bar, 70 ordered vanilla ice cream, 42, chocolate, and 48, other flavors. Is this experience consistent with the hypothesis that 50% of its patrons order vanilla, 30% chocolate, and 20% other flavors?

7. A large ice cream manufacturing company tested its product against that of its competitor by offering to each of 882 individuals two samples of ice cream, for one of which a preference was to be stated. The same individual was then given another two samples, for one of which a preference was to be stated. Unknown to the taster, the two brands A and B of the first test were the same as those of the second test. The results follow. B represents the brand of the competitor. Discuss these results as fully as possible.

Preference		Frequency
(1)	(2)	
A	A	331
B	B	135
A	B	416
B	A	

8. In a study of the evaluation of a certain social project, four levels A, B, C, D, of judgment were used. It was expected that, in general, these levels would be given 10, 40, 40, and 10% of the time, respectively. In one study, 16 judges showed the following results:

	A	B	C	D
Expected	1.6	6.4	6.4	1.6
Actual	1	7	8	0

It was found that

$$\chi^2 = \frac{(0.6)^2}{1.6} + \frac{(0.6)^2}{6.4} + \frac{(1.6)^2}{6.4} + \frac{(1.6)^2}{1.6} = 2.29.$$

Comment on this method.

In each of the exercises 9–13, test for independence by means of Chi-square.

9. The effect of a new treatment on patients afflicted with a certain disease.

	Recovered	Died	Total
Treated	73	12	85
Not treated	50	21	71
Total	123	33	156

10. Is any relationship between sex and performance indicated in the following data taken from an examination?

	No. Right	No. Wrong
Boys	56	24
Girls	34	36

11. Influence of the duration of a certain mental disorder on the intelligence quotient.

IQ Duration	Below 70	70 or Above	Total
Less than 10 years	62	55	117
More than 10 years	44	26	70
Total	106	81	187

12. Is there a significant difference between Plots 1 and 2?

	No. Seeds Germinating	No. Seeds Not Germinating
Plot 1	300	100
Plot 2	400	100

13. A drug manufacturing company made a survey of the number of doctors prescribing a certain product. According to the data shown below, does the general practitioner differ materially from the specialist in prescribing this drug?

	Prescribing	Not Prescribing
General practitioners	33	204
Specialists	18	47

In exercises 14 and 15, test the hypothesis of independence ($\alpha = 0.05$) with the aid of the tables of References 15 or 19, if available.

14.

	B	$\bar{B}$
A	1	9
$\bar{A}$	6	2

15.

	Inoculated	Not Inoculated
Attacked	3	7
Not attacked	8	4

16. A professor thinks that students in Monday, Wednesday, Friday classes are more likely to be absent on Mondays and Fridays than on Wednesdays. He noted that in a randomly selected class there were 35 absences on Mondays, 23 on Wednesdays, and 32 on Fridays. Test the hypothesis that absences on the three days in question are about equally numerous.

17. A safety engineer at the *ABC* Company claimed that accidents were more likely to occur at the beginning and the end of the week and just before lunch and closing time. Do the data shown for a month at the factory of this company bear out his contention?

Day of the Week	Hour of Day		
	11–12	4–5	Other
Monday	7	10	52
Friday	9	13	57
Other	16	28	112

18. Four closely related species of plants have their seeds mixed in numbers of 10, 30, 40, and 20. A student attempts to separate them, and obtains the numbers shown. Does he do a good job?

Species	Mixture	Results
A	10	8
B	30	37
C	40	20
D	20	35

19. For the following data, test the hypothesis that inoculation does not affect recovery, with a significance level of 2%. Why is it safe to omit the correction factor here?

	Recoveries	Deaths	Total
Inoculated	89	53	142
Not inoculated	32	61	93
Total	121	114	235

20. Do the data shown below indicate any real difference between Methods A and B used in a manufacturing process?

	Defective	Nondefective
Method A	41	20
Method B	16	28

21. The scores on a Graduate Record Examination of 22 seniors from College A showed a standard deviation of 85. Test H_0: $\sigma = 100$ versus H_1: $\sigma < 100$, with $\alpha = 0.05$.

22. The mean purity of a compound is stated to be 94.6% and the standard deviation, 2.13. A sample of 10 from Laboratory Q showed $s = 2.52$. Test H_0: $\sigma = 2.13$ versus H_1: $\sigma \neq 2.13$. Let $\alpha = 0.02$.

23. Assume for a certain age group of American males that systolic blood pressures show a variance of 268. A selected sample of 20 men from this age group had a variance of 313. May one conclude that this group represents a population with $\sigma^2 \neq 268$? Let $\alpha = 0.04$.

24. The variance in the diameter of steel shafts is found to be 0.0052. Would 100 shafts, turned out by a certain machinist, with a variance of 0.0065 indicate greater variability than normal for this workman?

12

Distributions Related to Binomial and Normal Distributions

Probable evidence is essentially distinguished from demonstrative by this, that it admits of Degrees.

BISHOP JOSEPH BUTLER
The Analogy of Religion Natural and Revealed, 1736

12.1. THE DISTRIBUTION OF A PROPORTION

If p is the constant probability for success, then for N independent trials $\mu = Np$ and $\sigma^2 = Npq$. We may interpret p as the proportion of individuals or percentage of them (expressed as a decimal) having a given attribute in a population. The standard deviate is:

$$z = \frac{x - \mu}{\sigma}. \tag{12.1}$$

If p_1 is the proportion of individuals possessing a given characteristic in a sample of N, then $x = Np_1$ is the *actual* number of them in the sample, and Np is the corresponding *expected* number. Then Eq. (12.1) may be written:

$$z = \frac{Np_1 - Np}{\sqrt{Npq}}, \tag{12.2}$$

whence

$$z = \frac{p_1 - p}{\sqrt{pq/N}}. \tag{12.3}$$

If Np and Nq are not too small, say both exceed five, the distribution of p_1 about p will be practically normal, and the table of normal areas may be used to test hypotheses concerning p. An important thing to note is that the standard deviation of p_1, found in the denominator of Eq. (12.3), is given by the formula:

$$\sigma_p = \sqrt{\frac{pq}{N}}. \tag{12.4}$$

We can prove this fact easily. If x is the number of individuals in the sample having the desired attribute,

$$\sigma_p^2 = E\left(\frac{x}{N} - p\right)^2$$

$$= \frac{1}{N^2} E(x - Np)^2$$

$$= \frac{1}{N^2} \cdot Npq = \frac{pq}{N}. \qquad \text{(Section 8.9)}$$

In the application of formula (12.2), we found it desirable to apply a correction factor $\frac{1}{2}$ to the numerator of the fraction (Section 10.10). In formula (12.3) it will generally be desirable to apply a corresponding correction factor of $\pm \dfrac{1}{2N}$. For right- and left-tail probabilities, the signs to be used are respectively minus and plus.

> EXAMPLE 1. Suppose that a random sample of 1000 births in Graustark showed 53% males and 47% females. Test the hypothesis that the sex ratio is $\frac{1}{2}$ against the alternative that it is higher than $\frac{1}{2}$ for males. Let $\alpha = 0.05$.
>   Since we seek the probability for a proportion of males as great as 0.53 or greater, the correction factor $\dfrac{1}{2N} = \frac{1}{2000} = 0.0005$ is to be subtracted.
>
> $$p_1 = 0.530, \qquad p = 0.500, \quad \text{and} \quad \sigma = \sqrt{\frac{0.500 \times 0.500}{1000}} = 0.0158.$$
>
> Then
> $$z = \frac{p_1 - \dfrac{1}{2N} - p}{\sigma_p} \tag{12.5}$$
>
> $$= \frac{0.530 - 0.0005 - 0.500}{0.0158} = 1.87.$$

Since $P(z > 1.87) = 0.0307$, we conclude that the sex ratio is higher than $\frac{1}{2}$ for males in Graustark. Note that here, as in many problems where N is large, the correction factor is negligibly small.

EXAMPLE 2. A municipal election is expected to be close, with neither of the two contending candidates obtaining more than 55% of the votes cast. How large a pre-election polling sample is required if one is to forecast with a 90% chance of being within 2% of the true percentage of votes to be polled by the winning candidate? Discuss the risks to be made in such a prediction.

Although we do not know the true percentage of votes to be cast for a given candidate, let us, for reasons to be stated later, assume $p = q = \frac{1}{2}$. If we are to have a 90% chance of forecasting within 2% of the correct

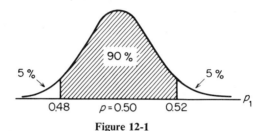

Figure 12-1

figure, then our forecast must be within the region from $p = 0.48$ to $p = 0.52$ (Fig. 12-1). Under the standard normal curve, the area between $z = \pm 1.645$ constitutes 90% of the total area. Applying formula (12.3) we have

$$\pm 1.645 = \frac{\pm 0.02}{\sqrt{\dfrac{(0.50 \times 0.50)}{N}}}$$

If, on both sides of the equation, we multiply by the radical, square, and then solve for N, we find that $N = 1689$. Thus our sample must contain 1689 voters.

If we employ the correction factor, the equation previously used becomes

$$\pm 1.645 = \frac{\pm 0.02 \pm \dfrac{1}{2N}}{\left(\dfrac{(0.50)^2}{N}\right)^{\frac{1}{2}}} \cdot$$

When this equation is cleared of fractions, and simplified, we arrive at the quadratic equation

$$0.0004N^2 - 0.6557N + 0.25 = 0.$$

The larger root of this equation is the useful one here and is 1638. Thus in this problem, the sample size necessary, computed with greater accuracy, is 1638 instead of 1689.

Why did we assume that $p = q = \frac{1}{2}$? The reason for this is related to a familiar question: "For a given perimeter, what must the relative dimensions of a rectangle be in order to have the greatest area?" The answer, of course, is that the length must equal the width: we must have a square. Phrased in the language of probability, this question becomes: "If $p + q = 1$, what values must p and q have in order that pq be a maximum?" The answer, then, is that $p = q = \frac{1}{2}$. Note that pq is the numerator in the radical above and that the larger this product is, the larger N must be. Thus this sample of 1638 is surely the largest necessary.

In pre-election polls one encounters a number of risks due to such circumstances as the following: The sample may not be representative of the total voting population; the persons sampled may change their minds about the candidates after the poll has been taken; the majority listed as undecided at the time of the poll may constitute a substantial group favoring one candidate; the persons sampled may not state truthfully how they expect to vote.

12.2. THE DIFFERENCE BETWEEN TWO PROPORTIONS

In two samples of N_x and N_y, let x and y individuals respectively possess a given attribute, so that $p_1 = x/N_x$ and $p_2 = y/N_y$ are the proportions having this characteristic. If the samples are assumed to be drawn from two independent populations with proportions p_x and p_y, then by formula (15.14) to be derived later, and by formula (12.4),

$$\sigma^2_{p_1-p_2} = \sigma^2_{p_1} + \sigma^2_{p_2}$$

$$= \frac{p_x q_x}{N_x} + \frac{p_y q_y}{N_y}. \tag{12.6}$$

If we set up the null hypothesis that x and y stem from the same population, that is, if we assume $p_x = p_y = p$, then we may write

$$\sigma^2_{p_1-p_2} = pq \left(\frac{1}{N_x} + \frac{1}{N_y} \right) \tag{12.7}$$

and employ the standard deviate

$$z = \frac{(p_1 - p_2) - (p_x - p_y)}{\sigma_{p_1-p_2}}$$

so that

$$z = \frac{(p_1 - p_2) - 0}{\left[pq \left(\frac{1}{N_x} + \frac{1}{N_y} \right) \right]^{1/2}}. \tag{12.8}$$

We test for significance with the aid of the normal curve, provided the values of p and q are not too close to 0 or 1.

Usually p is unknown so we use the following estimates:

$$\hat{p} = \frac{x + y}{N_x + N_y}, \qquad \hat{q} = 1 - \hat{p} \tag{12.9}$$

$$\hat{\sigma}_{p_1 - p_2} = \left[\hat{p}\hat{q}\left(\frac{1}{N_x} + \frac{1}{N_y}\right) \right]^{\frac{1}{2}}. \tag{12.10}$$

The correction factor for continuity, for reasons not easily shown here, comes out equal to

$$\frac{N_x + N_y}{2N_x N_y}. \tag{12.11}$$

For right- and left-tail probabilities, the signs to be used with it are, respectively, minus and plus.

Example. In an "attitude" test, 45 out of 113 persons of race R and 112 persons out of 381 persons of race S answered "yes" to a certain question. Do these races differ in their attitudes on this question? We wish to test the hypothesis that $p_x - p_y = 0$ against the alternative that $p_x - p_y \neq 0$. Choose $\alpha = 0.05$.

$$p_1 = \frac{45}{113} = 0.392, \qquad p_2 = \frac{112}{381} = 0.294$$

$$\hat{p} = \frac{45 + 112}{113 + 381} = 0.318, \qquad \hat{q} = 0.682$$

$$\hat{\sigma}_{p_1 - p_2} = \left[0.318 \times 0.682\left(\frac{1}{113} + \frac{1}{381}\right) \right]^{\frac{1}{2}} = 0.0500.$$

The correction factor is $\dfrac{(113 + 381)}{2(113 \times 381)} = 0.00574$ or approximately 0.006.

$$z = \frac{(0.392 - 0.294) - 0.006}{0.0500} = 1.84.$$

For a two-tail probability of 0.05, z would have to equal 1.96. Since $z < 1.96$, the hypothesis is not refuted. It is interesting to note that without the correction factor, z would equal 1.96. Unless one adheres strictly to a type I error of 0.05, there might well be grounds for suspecting racial differences to influence the attitudes in question.

12.3. THE POISSON DISTRIBUTION

In applying the normal curve approximation to the calculation of binomial probabilities, we assume that p is not very small. If the probability,

p, for an event to happen is excessively small, the approximation is poor and a better formula must be sought. In this case, the event may be termed rare. Examples of rare events are drawing the ace of diamonds from a pack of cards, throwing a double six with a pair of dice, or contracting a case of scurvy in Boston. The following theorem, the proof of which cannot be given here, becomes applicable.

In a binomial distribution, if N becomes infinite as p approaches 0 as a limit, in such a manner that Np remains constant (equal to μ), then the distribution approaches as a limit the Poisson distribution

$$f(x) = \frac{e^{-\mu}\mu^x}{x!}. \tag{12.12}$$

It can be shown that if N is large and p is very small, say $\mu = Np < 5$, an excellent approximation to the probability for exactly x successes in N trials is given by formula (12.12). The expression on the right of formula (12.12) is called the *Poisson exponential function*. The probabilities for exactly 0 occurrences, 1 occurrence, 2 occurrences, . . . , are given by the respective terms of the series

$$\sum_{x=0}^{\infty} \frac{e^{-\mu}\mu^x}{x!} = e^{-\mu}\left(1 + \frac{\mu}{1!} + \frac{\mu^2}{2!} + \frac{\mu^3}{3!} + \cdots\right). \tag{12.13}$$

This, like the binomial, defines a discrete distribution. The sample space $\{0,1,2,,,\}$ consists of a denumerably infinite set of outcomes with probabilities given by the respective terms of formula (12.13).

It may be proved that the expected value or population mean is:

$$E(x) = \mu = Np, \tag{12.14}$$

Proof.

$$E(x) = \sum_{x=0}^{\infty} \frac{e^{-\mu}\mu^x}{x!} x$$

$$= e^{-\mu} \sum_{x=1}^{\infty} \frac{\mu^x}{(x-1)!}$$

$$= e^{-\mu}\left[\mu + \mu^2 + \frac{\mu^3}{2!} + \cdots\right]$$

$$= \mu e^{-\mu}\left[1 + \mu + \frac{\mu^2}{2!} + \cdots\right].$$

The expression in the brackets defines e^{μ} as one learns in a first course in calculus; hence,

$$E(x) = \mu e^{-\mu}e^{\mu} = \mu.$$

The variance has the peculiar property of being equal to the mean, that is,

$$\sigma^2 = \mu. \tag{12.15}$$

Proof. We first find $E(x^2)$.

$$E(x^2) = \sum_{x=0}^{\infty} \frac{e^{-\mu}\mu^x}{x!} x^2$$

$$= e^{-\mu} \sum_{x=0}^{\infty} \frac{\mu^x}{x!} [x(x-1) + x]$$

$$= e^{-\mu} \left[\sum_{x=2}^{\infty} \frac{\mu^x}{(x-2)!} + \sum_{x=0}^{\infty} \frac{e^{-\mu}\mu^x}{x!} x \right]$$

$$= e^{-\mu} \left[\left(\mu^2 + \mu^3 + \frac{\mu^4}{2!} + \cdots \right) + \mu \right]$$

$$= e^{-\mu} \left[\mu^2 \left(1 + \mu + \frac{\mu^2}{2!} + \cdots \right) + \mu \right]$$

$$= e^{-\mu}\mu^2 e^{\mu} + \mu$$

$$= \mu^2 + \mu.$$

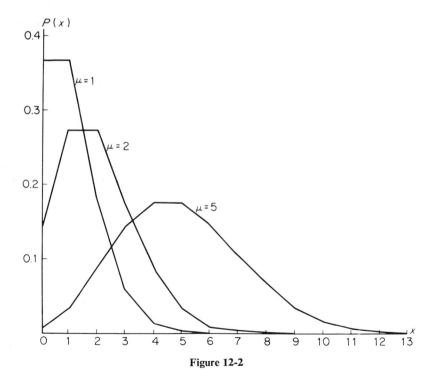

Figure 12-2

Then

$$\sigma^2 = E(x^2) - \mu^2 = \mu.$$

The Poisson distribution is skew for small values of μ but tends to become more symmetrical with increasing μ, as illustrated in Fig. 12-2.

It is not always clear when the Poisson distribution should be used rather than the normal to approximate to the binomial. Since the shape of the distribution is determined by the parameter, μ, and is nearly symmetrical when $\mu = 5$ (Fig. 12-2), a fairly safe rule is to use the Poisson approximation whenever $\mu < 5$. The binomial distribution is always accurate and in cases of doubt it may be employed.

The values of the individual probabilities given by formula (12.12) are tabulated in the *Biometrika Tables* (Reference 22) and in the *Fisher and Yates Tables* (Reference 16). These probabilities and the cumulated terms beginning with an arbitrary value of x

$$\sum_{x=k}^{\infty} f(x) = \sum_{x=k}^{\infty} \frac{e^{-\mu}\mu^x}{x!}$$

are also found in *Molina's Tables* (Reference 20), which are especially useful.

EXAMPLE 1. The mortality rate for a certain disease is 7 per 1000. What is the probability for just five deaths from this disease in a group of 400?

$$\mu = Np$$
$$= 400 \times 0.007 = 2.8.$$

From *Molina's Tables*, Part I, page 4 (here $a = \mu = 2.8$, $c = x = 5$), we find that

$$f(5) = \frac{e^{-2.8}(2.8)^5}{5!} = 0.0872.$$

EXAMPLE 2. As a rule, $\frac{1}{2}\%$ of certain manufactured products are defective. What is the probability that 1000 of them will have 10 or more defective?

$$\mu = 1000 \times 0.005 = 5;$$

$$P = \sum_{x=10}^{\infty} \frac{e^{-5}5^x}{x!}$$

$$= e^{-5}\left(\frac{5^{10}}{10!} + \frac{5^{11}}{11!} + \frac{5^{12}}{12!} + \cdots\right).$$

From *Molina's Tables* for cumulated terms, Part II, page 6, we find for

$$a = \mu = 5, \qquad c = x = 10,$$

that $P = 0.0318$; hence, the occurrence of 10 defective products in 1000 might well be considered unusual.

EXAMPLE 3. Von Bortkiewicz's classic example (1898) used the frequency distribution of the number of deaths from horse kicks per army corps per year in the Prussian army for 20 years, 1875–1894, to illustrate the agreement between actuality and theory. The data are given in the first two columns of Table 12-1.

TABLE 12-1

No. of Deaths x	Actual Frequency f	fx	fx^2	Theoretical Frequency
0	109	0	0	108.7
1	65	65	65	66.3
2	22	44	88	20.2
3	3	9	27	4.1
4	1	4	16	0.7
		122	196	

Number of deaths:	122
Number of army corps:	10
Number of years:	20

The mean number of deaths per army corps per year is:

$$\bar{x} = \tfrac{122}{200} = 0.61.$$

The variance is:

$$s^2 = \tfrac{196}{200} - (0.61)^2 = 0.61.$$

Here the agreement between $\bar{x}$ and s^2 is remarkably close and constitutes strong evidence that the distribution is Poissonian in character. Letting $\mu = 0.61$, we obtain the theoretical frequencies by multiplying by 200 the first five terms of Eq. (9.13), with $\mu = 0.61$.

$$200e^{-0.61}\left[1 + \frac{0.61}{1!} + \frac{(0.61)^2}{2!} + \frac{(0.61)^3}{3!} + \frac{(0.61)^4}{4!}\right]$$

$$= 108.7 + 66.3 + 20.2 + 4.1 + 0.7.$$

The agreement between the actual and theoretical frequencies is excellent.

12.4. THE HYPERGEOMETRIC DISTRIBUTION

Suppose that we have a finite population of N objects, each of which belongs to one of two mutually exclusive categories called success and failure, symbolized by 1 and 0 respectively. Assume that there are Np 1's and Nq 0's with $p + q = 1$. If a random sample of n is drawn *without replacement* from this population, what is the probability of obtaining exactly x 1's?

There are $(Np)!/[x!(Np - x)!]$ ways of drawing x 1's from Np of them, $(Nq)!/[(n - x)!(Nq - n + x)!]$ ways of drawing $n - x$ 0's from Nq of them, and $N!/[n!(N - n)!]$ ways of drawing n objects from N. Hence, the probability sought is:

$$P(x) = \frac{(Np)!}{x!(Np - x)!} \cdot \frac{(Nq)!}{(n - x)!(Nq - n + x)!} \bigg/ \frac{N!}{n!(N - n)!}$$

$$= \frac{C(Np, x)C(Nq, n - x)}{C(N,n)}. \qquad (12.16)$$

Formula (12.16) defines the *hypergeometric probability function* or *hypergeometric distribution*. Note that it contains three parameters, N, n, and p.

Example. A club consists of 12 women and eight men. A committee of five is to be selected by lot. What is the probability that three of the committee are women and two men?

Let p be the proportion of women in the club. Then $N = 20$, $Np = 12$, $Nq = 8$, $n = 5$, and $x = 3$; and

$$P(3) = \frac{12!}{3!9!} \cdot \frac{8!}{2!6!} \bigg/ \frac{20!}{5!15!} = 0.397.$$

It may be proved that

$$\mu = np$$

and

$$\sigma^2 = \frac{N - n}{N - 1} npq,$$

but the proofs are involved and will not be given here.[1] Note that the mean is the same as that for the binomial distribution which involves sampling *with* replacement, but that the variance is that for the binomial distribution multiplied by $(N - n)/(N - 1)$.

EXERCISES

1. In crossing certain varieties of peas, it was expected that 25% of the seeds would be green. However, it was found that of 3675 seeds 26.3% were green. Could this be the result of chance? Let $\alpha = 0.05$.

[1] See, for example, J. F. Kenney and E. S. Keeping, *Mathematics of Statistics,* (2nd ed.; New York: Van Nostrand, 1951) Part II, pp. 48–50.

2. It is claimed that 20% of the voters in a certain community are independent voters. A representative sample of 236 voters are polled, and of these, 40 state that they are independent. On the basis of this sample, is the claim justified? Let $\alpha = 0.05$.

3. On an average, 32% of the persons afflicted with a certain malady die. If under a new treatment 24% out of 200 die, might you say that the new treatment is effective? Let $\alpha = 0.04$.

4. The failures in a qualifying examination have been found to average 25%. (a) What can you say about a group of 156 pupils from School X who show 26 failures? (b) How large a sample is necessary in order that one may be 90% sure that the failures do not exceed 30%? You may omit the correction factor in solving (b).

5. A bag contains a very large number of black and white beads, all of uniform size and weight. There are twice as many white beads as black. If 24 beads are selected at random, what is the probability that 20 or more of them are white?

6. In the manufacture of a type of delicate filament, the per cent of defectives is found to average 12. It is decided to adopt a modified method of manufacture if and only if a random sample of 300 filaments shows the per cent of defectives equal to 9 or less. (a) What is the probability of adopting the new method if the mean per cent defective remains equal to 12? (b) What is the size of the type II error if the new method actually reduces the per cent defective to 8? (c) After the new method had been tried, a sample of 300 showed 25 filaments defective. Should the new process be adopted?

7. If 10% of the mice injected with a certain serum die, how large a group of mice must be tested in order that there be a probability of 0.02 that 5% or fewer die? Obtain the answer in two ways; (a) without and (b) with the use of the correction factor.

8. An insecticide usually kills 80% of the insects sprayed. How large a sample of them should be taken in order that we may be 95% sure that the per cent killed differs from the expected per cent by less than 10? Omit the correction factor.

9. In an opinion poll, 40 out of 160 women and 80 out of 240 men answered "yes" to a certain question. Test the hypothesis that the two sexes do not differ significantly on this matter, against the alternative that they do. Let $\alpha = 0.05$.

10. In a competitive examination, 45 pupils out of 600 in School X and 40 pupils out of 800 in School Y received scores of 90 or better. May one conclude, in general, that School X has more superior students than School Y? Let $\alpha = 0.10$.

11. In a certain college, the senior class consisted one year of 231 men and 193 women. From this class 19 men and 20 women were elected to Phi Beta Kappa. Does this indicate that, generally, a larger fraction of women are given this honor than men? Let $\alpha = 0.02$.

12. A group of 200 students was given an examination. One hundred and thirty students answered question 2 correctly and 148 answered question 3 correctly.

Test the hypothesis that these two questions are of equal difficulty, against the alternative that question 3 is easier. Let $\alpha = 0.10$.

13. The following data are given in the form of a 2×2 table. Let p_1 be the proportion of recoveries among those inoculated and p_2 the proportion among those not inoculated. Test the hypothesis that inoculation does not affect recovery, with a significance level of 2%. State your hypothesis and the alternative in the form of equations in the p's. Why is it safe to omit the correction factor here? Note that this is an alternative method to that of Chi-square (see exercise 19, Chapter 11).

	Recoveries	Deaths	Total
Inoculated	89	53	142
Not inoculated	32	61	93
Total	121	114	235

14. The number of vacancies on the Supreme Court Bench filled by the presidents of the United States up to 1932 were as follows:

No. Vacancies	No. Times Filled
0	59
1	27
2	9
3	1
Over 3	0

Show that the distribution is of the Poisson type by computing the theoretical frequencies.

15. The author's records of freshman classes averaging 25 students per class show that the number of A+ grades given per class were as follows:

No. Grades	Frequency
0	24
1	10
2	1
3 or more	0

Show that the distribution is of the Poisson form.

16. As a rule, 1% of certain units purchased by a manufacturer are unfit for use. What is the probability that (a) 12 or more in a lot of 500 will be unfit? (b) fewer than 4 in a lot of 400 will be unfit?

17. In a research on "flying bombs" fallen in London during World War II, an area of 144 square kilometers in the south of London was divided into 576 squares of $\frac{1}{4}$ square kilometer each. The results are shown in the table that follows. Show that the distribution is of the Poisson type (a) by comparing the mean with the variance, and (b) by comparing the theoretical frequencies with the actual.

No. Bombs Fallen	No. Observed Squares
0	229
1	211
2	93
3	35
4	7
5 and over	1

[Data used by permission of R. D. Clarke, *Journal of the Institute of Actuaries*, London. Vol. 72, 1946, p. 481.]

18. A sales-by-mail company receives orders, on an average, from 2% of the letters sent out. A new type of sales appeal is tried in 1000 letters, and 30 orders are received. Is the new type more effective than the old? Let $\alpha = 0.05$.

19. A factory produces items which are usually 5% defective. The process of manufacture is modified and then tested for possible improvement. A random sample of 200 shows only 6 defective. Would you say ($\alpha = 0.05$) that the modification reduces the number of defectives? Compare the probabilities obtained by using both the Poisson and binomial distributions.

20. If, on an average, two lost articles per day are reported on a certain railroad train, what is the probability that more than four are reported on a given day?

21. A box contains 10 fuses of which three are defective and seven are not. A sample of three is drawn without replacement from the box. What is the probability that two of them are defective?

22. The male voters on Maple Street comprise 12 Republicans and 6 Democrats. A random sample of 6 voters is selected. What is the probability that the ratio of Republicans to Democrats in the sample is the same as that on the street?

23. If the experiment of exercise 21 were repeated a large number of times, what is the expected number of defective fuses drawn and what is the standard deviation?

24. A true-false quiz in English history contains 50 statements of which 30 are true and 20 false. A student, not familiar with English history, is to select 10 statements, five of which are true and five false. (a) Write but do not evaluate the probability that his selection is a correct one. What is (b) the expected number of true statements in his selection? (c) the variance for these?

25. In 1964, a letter written to the editor of the Boston Herald discussed the frequency of murders that had been committed in the city for the year. There had been four in one week and an average for the year of one per week. The writer stated that it would be "usual" for a murder to occur four or even five times in a week and that if it did not occur the laws of probability would not be working. What law of probability underlies the writer's reasoning? Comment on the validity of his conclusions.

13

Inferences from Sample Means

Everywhere one observes the unfortu-
nate habit of generalizing, without
demonstration, from special cases.

NIELS ABEL, 1826

13.1. INTRODUCTION

Probably the largest area of statistical inquiry deals with the drawing of
conclusions concerning a population, from a sample selected from it. Such
conclusions will never be certain; a probability of being correct will be
attached to each inference. For this reason, we often speak of this aspect of
statistics as *uncertain inference*. The fact that useful inferences can be made
from small samples, even as small, say, as three or four observations, is
often difficult for persons to believe. As this book progresses, the reasons
therefore should become clear.

13.2. THE DISTRIBUTION OF
THE SAMPLE MEAN;
THE DISCRETE CASE

Given the probability function in Table 13-1, it is easily verified that
$\mu_x = 0.1$ and $\sigma_x^2 = 0.49$. If we draw random samples of two, with replacement, from the population characterized by Table 13-1 and list the possible

TABLE 13–1

x	-1	0	1
$f(x)$	0.2	0.5	0.3

outcomes (x_1, x_2) with their respective probabilities, we obtain the following:

$\{(x_1, x_2)\}$: $\{(-1,-1), (-1,0), (-1,1), (0,-1), (0,0), (0,1), (1,-1), (1,0), (1,1)\}$
$P(x_1, x_2)$:   0.04   0.10   0.06   0.10   0.25 0.15   0.06   0.15 0.09

From these outcomes, we derive the probability function for $\bar{x} = \frac{1}{2}(x_1 + x_2)$.

$\bar{x}$	-1	-0.5	0	0.5	1
$f(\bar{x})$	0.04	0.20	0.37	0.30	0.09

Note that the sum of the probabilities is 1, thus furnishing a check on our calculations. The mean of $\bar{x}$, $\mu_{\bar{x}} = 0.10$ and the variance of $\bar{x}$, $\sigma_{\bar{x}}^2 = E(\bar{x}^2) - \mu_{\bar{x}}^2 = 0.255 - 0.010 = 0.245$. These conclusions follow:

$$\mu_x = \mu_{\bar{x}} = 0.10$$

and

$$\sigma_{\bar{x}}^2 = \frac{\sigma_x^2}{2} = \frac{0.49}{2} = 0.245.$$

This example illustrates a general theorem, 13.1, which will be proved in Sections 15.5 and 15.6.

Theorem 13.1. If $\bar{x}$ is the mean of a random sample of N drawn with replacement from a population with a given probability function, then

$$\mu_{\bar{x}} = \mu_x \tag{13.1}$$

and

$$\sigma_{\bar{x}}^2 = \frac{\sigma_x^2}{N}. \tag{13.2}$$

13.3. THE DISTRIBUTION OF
THE SAMPLE MEAN;
THE CONTINUOUS CASE

The theorem just stated can be shown to be valid for samples of N drawn from a continuously distributed population. Of great importance is the fact that, if the population is normal, it can be proved by the more advanced

methods of mathematical statistics that the sample mean, $\bar{x}$, has precisely
a normal distribution. In this connection, it is worthwhile to state a very
important theorem of statistics.

The Central Limit Theorem. If $\overline{X}$ is the mean of a sample, N, drawn from
any population (continuous or discrete) with mean, μ, and finite variance, σ^2,
the standardized variable $\overline{Z} = \dfrac{\overline{X} - \mu}{\sigma/\sqrt{N}}$ will have a distribution that approaches,
as N becomes infinite, the normal distribution with mean, 0, and variance, 1.

The proof of this theorem also demands advanced mathematical
methods, and cannot be given here.

It will be noted that this theorem implies that for large N, $\overline{X}$ has practically a normal distribution, even if the population is not normal. Whether
it is normal or not, Eqs. (13.1) and (13.2) hold. In the work of this book, we
shall assume all the populations from which the samples are drawn to be
approximately normal; hence we may assume $\overline{X}$ to have a normal distribution.

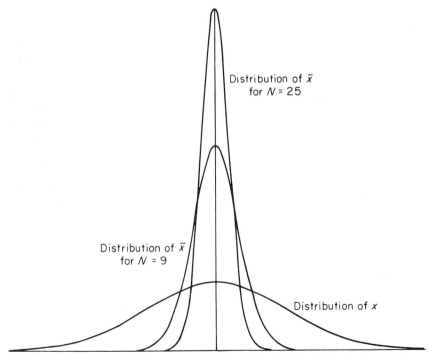

Distribution of $\bar{x}$
for $N = 25$

Distribution of $\bar{x}$
for $N = 9$

Distribution of x

Fig. 13-1. The normal distribution of x and the distributions of $\bar{x}$ for samples
of 9 and 25.

The quantity obtained when we take the positive square root of formula (13.2),

$$\sigma_{\bar{x}} = \frac{\sigma_x}{\sqrt{N}}, \tag{13.3}$$

is often called the *standard error of the mean*. The relationship of the frequency functions of $\bar{X}$ for samples of 9 and 25 to the parent normal population is illustrated in Fig. 13-1.

13.4. APPLICATIONS

In most practical problems, $\bar{X}$ has essentially a normal distribution; therefore, we may test a hypothesis about a population mean, μ_x, by drawing a sample of N from the population and calculating its mean, $\bar{x}$. In the type of problem now under discussion, we assume that the population standard deviation, σ_x, is known. The standard variable now becomes

$$Z = \frac{\bar{X} - \mu_{\bar{x}}}{\sigma_{\bar{x}}}, \qquad \text{where} \quad \mu_{\bar{x}} = \mu_x, \quad \text{and} \quad \sigma_{\bar{x}} = \frac{\sigma_x}{\sqrt{N}};$$

hence

$$Z = \frac{(\bar{X} - \mu_x)\sqrt{N}}{\sigma_x}. \tag{13.4}$$

EXAMPLE 1. Suppose that the mean length of life of 40-watt electric light bulbs is guaranteed to be at least 1000 hours and that the standard deviation is 200 hours. A sample of 16 is drawn from a shipment of bulbs and shows a mean length of life of 910 hours. Does this indicate that the shipment does not meet the guarantee and should be rejected?

Let the null hypothesis, H_0, be $\mu \geq 1000$, the alternative hypothesis, H_1 be $\mu < 1000$, and $\alpha = 0.05$. Here the buyer is primarily interested in *not* accepting a lot of bulbs whose lives have a mean *below* that guaranteed. By Eq. (13.4)

$$z = \frac{(910 - 1000)\sqrt{16}}{200} = -1.80.$$

The probability that a mean of 16 is 910 or less (left-tail area),

$$P(\bar{x} \leq 910) = \int_{-\infty}^{-1.80} \phi(z)\, dz = 0.0359.$$

[See Fig. 13-2a and b.] Since $P < 0.05$, the sample indicates that the shipment contains too many bulbs with lives below 1000 hours and should be rejected.

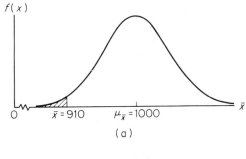

(a)

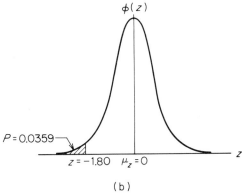

(b)

Figure 13-2

EXAMPLE 2. On a nation-wide examination, the scores showed $\mu = 72$ and $\sigma = 10$. How large a sample of candidates from the University of X must be taken, in order that there be a 10 per cent chance that its mean score is less than 70?

Since $P(\bar{x} < 70)$ is to equal 0.10, we seek the value of z_1 such that

$$0.10 = \int_{-\infty}^{z_1} \phi(z)\, dz.$$

By inverse interpolation in the table of normal areas, we find that z_1 must equal -1.28.

Since

$$z = \frac{(\bar{x} - \mu)\sqrt{N}}{\sigma_x},$$

$$-1.28 = \frac{(70 - 72)\sqrt{N}}{10}$$

whence

$$N = 40.96.$$

Therefore we must take a sample of 41.

EXAMPLE 3. Suppose that we are testing the breaking strength, x, of a certain type of cord by means of a random sample of 9 pieces of cord. Let $\sigma = 5$ pounds and set up the hypothesis, H_0, that the population mean breaking strength, $\mu_0 \geqq 50$ pounds. Assume that the alternative, H_1, to this hypothesis is $\mu < 50$. Choose the type I error to be (say) 0.05.
(a) Find the rejection and acceptance regions for H_0.
(b) If the alternative hypothesis, H_1, were true with $\mu = 45$, what would be the size of the type II error, β.
It would be wise for the reader, at this point, to review Section 8.5.

(a) By the use of formula (13.4) we find that, corresponding to a left-tail area of 0.05, $z = -1.645$. Then

$$-1.645 = \frac{(\bar{x} - 50)\sqrt{9}}{5} ,$$

whence $\bar{x} = 47.3$. Thus there is a probability of not more than 0.05 that a sample of 9 will yield by chance, an $\bar{x}$ as low as 47.3 or lower when $\mu \geqq 50$. (Fig. 13-3.) If, then, our sample yields an $\bar{x}$

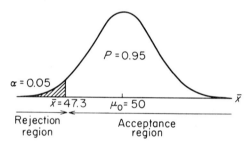

Figure 13-3

lower than 47.3, we reject H_0 and accept as an alternative the conclusion that $\mu < 50$. The interval $\bar{x} < 47.3$ constitutes the critical or rejection region for the hypothesis $H_0: \mu \geqq 50$. The interval, $\bar{x} > 47.3$ is the acceptance region for H_0. If, however, H_0 were true, repeated tests of samples of 9 would produce $\bar{x}$'s lying in the rejection region 5 per cent of the time, and we would then be committing a type I error of size $\alpha = 0.05$. Also, if H_0 were true, the $\bar{x}$'s would lie in the acceptance region 95 per cent of the time, and this is the percentage of times that we would be making a correct decision.
(b) If H_0 were false then the true mean would be less than 50. The magnitude of the type II error, β, will depend upon the true value of μ which we shall now assume to be $\mu_1 = 45$. How often would we accept $H_0: \mu \geqq 50$ when $H_1: \mu_1 = 45$ is true? The chance of

obtaining an $\bar{x} > 47.3$ when $\mu = 45$ is found thus:

$$z = \frac{(47.3 - 45)\sqrt{9}}{5} = 1.38,$$

and the corresponding probability is 0.0838. (See the horizontally shaded area in Fig. 13-4.) Thus β is about 0.08; in other words,

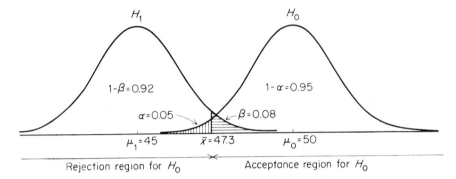

Figure 13-4

we shall accept the hypothesis that $\mu \geq 50$ when actually $\mu = 45$, about 8 per cent of the time. Note also that we shall accept the alternative $\mu < 50$, that is, reject H_0, about 92 per cent of the time when $\mu_1 = 45$, and this would be the correct decision.

As an additional illustration, suppose that $\mu_1 = 48$ instead of 45. How often would we accept $H_0:\mu_0 \geq 50$?

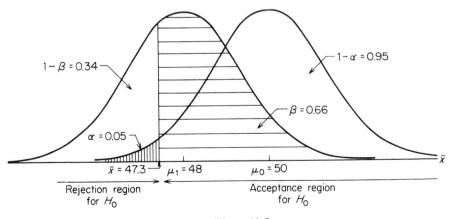

Figure 13-5

The chance of obtaining an $\bar{x} > 47.3$ when $\mu = 48$ is found in the same manner as before.

$$z = \frac{(47.3 - 48)\sqrt{9}}{5} = -0.42,$$

whence the probability, β, sought is 0.6628 (Fig. 13-5.) Thus we shall accept the hypothesis that $\mu_0 \geqq 50$ when it is false about 66 per cent of the time, provided the true mean is 48. Also, we shall accept $H_1 : \mu < 50$ or, what is equivalent, reject $H_0 : \mu \geqq 50$ about 34 per cent of the time when $\mu = 48$.

From Fig. 13-4, observe that the farther μ_1 is below μ_0, the smaller the chance of committing a type II error. Intuitively we should expect that the smaller the μ_1's are, the less likely we are to get $\bar{x}$'s in the acceptance region, that is, large enough to cause us to accept H_0. From Fig. 13-5, μ_1 is closer to μ_0 so that it is more difficult to discriminate between them by means of a statistical test. The error, β, becomes larger as μ_1 approaches μ_0. Considerations such as these lead us to the concept of the *power function* (see Section 13.11).

13.5. A GENERAL THEOREM

In Chapter 15, we shall prove (Theorems 15.1 and 15.5) that:

If X and Y are random variables with probability functions having means μ_X and μ_Y, the mean of their difference, X − Y, (or sum, X + Y) is the respective difference (or sum) of their means, that is,

$$\mu_{X-Y} = \mu_X - \mu_Y \tag{13.5}$$

$$\mu_{X+Y} = \mu_X + \mu_Y \tag{13.6}$$

and if the variables are independent with variances σ_X^2 and σ_Y^2 respectively, then the variance of their difference (or sum) is the sum of their variances, that is,

$$\sigma_{X \pm Y}^2 = \sigma_X^2 + \sigma_Y^2. \tag{13.7}$$

One can prove by the methods of mathematical statistics that the foregoing theorems hold also if X and Y are continuous random variables. It is interesting that the last formula holds for either $X − Y$ or $X + Y$. Furthermore, it is possible to prove that:

If X and Y are normally distributed, then X − Y and X + Y are also.

If $\bar{X}$ and $\bar{Y}$ are means of sample sizes N_X and N_Y respectively, which are normally and independently distributed, then by the preceding theorems their difference, $\bar{X} − \bar{Y}$, is also normally distributed with

$$\mu_{\bar{X}-\bar{Y}} = \mu_{\bar{X}} - \mu_{\bar{Y}} = \mu_X - \mu_Y, \tag{13.8}$$

$$\sigma_{\bar{X}-\bar{Y}}^2 = \sigma_{\bar{X}}^2 + \sigma_{\bar{Y}}^2$$

$$= \frac{\sigma_{\bar{X}}^2}{N_X} + \frac{\sigma_{\bar{Y}}^2}{N_Y}, \tag{13.9}$$

by formula (13.2). It follows that a hypothesis on $\mu_X - \mu_Y$ can be tested by means of the standard variable

$$Z = \frac{(\bar{X} - \bar{Y}) - \mu_{\bar{X} - \bar{Y}}}{\sigma_{\bar{X} - \bar{Y}}}$$

$$= \frac{(\bar{X} - \bar{Y}) - (\mu_X - \mu_Y)}{\sqrt{\sigma_X^2/N_X + \sigma_Y^2/N_Y}}. \qquad (13.10)$$

Example. Suppose that 64 senior girls from College A and 81 senior girls from College B had mean statures of 68.2 inches and 67.3 inches respectively. If the standard deviation for statures of all senior girls is 2.43 inches, is the difference between the two groups significant?

Since mean statures are normally distributed, the difference $\bar{X} - \bar{Y}$ is also, and formula (13.10) is applicable. We take as our null hypothesis, that there is no difference in mean height between the senior girls of Colleges A and B; in symbols,

$$H_0 : \mu_X - \mu_Y = 0.$$

Let us take as our alternative hypothesis,

$$H_1 : \mu_X - \mu_Y \neq 0$$

so that a two-tail test is called for. We also assume that

$$\sigma_x = \sigma_y = 2.43$$

and take $\alpha = 0.05$. Then from formula (13.10),

$$z = \frac{(68.2 - 67.3) - 0}{\sqrt{\dfrac{(2.43)^2}{64} + \dfrac{(2.43)^2}{81}}} = 2.21.$$

Since $2\int_{1.96}^{\infty} \phi(z)\,dz = 0.05$, the rejection region for H_0 consists of the two intervals $z < -1.96$ and $z > +1.96$. The number 2.21 corresponds to a point in the right-tail rejection interval so the hypothesis, H_0, is refuted; the girls from the two colleges differ significantly in their statures.

13.6. REMARKS

It is important to note that the method of the preceding section as well as that of Section 13.4 requires that the population variances be known. In many cases they are not known and must be estimated from the sample. If the sample is large, say $N \geq 50$, the sample variance s^2 may be used in place of the unknown parameter, σ^2, without too much risk. When N is small, it is necessary to employ the t-distribution which will be explained in the next section.

Example. Two sections of 54 and 67 students each took the same examination in statistics. The first section had a mean score of 73.1 with a standard deviation of 11.2; the second had a mean score of 76.6 with a standard deviation of 13.0. Can the difference in mean scores be attributed to chance? Let $H_0 : \mu_x - \mu_y = 0$ and $H_1 : \mu_x - \mu_y \neq 0$. Let $\alpha = 0.05$.

Since both sample numbers are moderately large, assume $\sigma_x = s_x = 11.2$ and $\sigma_y = s_y = 13.0$. Then by Eq. (13.10),

$$z = \frac{(73.1 - 76.6) - 0}{\left[\dfrac{(11.2)^2}{54} + \dfrac{(13.0)^2}{67}\right]^{\frac{1}{2}}} = -1.59.$$

Since the standard deviate is less numerically than 1.96, we accept H_0; there is no evidence that the difference is not due to chance.

13.7. THE STUDENT-FISHER t-DISTRIBUTION

The problem of testing the significance of the deviation of a sample mean from a given population mean when N is small and only the sample variance is known was first solved (1908) by W. S. Gossett, writing under the pen name of *Student*. His method was later modified by R. A. Fisher. When the population of X is normal, they proved that the variable[1]

$$t = \frac{(\bar{X} - \mu)(N - 1)^{\frac{1}{2}}}{s} \tag{13.11}$$

has a symmetrical, bell-shaped, but non-normal distribution with $\mu_t = 0$. Its probability density function is of the form:

$$y = C\left(1 + \frac{t^2}{n}\right)^{-(n+1)/2} \tag{13.12}$$

where the parameter $n = N - 1$ is the number of degrees of freedom (see Section 11.4). C is a constant depending upon n and determined so as to make the area under the density curve equal to 1. The curve for $n = 20$, together with a normal curve, is shown in Fig. 13-6. As n increases, the t-curve approaches a normal curve as a limiting form.

---

[1] The lower-case t and s are used here instead of T and S because of general usage in the past and to avoid confusion with other meanings of T and S.

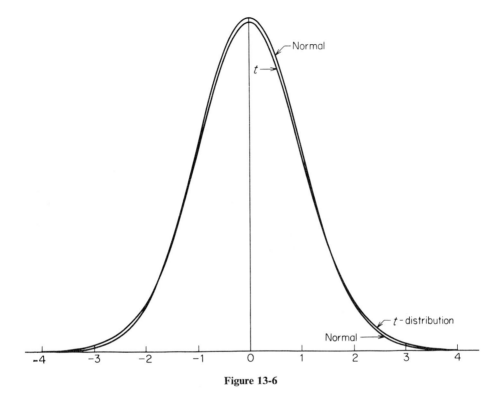

Figure 13-6

Fisher tabulated the values of t corresponding to various levels of significance for different useful values of n. A modified form of his table appears in Table F of the Appendix. From this table, for example, we find for $n = 10$ and $P = 0.01$ that $t = 2.76$. Thus (Fig. 13-7) we find that

$$P(t > 2.76) = P(t < -2.76) = 0.01,$$

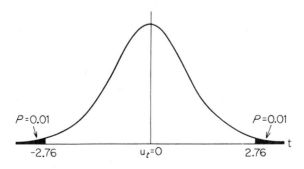

Figure 13-7

or that

$$P(|t| > 2.76) = 0.02.$$

In order to use the Student-Fisher distribution, we take into account the number of degrees of freedom of the N variates, $x_1, x_2, \ldots, x_N$, constituting the sample from which $\bar{x}$ and s are computed.

13.8. DEGREES OF FREEDOM

In the case of the t-distribution, we may ask: Given a sample of N which determines a mean $\bar{x}$, or its deviation from the population mean, $\bar{x} - \mu$, how can t in formula (13.11) vary? Clearly, the variation of t, for any $\bar{x}$, depends upon that of the denominator, s. For a given $\bar{x}$, the N variates comprising the sample, $x_1, x_2, \ldots, x_N$, are free to vary and thus to determine various values of s, subject to the restriction

$$\bar{x} = \frac{1}{N} \sum_{i=1}^{N} x_i.$$

Thus, the t-distribution has $N - 1$ degrees of freedom.

13.9. APPLICATIONS

EXAMPLE 1. A machine is to turn out engine parts with axle diameters of 0.700 in. The hypothesis $H_0 : \mu = 0.700$ is to be tested against the alternative $H_1 : \mu > 0.700$, with $\alpha = 0.025$. A random sample of ten parts shows $\bar{x} = 0.712$ inches and $s = 0.040$ inches. What does this indicate?

Solution. Since N is small and σ is not known, we use the t-test [formula (13.11)]. For $n = 9$ and $P = 0.025$ it follows from Table F that $t = 2.262$. Then

$$t = \frac{(0.712 - 0.700)\sqrt{9}}{0.040} = 0.900.$$

Since $P(t > 2.262) = 0.025$, this value, 0.900, is not large enough to cause us to reject H_0. It appears that the machine is working properly.

EXAMPLE 2. The grades of students in a certain course averaged 77 over a period of years. A class of 40 has a mean grade of 70 with a standard deviation of 9. Can this lower mean be attributed to ordinary sampling variation?

Solution. By formula (13.11),

$$t = \frac{(70 - 77)(39)^{\frac{1}{2}}}{9} = -4.86.$$

Inasmuch as the sample is moderately large, we may, instead of referring to the *t*-table, use the normal distribution. Obviously, a difference of almost five sigmas can hardly be attributed to the ordinary fluctuations of sampling.

13.10. THE DIFFERENCE BETWEEN TWO SAMPLE MEANS; POPULATION VARIANCES UNKNOWN

When the population variances are not known but are assumed to be equal, the following methods may be used for testing the significance of the difference between two sample means obtained from two populations.

Mathematical statistics has proved that the variable

$$t = \frac{(\bar{X} - \bar{Y}) - (\mu_X - \mu_Y)}{\left[\left(\dfrac{N_x s_x^2 + N_y s_y^2}{N_x + N_y - 2}\right)\left(\dfrac{1}{N_x} + \dfrac{1}{N_y}\right)\right]^{\frac{1}{2}}} \tag{13.13}$$

has a *t*-distribution with $n = N_x + N_y - 2$ degrees of freedom. As in Section 13.5, the null hypothesis is that $\mu_x - \mu_y = 0$. If the samples are large, we revert to the method of Section 13.6.

The reason for the complex denominator in formula (13.13) will appear in Section 16.5 [formula (16.7)]. Ordinarily, if the two sample variances s_x^2 and s_y^2 are not too far apart, we assume $\sigma_x^2 = \sigma_y^2$. If we are in doubt concerning this, the *F*-test, not included in this book, may be employed as a test of the hypothesis, $\sigma_x^2 = \sigma_y^2$. (See Reference 8.) If the two samples are drawn from populations with different variances, that is, if $\sigma_x^2 \neq \sigma_y^2$, the foregoing procedures may be questioned. Alternative tests are available for the case where the variances differ significantly.

Example. The mean life of a sample of ten electric light bulbs was found to be 1456 hours with $s = 423$ hours. A second sample of 17 bulbs chosen from a different batch showed a mean life of 1280 hours with $s = 398$ hours. Is there a significant difference between the means of the two batches? Let $\alpha = 0.05$.

Let H_0 be $\mu_x - \mu_y = 0$, and let H_1 be $\mu_x - \mu_y \neq 0$. By formula (13.13),

$$t = \frac{(1456 - 1280) - 0}{\left[\left(\dfrac{(10 \times 423^2) + (17 \times 398^2)}{10 + 17 - 2}\right)\left(\dfrac{1}{10} + \dfrac{1}{17}\right)\right]^{\frac{1}{2}}} = 1.04.$$

For $t = 1.04$ and $n = 25$, we find from Table F that $P = 0.15$, approximately, so that the two-tail probability $2P = 0.30$. We can say that there is no evidence that the two batches are significantly different in length of life. In other words, the null hypothesis, $\mu_x = \mu_y$, is not denied.

13.11. THE POWER OF A TEST

If we examine Figs. 13-4 and 5 and note the behavior of β as μ_1 recedes to the left away from μ_0, we see that β becomes smaller and will eventually approach 0. Similarly, as μ_1 moves to the right, β increases. The graph of $1 - \beta$ plotted against μ_1 for $\mu_1 < \mu_0$ is shown in Fig. 13-8 and exhibits the

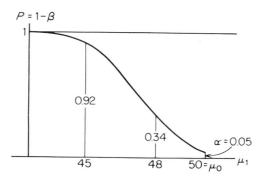

Fig. 13-8. Probability of rejecting $H_0:\mu_0 \geq 50$ in favor of $H_1:\mu_1 < 50$.

change in the probability of accepting H_1, that is, rejecting H_0 as μ_1 varies. The probability, $1 - \beta = 1 - 0.08 = 0.92$ obtained earlier (Section 13.4) is called the *power of the test* of the hypothesis that $\mu_0 \geq 50$ with respect to the alternative, $\mu_1 = 45$; it is the probability of rejecting H_0 when the alternative H_1 is true. Similarly, the probability $1 - 0.66 = 0.34$ is the power of the test of $H_0:\mu_0 \geq 50$ with respect to the alternative $H_1:\mu_1 = 48$. For the case that $\mu_1 = \mu_0$, $\beta = 1 - \alpha$, whence $1 - \beta = \alpha$. The probability $P = 1 - \beta$ obviously varies with μ_1, that is, it is a function of μ_1. This function, $P(\mu)$ is called the *power function*.

If we test $H_0:\mu_0 = 50$ against $H_1 : \mu_1 \neq 50$, which implies a two-tail test, we can verify that the power curve has the form shown in Fig. 13-9.

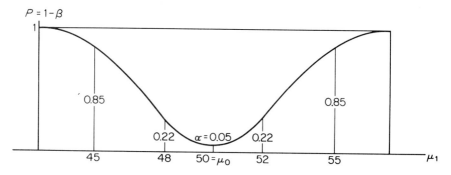

Fig. 13-9. Probability of rejecting $H_0:\mu_0 = 50$ in favor of $H_1:\mu_1 \neq 50$.

Naturally, we should like to keep the sizes of the two errors α and β as small as possible, but we cannot reduce both simultaneously since a decrease in α causes an increase in β and vice versa. Customarily, we select an appropriate α, say, $\alpha = 0.05$, and then select a rejection region that minimizes β. In this connection it should be pointed out that an infinite number of rejection regions are, in general, possible for a given H_0 and a given α, but that only a few have practical value. Thus, if we test $H_0:\mu_0 = 50$ and choose $\alpha = 0.05$, we might select among the many rejection regions possible the following:

(a) $\bar{x} > 52.7$. Thus an excessively large $\bar{x}$ causes rejection of H_0 (Fig. 13-10a).

(b) $\bar{x} < 47.3$. Thus an excessively small $\bar{x}$ causes rejection of H_0 (Fig. 13-10b).

(c) $\bar{x} < 46.7$, $\bar{x} > 53.3$. Thus either an excessively small or excessively large $\bar{x}$ causes rejection of H_0 (Fig. 13-10c).

(d) $51.9 < \bar{x} < 52.4$. This region is mathematically possible but unrealistic (Fig. 13-10d).

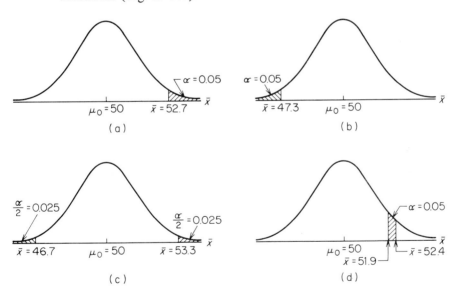

Figure 13-10

If the true value of $\mu = 45$, we can calculate the power of the test for each of the four regions selected. The respective values of $P(\mu)$ follow:

(a) 0.00; (b) 0.92; (c) 0.85; (d) 0.00.

It follows, then, that for the alternative, $H_1 : \mu_1 = 45$, test region (b) is the most powerful. Note that in this case $H_0:\mu_0 = 50$ is rejected more frequently (as it should be) for a critical region to the *left* of μ_0, provided the true mean, $\mu_1 < 50$. This conclusion confirms the simple intuition that $\bar{x}$'s will occur more frequently to the left of μ_0 if the true mean μ_1 lies to the left.

On the other hand, if the true mean $\mu = 55$, the power of the test for each of the same four regions becomes:

(a) 0.92; (b) 0.00; (c) 0.85; (d) 0.03.

Thus test (a) is the most powerful. Again, intuitively we should expect $\bar{x}$'s to occur more frequently to the *right* of μ_0 if the true mean μ_1 lies to the right. Test (c) is not as powerful as (a), since the right rejection region lies somewhat farther down the right tail.

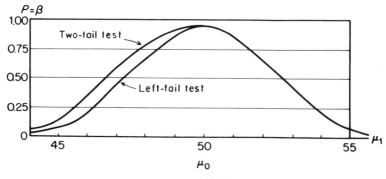

Figure 13-11

In industrial statistics, the type I error is often called the *producer's risk*, because the rejection of the hypothesis H_0 means that manufactured articles will not be sold. The type II error is called the *consumers' risk*, since the consumer would then be accepting articles not meeting certain specifications.

If, instead of plotting $1 - \beta$ against μ, we plot β, we obtain an *operating-characteristic (OC) curve*. Figure 13-11 shows the two *OC* curves corresponding to the power curves of Figs. 8-9 and 10. The ordinate of an *OC* curve, for a given μ_1, represents the probability of accepting H_0 when it is false.

EXERCISES

1. Verify the calculations for μ_x, σ_x^2, $\mu_{\bar{x}}$, and $\sigma_{\bar{x}}^2$ in Section 13.2.

2. Given the probability function

x	0	1	2
$f(x)$	0.5	0.4	0.1

Find: (a) μ_x and σ_x^2; (b) the probability function for $\bar{x}$, the mean of a sample of 2; (c) $\mu_{\bar{x}}$ and $\sigma_{\bar{x}}^2$. (d) Check your answers by verifying Theorem 13.1.

3. Given the probability function

x	-1	0	1	2
$f(x)$	0.3	0.4	0.2	0.1

Find: (a) μ_x and σ_x^2; (b) the probability function for $\bar{x}$, the mean of a sample of 3; (c) $\mu_{\bar{x}}$ and $\sigma_{\bar{x}}^2$. (d) Check your answers by verifying Theorem 13.1.

4. A circular dial is divided into eight equal sectors. Two of these are marked 1, three are marked 2, two are marked 3, and one is marked 4. An arrow pivoted at the center is spun and the outcome is the number to which the arrow points. For three spins of the arrow, what is the expected mean of the numbers and the standard deviation of the mean?

5. If the scores of students in Graduate Record Examinations show a standard deviation of 100, what will the standard deviation be for the mean scores of samples of (a) 16? (b) 25? (c) 100?

6. A certain test has been administered to thousands of pupils with a mean score of 80 and a standard deviation of 6. The same test given to 64 pupils of race R showed a mean of 78. Are scores for this race substantially lower than those in general? Let $\alpha = 0.05$.

7. Experience shows that a fixed dose of a certain drug causes an average increase of pulse rate of ten beats per minute with a standard deviation of 4. A group of nine patients given the same dose showed the following increases:

$$13, \quad 15, \quad 14, \quad 10, \quad 8, \quad 12, \quad 16, \quad 9, \quad 20.$$

Is there evidence that this group is different in response to the drug? ($\alpha = 0.05$.)

8. A certain drug is found, on the average, to lower the systolic blood pressure by 12.3 with $\sigma = 4.70$. When administered to a group of 16 selected patients, it was found that their blood pressures were changed by the following amounts: -15, -7, -3, -12, -20, -9, -5, -9, -11, -10, 0, -7, -18, $+5$, -21, -15. Test the hypothesis that this type of patient reacts no differently with respect to the drug than other patients in general.

9. The I.Q.'s for a large population of five year-old boys were determined and found to have a mean of 110 and a variance of 144. How large a sample would we have to take in order to have a probability of 0.90 that the mean I.Q. of the sample would not differ from the expected value, 110, by more than five?

10. Assume that the mean specific gravity of U.S.P. coal tar available to pharmacists for use in coal tar preparations is 1.185 with $\sigma = 0.012$. Ten samples of nonofficial coal tar showed a mean S.G. of 1.172. Do these differ significantly ($\alpha = 0.05$) with respect to S.G. from the U.S.P. mean?

11. For the ampuls of Arsenical I manufactured by a company, the mean weight is 145.3 mg with $\sigma = 4.82$ mg. How large a sample of such ampuls should we take in order that we may be 95% sure that the mean weight does not exceed 147.0 mg?

12. A manufacturer requires cotton thread with a mean breaking strength of 6.50 ounces and a $\sigma = 0.25$. He tests a new lot of thread by means of a sample of 16 pieces and finds $\bar{x} = 6.65$ ounces. Does this indicate that the lot is stronger than required?

13. Assume a population to have $\sigma = 10$. Choose $\alpha = 0.05$. Find the rejection and acceptance regions for the hypothesis $\mu \leq 50$. What is the type II error, β, when the true mean is 53? 55? Assume $N = 25$.

14. Assume that the mean weight of some newly compounded tablets is to be equal to 4.00 grams and that the standard deviation is expected to be 0.20 grams. Samples of 16 tablets are to be tested and the rejection region for $H_0 : \mu_0 \leq 4.00$ is $\bar{x} > 4.10$. (a) Find the value of α. (b) Find the value of β if $H_1 : \mu_1 = 4.10$.

15. We are to test the hypothesis $H_0 : \mu_0 \leq 150$ by means of a sample of 25. Assume $\sigma = 20$ and $\alpha = 0.07$. (a) Find β when $H_1 : \mu_1 = 160$. (b) Find the power of this test.

16. Assume that pulse rates for American males of age 25 have $\sigma = 9.00$. For samples of 100, with $\alpha = 0.03$, find (a) the acceptance region for the hypothesis that $\mu_0 = 72.0$ when the alternative $\mu_1 \neq 72.0$; (b) β if the alternative hypothesis is $\mu_1 = 71.0$; (c) the power of the test for the alternative in (b).

17. In example 3 of Section 13.4, replace the hypothesis $\mu_0 \geq 50$ which calls for a one-tail test by the hypothesis $\mu_0 = 50$ which demands a two-tail test for the alternative $H_1 : \mu_1 \neq 50$. Let $\alpha = 0.05$ and show that the rejection region consists of the two intervals $\bar{x} < 46.7$ and $\bar{x} > 53.3$. If $\mu_1 = 45$, show that $\beta = 0.15$. This choice of critical region produces a test not as good as the earlier one for $\mu_0 \geq 50$, because the same α corresponds to a larger β.

18. A sample of 49 tablets is to be tested for weight. Assuming $\sigma = 0.25$ grams and $\alpha = 0.10$, find the acceptance region for the hypothesis, $\mu = 2.50$ grams when the alternative is that $\mu > 2.50$ grams. Find the power of the test when the true mean $\mu = 2.60$ grams. What does your answer mean?

19. The heights of the 16-year-old boys in two schools of the same city have been sampled. Fifty boys from School X have a mean height of 66.00 inches and an equal number from School Y have a mean height of 65.50 inches. If σ for the heights of all 16-year-old boys is 2.00 inches can we say that the difference in heights is significant at the 5% level?

20. The systolic blood pressures of a group of 60 patients showed $\bar{x} = 140$ and $s_x = 10$. A second group of 60 showed $\bar{y} = 145$ and $s_y = 13$. Compare the two groups and give reasons for your statements.

21. The total nitrogen (N) content (mg per cc) of rat blood plasma was determined for a group of 60 rats of age 50 days and for a group of 70 rats of age 80 days. The mean N content for the first group was 0.983 and the variance was 0.00253; for the second group the corresponding statistics were 1.042 and 0.00224,

respectively. Test the hypothesis that the N content does not vary with age. Let $\alpha = 0.01$.

22. A drug manufactured by two different laboratories, A and B, is tested for per cent of purity. The product from A tested in 40 samples shows 94.6% of purity; the product from B tested in 50 samples shows 96.3%. Assume that σ for both is 0.73%. (a) With $\alpha = 0.05$ test the hypothesis that $\mu_B - \mu_A = 1.00\%$. (b) What is the size of β if $\mu_B - \mu_A = 1.50$?

23. In a biological experiment, the time in seconds elapsed for a reaction after a given stimulus has a variance of 14. A set of 10 individuals shows a mean time interval of 21; another set of 13 shows a mean time interval of 24. Is there an unusual difference in means? Interpret "unusual" as a result corresponding to $P < 0.05$.

In the following exercises, assume the distributions of the original variables to be normal so that the t-distribution may be applied where necessary. State clearly what you assume H_0, H_1, or α to be in case they are not specified.

24. In a time and motion study, it is found that a certain manual operation averages 36 seconds. A group of 17 workers are given special training and then found to average only 33 seconds with $s = 6$ seconds. Is the argument valid that special training speeds up this operation? Let $\alpha = 0.05$.

25. The numbers of correct answers given by a selected group of ten persons taking a test were as follows:

$$8, \quad 15, \quad 11, \quad 9, \quad 10, \quad 8, \quad 11, \quad 18, \quad 17, \quad 13,$$

Test the hypothesis that $\mu = 15$ against the alternative that $\mu \neq 15$. Let $\alpha = 0.05$.

26. The scores, x, of ten students in a psychology test were as follows:

$$61, \quad 70, \quad 85, \quad 81, \quad 76, \quad 79, \quad 94, \quad 43, \quad 67, \quad 74.$$
$$\Sigma x = 730, \quad \Sigma x^2 = 55,074.$$

If the mean score of students in general in this test is 70, would you consider this sample an unusual one?

27. The changes in the blood pressures of 18 patients given the same dose of a drug were as follows:

$$6, -2, 1, -1, -6, 10, 3, 5, -3, -4, 2, 4, -2, 8, 1, 3, 7, 8.$$

Is the assertion that this drug generally increases the blood pressure substantiated?

28. After remedial work in arithmetic, a class of 11 pupils showed the following changes in scores on a test.

$$+6, +1, +10, -2, +3, -1, +5, +2, -6, +8, +3.$$

Is the claim justified that this remedial work is beneficial? Let $\alpha = 0.05$.

29. A halibut liver oil product was analyzed by means of eight random samples. The Vitamin A contents (measured in international units per gram) were as follows:

$$33,600, \quad 24,900, \quad 24,600, \quad 20,700, \quad 27,000, \quad 25,100, \quad 0, \quad 18,400.$$

Test the hypothesis that μ for Vitamin A equals at least 27,000. Choose $\alpha = 0.05$.

30. Two laboratory assistants make ten observations each on the same galvanometer for the same experiment. The average readings were 61 and 58 with variances of 0.60 and 0.40 respectively. Comment on the difference between the two readings.

31. Fifteen city drug stores showed a mean percentage of profit of 6.37 with a variance of 0.932. Ten suburban drug stores showed a mean percentage of profit of 7.04 with a variance of 1.21. Do these statistics refute the hypothesis that there is no difference in profit between city and suburban stores?

32. Four rats were fed a special ration during the first three months of their lives. The following gains in weight (grams) were noted: 55, 62, 58, 65. Test the hypothesis that $\mu = 65$ against the alternative that $\mu < 65$. Let $\alpha = 0.10$.

33. Ten pupils from one school have a mean I.Q. of 108 and a variance of 60; 17 pupils from another school show a mean of 114 with a variance of 80. Is there a significant difference ($\alpha = 0.05$) between the mean I.Q.'s?

34. The microflavin content (measured in micrograms per 100 grams) of two varieties of turnip greens was determined from samples of 40 turnips each from each variety. The results follow:

$$\text{Variety X:} \quad \Sigma x = 100,000, \quad \Sigma x^2 = 258,800,000;$$
$$\text{Variety Y:} \quad \Sigma y = 92,000, \quad \Sigma y^2 = 219,080,000.$$

Is there evidence of a higher content in variety X than in variety Y?

35. Two machines stamp out washers. During one morning, their products were tested by taking random samples from their lots. The outcomes of the measurements made on the two samples are given.

Machine A	Machine B
$\bar{x} = 2.33$	$\bar{y} = 2.61$
$s_x = 0.24$	$s_y = 0.30$
$N_x = 21$	$N_y = 21$

Test the hypothesis, H_0, that $\mu_x = \mu_y$ against the alternative that $\mu_x \neq \mu_y$.

36. Two tinctures of strophanthus were tested by the cat method, each tincture being administered to seven cats. The mean lethal dose in cubic centimeters of undiluted tincture per kilogram of cat was 0.0168 for tincture A, and 0.0199 for tincture B. The respective standard deviations were 0.00328 and 0.00309. Do the tinctures appear to have significantly different effects?

37. Assume sample sizes, $N = 25$ with $\sigma = 2$. From $\bar{x}$, we are to test the hypothesis, H_0, that $\mu_0 \leq 20$ against the alternatives $\mu_1 = 20.5$, $\mu_2 = 21$, and $\mu_3 = 22$. When $\bar{x} > 20.7$ we reject H_0. (a) What is the value of α? (b) Calculate β for each of the alternatives. (c) Plot the graph of the power function from the values obtained in (b).

38. A certain kind of linen thread is to have a mean breaking strength of 25.8 ounces with a variance of 2.34. When tests are made of random samples of 16 pieces each, a mean breaking strength of 25.0 or lower causes rejection of the lot from which the sample was drawn. (a) What is the size of the type I error? (b)

Compute the size of the type II error for the alternatives $\mu_1 = 24.5$, $\mu_2 = 25.4$, and $\mu_3 = 25.2$. (c) Sketch the power function.

39. Suppose that hand grenades are timed to explode in five seconds after the catch is released. If you were the manufacturer of these grenades and testing the timing mechanisms periodically, (a) would you use a one-tail or a two-tail test? Why? (b) Would you choose a larger or a smaller type I error for these tests than you would for testing other nonmilitary timing mechanisms. Why?

40. A manufacturer turns out steel axles with a standard deviation of their diameters equal to 0.50 mm. A buyer desires a sampling plan such that there is a 95% chance of accepting shipments of axles with mean diameters of 10.3 mm. or less, and a 10% chance of accepting shipments with mean diameters of 10.8 or more. What should the sample size for testing be and what is the critical value of $\bar{x}$, that is, the value of the sample mean that separates acceptable shipments from those that are not acceptable?

41. For what alternative hypothesis would the two-tail test illustrated in Fig. 13-10c be appropriate?

14

The Bivariate Binomial
Probability Function

Indeed the intellectual basis of all
empirical knowledge may be said to be
a matter of probability . . . .

WILLIAM C. D. DAMPIER-WHETHAM
A History of Science[1]

14.1. GENERAL PROPERTIES

Consider the 2×2 table shown below where the random variables X and Y may each have only two possible outcomes: success denoted by x_1 and y_1, and failure, by x_0 and y_0 respectively.

TABLE 14-1

x \ y	y_1	y_0	$f(x)$
x_1	p_{11}	p_{10}	p_1
x_0	p_{01}	p_{00}	q_1
$g(y)$	p_2	q_2	1

This table defines a *bivariate* or *joint probability function* $P(X, Y)$, whose sample space is the set $\{(x_1,y_1), (x_0,y_1), (x_1,y_0), (x_0,y_0)\}$ so that

$$P(X = x_i, \ Y = y_j) = p_{ij}, \ i = 1, 2; \quad j = 1, 2.$$

[1] Cambridge University Press, by permission.

The *marginal probabilities* are

$$p_1 = P(X = x_1), q_1 = P(X = x_0), p_2 = P(Y = y_1), \quad \text{and} \quad q_2 = P(Y = y_0),$$

where

$$p_1 = p_{11} + p_{10}, q_1 = p_{01} + p_{00}, p_2 = p_{11} + p_{01}, \quad \text{and} \quad q_2 = p_{10} + p_{00}.$$

Of course, $p_{11} + p_{01} + p_{10} + p_{00} = p_1 + q_1 = p_2 + q_2 = 1$. The marginal probability functions $f(x)$ and $g(y)$ are of the simple binomial type. The determinant, D, of this table is defined as:

$$D = p_{11}p_{00} - p_{01}p_{10}. \tag{14.1}$$

Tables such as that shown are often exhibited in the following form (Table 14-2):

TABLE 14-2

	B	$\bar{B}$
A	p_{11}	p_{10}
$\bar{A}$	p_{01}	p_{00}

EXAMPLE 1. A set of ten cards contains seven hearts and three spades. Two cards are drawn in succession without replacement. Let the events H_1 and S_1 be the appearance of hearts and spades, respectively, on the first card, and let H_2 and S_2 be the appearance of hearts and spades, respectively, on the second card. The 2×2 table corresponding to this experimental model is shown as Table 14-3.

TABLE 14-3

	H_2	S_2	
H_1	$\frac{7}{15}$	$\frac{7}{30}$	$\frac{7}{10}$
S_1	$\frac{7}{30}$	$\frac{1}{15}$	$\frac{3}{10}$
	$\frac{7}{10}$	$\frac{3}{10}$	1

Here $p_{11} = (\frac{7}{10})(\frac{6}{9}) = \frac{7}{15}$, $p_{10} = (\frac{7}{10})(\frac{3}{9}) = \frac{7}{30}$, etc. We can let the outcome, hearts, be designated by 1, and that of no hearts (spades) by 0; then X and Y can symbolize two random variables with numerically valued outcomes. Here

$$D = \left(\frac{7}{15}\right)\left(\frac{1}{15}\right) - \left(\frac{7}{30}\right)^2 = \frac{-7}{300} = -0.0233.$$

Theorem 14.1. *If any one of the equalities, $p_{11} = p_1p_2$, $p_{01} = p_2q_1$, $p_{10} = p_1q_2$, $p_{00} = q_1q_2$, hold, then all of them do.*

The proof is left as an exercise. See exercise 4.

Definition. X and Y are independent random variables if P(x,y) = f(x) g(y) for each of the four pairs of possible outcomes.

From the preceding definition and theorem, it follows that, for independent random variables, $p_{11}p_{00} = p_1p_2q_1q_2 = p_{01}p_{10}$; whence,

$$D = p_{11}p_{00} - p_{10}p_{01} = 0.$$

EXAMPLE 2. If, in the experiment of example 1, we draw *with* replacement, then X and Y become independent variables. Table 14-2 is replaced by Table 14-4.

TABLE 14-4

	H_2	S_2	
H_1	0.49	0.21	0.70
S_1	0.21	0.09	0.30
	0.70	0.30	1

Here $D = (0.49)(0.09) - (0.21)^2 = 0$.

Imagine a population of individuals with characteristics (x_1,y_1), (x_0,y_1), (x_1,y_0), and (x_0,y_0) occurring in the proportions given by p_{11}, p_{01}, p_{10}, and p_{00}, respectively, from which we draw a random sample of N with replacement after each drawing. Let the frequencies of the pairs be represented by a, b, c, and d as in Table 14-5. The probability that (x_1,y_1) occurs a times, (x_0,y_1),

TABLE 14-5

	y_1	y_0	
x_1	a	c	$a + c$
x_0	b	d	$b + d$
	$a + b$	$c + d$	N

b times, (x_1,y_0), c times, and (x_0,y_0), d times in N trials is given by a term of the multinomial expansion of

$$(p_{11} + p_{01} + p_{10} + p_{00})^N \tag{14.2}$$

and is

$$\frac{N!}{a!b!c!d!} p_{11}^a p_{01}^b p_{10}^c p_{00}^d. \tag{14.3}$$

This form yields the probability for a given four-fold outcome of (x,y)'s in N trials and, hence, is a function of x and y.

14.2. BINOMIAL CORRELATION

In what follows, we shall assume that success and failure are designated 1 and 0, respectively, so that Table 14-1 becomes Table 14-6.

TABLE 14-6

x \ y	1	0	
1	p_{11}	p_{10}	p_1
0	p_{01}	p_{00}	q_1
	p_2	q_2	1

For a sample of N drawn with replacement from this table, we see that

$$\mu_x = Np_1, \qquad \mu_y = Np_2, \qquad \sigma_x^2 = Np_1q_1, \quad \text{and} \quad \sigma_y^2 = Np_2q_2,$$

since each variable separately has a binomial distribution.

We now introduce a new function of two random variables called the *covariance* and symbolized by σ_{XY}. We define it as

$$\sigma_{XY} = E(X - \mu_X)(Y - \mu_Y) \qquad \text{(14.4)}$$

$$= \sum_{j=1}^{2} \sum_{i=1}^{2} p_{ij}(x_i - \mu_X)(y_j - \mu_Y)$$

The meaning of this double sum becomes more evident when we expand it.

$$\sum_{j=1}^{2} \sum_{i=1}^{2} p_{ij}(x_i - \mu_X)(y_j - \mu_Y)$$

$$= \sum_{j=1}^{2} [p_{1j}(x_1 - \mu_X)(y_j - \mu_Y) + p_{2j}(x_2 - \mu_X)(y_j - \mu_Y)].$$

Note that we have written out the sum with respect to i first. Next we expand with respect to j, so that

$$\sigma_{XY} = p_{11}(x_1 - \mu_X)(y_1 - \mu_Y) + p_{21}(x_2 - \mu_X)(y_1 - \mu_Y) +$$
$$p_{12}(x_1 - \mu_X)(y_2 - \mu_Y) + p_{22}(x_2 - \mu_X)(y_2 - \mu_Y).$$

If successes of X tend to be associated with those of Y, while failures of X tend to be associated with those of Y, then $X - \mu_X$ and $Y - \mu_Y$ will both tend to be of the same sign and the product will be positive. On the other hand, if successes of one variable tend to be associated with failures of the other, then the corresponding product will be negative. Thus, the sign and the magnitude of the covariance indicate the nature and the degree of the association between X and Y when appropriate units of these variables are used.

Theorem. 14.2. *For a bivariate binomial probability function,*

$$\sigma_{XY} = p_{11} - p_1 p_2 = p_{10} - q_1 q_2 = D. \tag{14.5}$$

Proof.

$$E(X - \mu_X)(Y - \mu_Y) = \sum_{j=1}^{2} \sum_{i=1}^{2} p_{ij}(x_i - \mu_X)(y_j - \mu_Y).$$

Since $x_1 = 1$, $x_0 = 0$, $y_1 = 1$, and $y_0 = 0$, we expand the right member of this equation bearing in mind that $N = 1$.

$$\sigma_{XY} = \sum_{j=1}^{2} \sum_{i=1}^{2} p_{ij}(x_i y_j - x_i \mu_Y - y_j \mu_X + \mu_X \mu_Y).$$

$$= p_{11}(1 - p_2 - p_1 + p_1 p_2) + p_{01}(-p_1 + p_1 p_2)$$

$$+ p_{10}(-p_2 + p_1 p_2) + p_{00} p_1 p_2$$

$$= p_{11} + p_1 p_2(p_{11} + p_{01} + p_{10} + p_{00}) - p_{11}(p_1 + p_2) - p_{01} p_1 - p_{10} p_2$$

$$= p_{11} + p_1 p_2 - p_1(p_{11} + p_{01}) - p_2(p_{11} + p_{10})$$

$$= p_{11} + p_1 p_2 - p_1 p_2 - p_2 p_1$$

$$= p_{11} - p_1 p_2.$$

The proof that $D = p_{11} - p_1 p_2 = p_{00} - q_1 q_2$ is left as an exercise. (Exercise 5.)

Theorem 14.3. *If X and Y are independent, the covariance is zero, and conversely.*

The proof is left as an exercise. (Exercise 12.)

The degree of correlation or the association between two random variables is measured by the *correlation coefficient* ρ, which may be defined as the covariance between two standardized random variables. Thus,

$$\rho = E\left(\frac{X - \mu_X}{\sigma_X}\right)\left(\frac{Y - \mu_Y}{\sigma_Y}\right). \tag{14.6}$$

When $N = 1$, $\sigma_X = \sqrt{p_1 q_1}$, $\sigma_Y = \sqrt{p_2 q_2}$, and the covariance $\sigma_{XY} = p_{11} - p_1 p_2$; hence,

$$\rho = \frac{p_{11} - p_1 p_2}{\sqrt{p_1 p_2 q_1 q_2}} = \frac{D}{\sqrt{p_1 p_2 q_1 q_2}}. \tag{14.7}$$

An advantage in using standardized variables is that we can prove that $-1 \le \rho \le 1$.

For perfect positive correlation between X and Y, only successes of X

are paired with those of Y, and similarly for failures. In this event, the four-fold table would have the aspect of Table 14-7a.

TABLE 14-7a

x \ y	y_1	y_0	
x_1	p_{11}	0	p_1
x_0	0	p_{00}	q_1
	p_2	q_2	1

TABLE 14-7b

x \ y	y_1	y_0	
x_1	0	p_{10}	p_1
x_0	p_{01}	0	q_1
	p_2	q_2	1

Then, since $p_{11} = p_1 = p_2$ and $p_{00} = q_1 = q_2$,

$$\rho = \frac{p_1 - p_1^2}{p_1 q_1} = 1.$$

For perfect negative correlation, only successes of X can be paired with failures of Y and vice versa. Thus, Table 14-7b is representative. Then $p_{10} = p_1 = q_2$ and $p_{01} = p_2 = q_1$.

$$\rho = \frac{-p_1 p_2}{p_1 p_2} = -1$$

EXAMPLE 1. For the experiment of Table 14-3,

$$\rho = \frac{\frac{7}{15} - (\frac{7}{10})^2}{(\frac{7}{10})(\frac{3}{10})} = \frac{-1}{9}.$$

EXAMPLE 2. For the experiment of Table 14-4,

$$\rho = 0.$$

This last value is predictable by Theorem 14.3.

EXAMPLE 3. Given Table 14-8.

TABLE 14-8

x \ y	y_1	y_0	$f(x)$
x_1	$\frac{5}{12}$	$\frac{1}{12}$	$\frac{1}{2}$
x_0	$\frac{1}{12}$	$\frac{5}{12}$	$\frac{1}{2}$
$g(y)$	$\frac{1}{2}$	$\frac{1}{2}$	1

$$\rho = \frac{\frac{5}{12} - \frac{1}{4}}{\frac{1}{4}} = \frac{2}{3}.$$

Notice here that p_{11} and p_{00} are large relative to p_{01} and p_{10}.

Theorem 14.4. *If* **X** *and* **Y** *are random variables governed by a bivariate binomial probability function with* $\rho = 0$, **X** *and* **Y** *are independent.*

The proof follows from that of Theorem 14.3. A caution should be stated here. In subsequent work with bivariate probability functions not of the binomial type, it will be shown that if $\rho = 0$, X and Y are not necessarily independent. See the remark following example 3 of Section 15.5.

14.3. χ^2 AND ρ^2

Table 14-1 may be conceived as a model for the 2×2 tables discussed in Sections 11.7–11.10. A typical 2×2 table is of the form:

	A	$\bar{A}$	
B	a	b	r_1
$\bar{B}$	c	d	r_2
	c_1	c_2	N

Table 14-1 assumes that the probabilities p_{ij} are known. In the applications of the χ^2-test, they are not known; hence we employ estimates under the hypothesis of independence (see Section 11.7). To clarify this statement, consider formula (11.12):

$$\chi^2 = \frac{N(ad - bc)^2}{r_1 r_2 c_1 c_2}.$$

For large N we may write this as:

$$\chi^2 = \frac{N[(a/N)(d/N) - (b/N)(c/N)]^2}{(r_1/N)(r_2/N)(c_1/N)(c_2/N)}$$

$$= \frac{N(p'_{11}p'_{00} - p'_{10}p'_{01})^2}{p'_1 q'_1 p'_2 q'_2},$$

where the prime superscripts denote estimates of the probabilities. If we compare this χ^2 with formula (14.7) where $D = p_{11}p_{00} - p_{01}p_{10}$ and let $N = 1$, we see that χ^2 is an estimate of ρ^2 and will be approximately equal to it for large N. Since both ρ and χ^2 are used to test the degree of dependence between two variables, it should not be surprising that ρ^2 and χ^2 are so closely related.

14.4. THE LIMITING FUNCTION

Let us consider a population defined by means of the bivariate function of Table 14-9, and assume that samples of 3 are drawn from it with replacement. Let the random variables X and Y be the number of occurrences of

TABLE 14-9

	B	B̄
A	0.4	0.3
Ā	0.1	0.2

A and B, respectively. Then the sample space for (X, Y) is the set of 16 bivariate elements:

$$S = \{x \mid x = 0,1,2,3\} \times \{y \mid y = 0,1,2,3\}$$
$$= \{(0,0), (0,1), , , (3,2), (3,3)\}.$$

The probability associated with each point of S is given by the multinomial formula (14.3). For example, for the point $(0,0)$ we have the only possible outcome shown in Table 14-10. Whence $P(0,0) = \dfrac{3!}{0!0!0!3!} (0.2)^3 = 0.008$; for

TABLE 14-10

	B	B̄	
A	0	0	$x = 0$
Ā	0	3	3
$y = 0$	3	3

the point $(1,1)$ we have the two possible outcomes shown in Tables 14-11a, b. The corresponding probabilities are

$$P(1,1) = \frac{3!}{0!1!1!1!} (0.3)(0.2)(0.1) + \frac{3!}{1!0!0!2!} (0.4)(0.2)^2$$

$$= 0.036 + 0.048 = 0.084.$$

The probabilities attached to the elements of S may be represented geometrically by parallelepipeds having bases of area 1 and altitudes equal to $P(x,y)$, as shown in the solid histogram of Fig. 14-1.

TABLE 14-11

(a)

	B	B̄	
A	0	1	$x = 1$
Ā	1	1	2
$y = 1$	2	3

(b)

	B	B̄	
A	1	0	$x = 1$
Ā	0	2	2
$y = 1$	2	3

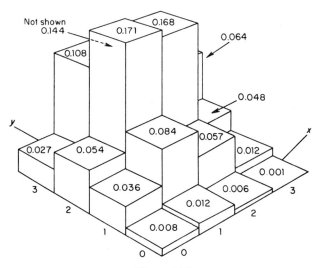

Figure 14-1

We advance now to the general case illustrated in Table 14-12.

If samples of N are drawn from a bivariate population governed by the probabilities of Table 14-12, with X and Y the random variables symbolizing occurrences A and B, respectively, then

$$\mu_X = Np_1, \quad \mu_Y = Np_2, \quad \sigma_X^2 = Np_1q_1, \quad \sigma_Y^2 = Np_2q_2.$$

TABLE 14-12

	B	$\bar{B}$	
A	p_{11}	p_{10}	p_1
$\bar{A}$	p_{01}	p_{00}	q_1
	p_2	q_2	1

Just as we noted that the simple binomial probability function led to the normal density function, so also for the bivariate binomial, if we change to standardized variables

$$Z_1 = \frac{X - Np_1}{\sqrt{Np_1q_1}}, \quad Z_2 = \frac{Y - Np_2}{\sqrt{Np_2q_2}},$$

and let N become infinite, the solid histogram approaches as a limiting form, the space under a *bivariate normal frequency surface*. Such a surface is pictured in Fig. 18-5 and defined by the equation:

$$\Phi(Z_1,Z_2) = \frac{1}{2\pi\sqrt{1 - \rho^2}} \, e^{-\frac{1}{2(1-\rho^2)}(Z_1^2 - 2\rho Z_1 Z_2 + Z_2^2)} . \qquad \textbf{(14.8)}$$

Here $\Phi(Z_1,Z_2)$ is a density function of two continuous random variables, where ρ is a parameter to be defined later. The properties of the surface [Eq. (14.8)] will be described in Chapter 18. Suffice it to say now that, for large N and for values of $p_1, q_1, p_2,$ and q_2 which are not too small, the probability for a given outcome (x,y) can be well approximated by the corresponding volume under the surface.

EXERCISES

Construct 2×2 probability tables for the experiments of exercises 1–3. Indicate the marginal probability functions.

1. An urn contains five uniform balls, three of which are marked $+$ and two are marked $-$. Two balls are drawn in succession without replacement.

2. A box contains twenty 40-watt electric light bulbs of which five are defective. A person selects two bulbs from the box.

3. A penny is tossed twice. Let X be the outcome on the first toss and Y the outcome on both tosses. Success for X is defined as head and success for Y is defined as heads on both tosses; all other outcomes are counted as failures.

4. Prove Theorem 14.1.

5. Prove that $D = p_{11} - p_1 p_2 = p_{00} - q_1 q_2$.

6. If the experiment of exercise 1 were repeated ten times with the results shown in the following table, what is the probability for exactly this result?

	+	−
+	3	2
−	5	0

7. Given the four-fold table of assumed probabilities for recovery and death from a disease when the patients have been either treated or not treated (Left-hand table).

	Recovered	Died			Recovered	Died
Treated	0.4	0.1		Treated	10	2
Not Treated	0.2	0.3		Not Treated	1	7

If a sample of 20 patients showed the results given in the right-hand table, what is the probability for exactly that outcome? Do not attempt to evaluate your answer.

8. A man and his wife enter two different gambling games. The husband's chance of winning is 0.45 and that of his wife, 0.48. (a) Construct a 2 × 2 probability table for this situation. (b) For one play with a dollar bet each, what is the expected return for the couple?

9. For exercise 1, what is the probability that the second ball drawn is marked +, provided the first one is +?

10. In exercise 2, what is the probability that the second bulb is defective, provided the first one is?

11. Find the covariance for each of the tables of exercises 1-3.

12. Prove Theorem 14.3.

13. Find ρ for each of the tables of exercises 1, 2, 3, and 7.

14. Given the following incomplete 2 × 2 table, construct all possible 2 × 2 tables meeting the given conditions.

	B	$\bar{B}$	
A	–	–	3
$\bar{A}$	–	–	–
	5	–	10

15. Given the data shown in the following 2 × 2 table, estimate the coefficient of correlation between inoculation and recovery if 250 individuals comprise a random sample from a given population. Discuss the accuracy of this estimate.

	Recovered	*Died*
Inoculated	110	30
Not Inoculated	20	90

16. Prove that the maximum value of the determinant, D, is $\frac{1}{4}$ and that the minimum value is $-\frac{1}{4}$. Recall that the product of two numbers having a given sum is a maximum when the numbers are equal.

17. We defined

$$\rho = \frac{p_{11} - p_1 p_2}{\sqrt{p_1 p_2 q_1 q_2}}.$$

Show that

$$\rho = \frac{p_{00} - q_1 q_2}{\sqrt{p_1 p_2 q_1 q_2}} = \frac{p_{10} - p_1 q_2}{\sqrt{p_1 p_2 q_1 q_2}} = \frac{p_{01} - q_1 p_2}{\sqrt{p_1 p_2 q_1 q_2}}.$$

15

Discrete Bivariate
Probability Functions

But if probability is a measure of the
importance of our state of ignorance, it
must change its value whenever we add
new knowledge. And so it does.

THORNTON C. FRY
Probability and Its Engineering Uses[1]

15.1. INTRODUCTION

It has already been noted in Section 2.1 that elements of a sample space
do not need to be individual objects but may be groups of them. We might
have a set of pairs such as $\{HH, HT, TH, TT\}$ or $\{(1,1), (1,0), (0,1), (0,0)\}$, or a
set of triples such as $\{ggg, ggr, grg, rgg, grr, rgr, rrg, rrr\}$, or a set of n-tuples,
$\{(a_1,a_2, , , a_n), (b_1,b_2, , , b_n), , , (k_1,k_2, , , k_n)\}$. In the preceding chapter, we
studied a special type of bivariate probability function. In this chapter, we
shall consider in detail sample spaces consisting of sets of pairs but shall,
occasionally, refer to the more general case of n-tuples.

15.2. SOME EXAMPLES

EXAMPLE 1. Two players, A and B, each hold five cards of the same kind:
two marked 0, two marked 1, and one marked 2. A draws a card from B's
hand, then B draws a card from A's hand. Let X be the number showing
on A's draw and let Y be the number showing on B's draw. The following

---

[1] Copyright 1928, D. Van Nostrand Company, Inc., Princeton, N.J.

pairs of outcomes constitute the sample space S for this experiment:

$$S = \{(0,0), (0,1), (0,2), (1,0), (1,1), (1,2), (2,0), (2,1), (2,2)\}.$$

Since the outcome for B is independent of that for A, the respective probabilities for these outcomes are:

$$\frac{4}{25}, \frac{4}{25}, \frac{2}{25}, \frac{4}{25}, \frac{4}{25}, \frac{2}{25}, \frac{2}{25}, \frac{2}{25}, \frac{1}{25}.$$

It is convenient to represent this joint probability function by means of Table 15-1.

TABLE 15-1

x \ y	0	1	2	$f(x)$
0	$\frac{4}{25}$	$\frac{4}{25}$	$\frac{2}{25}$	$\frac{2}{5}$
1	$\frac{4}{25}$	$\frac{4}{25}$	$\frac{2}{25}$	$\frac{2}{5}$
2	$\frac{2}{25}$	$\frac{2}{25}$	$\frac{1}{25}$	$\frac{1}{5}$
$g(y)$	$\frac{2}{5}$	$\frac{2}{5}$	$\frac{1}{5}$	1

The probability $P(X = x_i, Y = y_j)$ will be denoted by $P(x_i,y_j)$ or p_{ij}. This probability for the joint outcome (x_i,y_j) is found at the intersection of x_i row and the y_j column. Thus $p_{12} = P(1,2) = P(X = 1, Y = 2) = \frac{2}{25}$ and $p_{22} = P(2,2) = P(X = 2, Y = 2) = \frac{1}{25}$.

The conditional probability function (Section 4.2) $g(Y \mid X = 1)$ is obtained as follows:

Since $g(Y \mid 1) = P(1, Y)/f(1)$, it follows that

$$g(0 \mid 1) = \frac{P(1,0)}{f(1)} = \frac{4/25}{2/5} = \frac{2}{5}$$

$$g(1 \mid 1) = \frac{P(1,1)}{f(1)} = \frac{4/25}{2/5} = \frac{2}{5}$$

$$g(2 \mid 1) = \frac{P(1,2)}{f(1)} = \frac{2/25}{2/5} = \frac{1}{5}.$$

Thus, the conditional probability function of Y given $X = 1$ is defined by Table 15-2.

TABLE 15-2

y	0	1	2
$g(y \mid 1)$	$\frac{2}{5}$	$\frac{2}{5}$	$\frac{1}{5}$

Similarly, the conditional probability function of X given $Y = 0$ can be verified to be that in Table 15-3.

TABLE 15-3

x	0	1	2
$f(x \mid 0)$	$\frac{2}{5}$	$\frac{2}{5}$	$\frac{1}{5}$

EXAMPLE 2. Let us change the second random variable of example 1 so Y is the sum of the numbers drawn by A and B. Obviously, the sum is influenced by the outcome of A's draw. The joint probabilities $P(x,y)$, for this altered experiment are shown in Table 15-4.

TABLE 15-4

x \ y	0	1	2	3	4	$f(x)$
0	$\frac{4}{25}$	$\frac{4}{25}$	$\frac{2}{25}$	0	0	$\frac{2}{5}$
1	0	$\frac{4}{25}$	$\frac{4}{25}$	$\frac{2}{25}$	0	$\frac{2}{5}$
2	0	0	$\frac{2}{25}$	$\frac{2}{25}$	$\frac{1}{25}$	$\frac{1}{5}$
$g(y)$	$\frac{4}{25}$	$\frac{8}{25}$	$\frac{8}{25}$	$\frac{4}{25}$	$\frac{1}{25}$	1

It should be easy to identify the following: the marginal probability functions, $f(X)$ and $g(Y)$, and the conditional probability functions, $f(X \mid Y)$ and $g(Y \mid X)$. There is, however, an important difference between the probability functions of Tables 15-1 and 15-4. We know that, in the former, the random variables X and Y are independent; hence,

$$P(X, Y) = f(X)g(Y) \qquad \text{for all } (x,y).$$

For example, in Table 15-1,

$$P(1,2) = f(1)g(2) = \frac{2}{5} \times \frac{1}{5} = \frac{2}{25}$$

and

$$P(2,0) = f(2)g(0) = \frac{1}{5} \times \frac{2}{5} = \frac{2}{25}.$$

This leads us to the definition of independence stated in the next section.

In Table 15-4, $P(X, Y) \neq f(X)g(Y)$ for any pair (x,y). For example,

$$P(1,3) = \frac{2}{25} \neq f(1)g(3) = \frac{2}{5} \times \frac{4}{25}.$$

In this case, we say that X and Y are dependent. Clearly, the sum of the

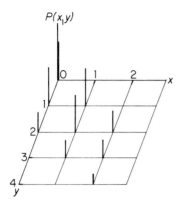

Figure 15-1

numbers drawn depends to some extent upon the number appearing on A's draw.

Table 15-4 can be represented by a three-dimensional graph as in Fig. 15-1. The length of each vertical line is proportional to the probability associated with the coordinates (x,y) of the point at which the line is erected. One may also use the solid histogram as in Fig. 14-1.

15.3. A FORMAL SUMMARY

Let the sets

$$\{x_1, x_2, , , x_m\} \text{ and } \{y_1, y_2, , , y_n\}$$

be sample spaces for the random variables X and Y, respectively. Let

$$P(X = x_i) = f(x_i) > 0, \quad i = 1, 2, , , m \quad \text{and let } \sum_{i=1}^{m} f(x_i) = 1$$

$$P(Y = y_j) = g(y_j) > 0, \quad j = 1, 2, , , n \quad \text{and let } \sum_{j=1}^{n} g(y_j) = 1.$$

The joint or bivariate probability function $P(X, Y)$ is defined by Table 15-5.

TABLE 15-5

x \ y	y_1	y_2	$\cdots$	y_n	$f(x)$
x_1	$P(x_1, y_1)$	$P(x_1, y_2)$	$\cdots$	$P(x_1, y_n)$	$f(x_1)$
x_2	$P(x_2, y_1)$	$P(x_2, y_2)$	$\cdots$	$P(x_2, y_n)$	$f(x_2)$
.	.	.	$\cdots$	.	.
.	.	.	$\cdots$	.	.
.	.	.	$\cdots$	.	.
x_m	$P(x_m, y_1)$	$P(x_m, y_2)$	$\cdots$	$P(x_m, y_n)$	$f(x_m)$
$g(y)$	$g(y_1)$	$g(y_2)$	$\cdots$	$g(y_n)$	1

In the table

$$\sum_{j=1}^{n} \sum_{i=1}^{m} P(x_i, y_j) = 1 \tag{15.1}$$

$$\sum_{i=1}^{m} P(x_i, y_j) = g(y_j), \quad j = 1, 2, , , n \tag{15.2}$$

$$\sum_{j=1}^{n} P(x_i, y_j) = f(x_i), \quad i = 1, 2, , , m. \tag{15.3}$$

TABLE 15-6

x	x_1	x_2	$\cdots$	x_m
$f(x)$	$f(x_1)$	$f(x_2)$	$\cdots$	$f(x_m)$

TABLE 15-7

y	y_1	y_2	$\cdots$	y_n
$g(y)$	$g(y_1)$	$g(y_2)$	$\cdots$	$g(y_n)$

The marginal probability function of X is defined in Table 15-6, and the marginal probability function of Y, in Table 15-7.

The conditional probability function of Y given x_i, $g(Y \mid x_i)$ is defined in Table 15-8, and the conditional probability function of X given y_j, $f(X \mid y_j)$ is defined in Table 15-9.

Definition. The random variables, X and Y, of a joint probability function, P(X,Y), are said to be independent if

$$P(x_i, y_j) = f(x_i)g(y_j) \tag{15.4}$$

for every pair of possible outcomes (x,y); that is, for $i = 1, 2, , , , m$ and $j = 1, 2, , , n$; otherwise X and Y are said to be dependent.

TABLE 15-8

y	y_1	y_2	$\cdots$	y_n
$g(y \mid x_i)$	$\dfrac{P(x_i,y_1)}{f(x_i)}$	$\dfrac{P(x_i,y_2)}{f(x_i)}$	$\cdots$	$\dfrac{P(x_i,y_n)}{f(x_i)}$

TABLE 15-9

x	x_1	x_2	$\cdots$	x_m
$f(x \mid y_j)$	$\dfrac{P(x_1,y_j)}{g(y_j)}$	$\dfrac{P(x_2,y_j)}{g(y_j)}$	$\cdots$	$\dfrac{P(x_m,y_j)}{g(y_j)}$

15.4. FUNCTIONS OF TWO RANDOM VARIABLES

From the data of Table 15-1, we can construct Table 15-10.

It should be evident that U is also a random variable as well as X and Y. Its probability function follows in Table 15-11. The probability of obtaining

TABLE 15-10

(x,y)	(0,0)	(0,1)	(0,2)	(1,0)	(1,1)	(1,2)	(2,0)	(2,1)	(2,2)
x	0	0	0	1	1	1	2	2	2
y	0	1	2	0	1	2	0	1	2
$u = x + y$	0	1	2	1	2	3	2	3	4
$P(x,y)$	$\dfrac{4}{25}$	$\dfrac{4}{25}$	$\dfrac{2}{25}$	$\dfrac{4}{25}$	$\dfrac{4}{25}$	$\dfrac{2}{25}$	$\dfrac{2}{25}$	$\dfrac{2}{25}$	$\dfrac{1}{25}$

a possible value of U is the sum of the probabilities of the pairs, whose sums yield the given U. Thus,

$$P(U = 2) = P(X = 0, Y = 2) + P(X = 1, Y = 1) + P(X = 2, Y = 0)$$

$$= \frac{2}{25} + \frac{4}{25} + \frac{2}{25} = \frac{8}{25},$$

and

$$P(U = 3) = P(X = 1, Y = 2) + P(X = 2, Y = 1)$$

$$= \frac{2}{25} + \frac{2}{25} = \frac{4}{25}.$$

It is possible to construct many useful functions of two (or more) random variables. Fortunately, some of the most important of these are quite simple ones, such as $X + Y$, $X - Y$, and XY.

TABLE 15-11

u	0	1	2	3	4
$P(u)$	$\dfrac{4}{25}$	$\dfrac{8}{25}$	$\dfrac{8}{25}$	$\dfrac{4}{25}$	$\dfrac{1}{25}$

15.5. THE MEAN OR EXPECTED VALUE

Let $P(X,Y)$ be a bivariate probability function of the random variables X and Y defined as in Table 15-5, and let $U(X, Y)$ denote a function of X and Y such that U has a numerical value for each (x,y) in the table. The mean or expected value of U is defined thus:

$$E(U) = \sum_{j=1}^{n} \sum_{i=1}^{m} P(x_i, y_j) U(x_i, y_j). \tag{15.5}$$

EXAMPLE 1. Let $U(X, Y) = XY$ where X and Y are the random variables of Table 15-1. Then

$$E(U) = \tfrac{4}{25} \cdot 0 + \tfrac{4}{25} \cdot 0 + \tfrac{2}{25} \cdot 0$$
$$+ \tfrac{4}{25} \cdot 0 + \tfrac{4}{25} \cdot 1 + \tfrac{2}{25} \cdot 2$$
$$+ \tfrac{2}{25} \cdot 0 + \tfrac{2}{25} \cdot 2 + \tfrac{1}{25} \cdot 4 = \tfrac{16}{25}.$$

Note that

$$E(X) = \tfrac{2}{5} \cdot 0 + \tfrac{2}{5} \cdot 1 + \tfrac{1}{5} \cdot 2 = \tfrac{4}{5}$$
$$E(Y) = \tfrac{2}{5} \cdot 0 + \tfrac{2}{5} \cdot 1 + \tfrac{1}{5} \cdot 2 = \tfrac{4}{5}.$$

Therefore, $E(X)E(Y) = \tfrac{16}{25} = E(XY)$. The last relation holds because X and Y are independent (see Theorem 15.2.); however, it is not generally true as in the case of Table 15-4.

$$E(X) = \frac{4}{5}, \qquad E(Y) = \frac{8}{5}$$

$$E(XY) = \frac{46}{25} \neq E(X)E(Y) = \frac{32}{25}.$$

EXAMPLE 2. Let $U = X - Y$, where X and Y are again the random variables of Table 15-4. Then,

$$E(U) = \tfrac{4}{25} \cdot 0 + \tfrac{4}{25}(-1) + \tfrac{2}{25}(-2) + 0 + 0$$
$$+ 0 + \tfrac{4}{25} \cdot 0 + \tfrac{4}{25}(-1) + \tfrac{2}{25}(-2) + 0$$
$$+ 0 + 0 + \tfrac{2}{25} \cdot 0 + \tfrac{2}{25}(-1) + \tfrac{1}{25}(-2)$$
$$= -\tfrac{4}{5}$$
$$E(X) = \tfrac{2}{5} \cdot 0 + \tfrac{2}{5} \cdot 1 + \tfrac{1}{5} \cdot 2 = \tfrac{4}{5}$$
$$E(Y) = \tfrac{4}{25} \cdot 0 + \tfrac{8}{25} \cdot 1 + \tfrac{8}{25} \cdot 2 + \tfrac{4}{25} \cdot 3 + \tfrac{1}{25} \cdot 4$$
$$= \tfrac{8}{5}.$$

Hence, $E(X) - E(Y) = \tfrac{4}{5} - \tfrac{8}{5} = -\tfrac{4}{5} = E(X - Y)$.

Theorem 15.1. Let X and Y be random variables with joint probability function $P(X, Y)$ defined as in Table 15-5. Then

$$E(X + Y) = E(X) + E(Y),$$

that is,

$$\mu_{X+Y} = \mu_X + \mu_Y. \qquad (15.6)$$

$$E(X - Y) = E(X) - E(Y),$$

that is,

$$\mu_{X-Y} = \mu_X - \mu_Y. \qquad (15.7)$$

Proof.

$$E(X + Y) = \sum_{j=1}^{n} \sum_{i=1}^{m} P(x_i,y_j)(x_i \pm y_j) \qquad \text{by formula (15.5)}$$

$$= \sum_{j=1}^{n} \sum_{i=1}^{m} P(x_i,y_j)x_i \pm \sum_{j=1}^{n} \sum_{i=1}^{m} P(x_i,y_j)y_j$$

$$= \sum_{i=1}^{m} x_i \sum_{j=1}^{n} P(x_i,y_j) \pm \sum_{j=1}^{n} y_j \sum_{i=1}^{m} P(x_i,y_j)$$

$$= \sum_{i=1}^{m} x_i f(x_i) \pm \sum_{j=1}^{n} y_j g(y_j) \qquad \text{by formulas (15.2) and (15.3)}$$

$$= E(X) \pm E(Y).$$

A generalization of Theorem 15.1 is the following:

Theorem 15.1a. Let $X_1, X_2, , , X_N$ be N random variables with probability function $P(X_1,X_2, , , X_N)$. Then,

$$E(X_1 + X_2 + \cdots + X_N) = E(X_1) + E(X_2) + \cdots + E(X_N). \quad (15.8)$$

The proof follows by mathematical induction but will only be outlined here. The theorem has just been proved for $N = 2$. We assume the theorem true for $N = k$ and let $U = X_1 + X_2 + \cdots + X_k$. We then prove the theorem true for $N = k + 1$ by considering $E(U + X_{k+1})$.

An important consequence of this theorem follows:

Corollary. If $\overline{X}$ is the mean of a random sample $X_1, X_2, , , X_N$ drawn from a population with probability function $f(X)$, then,

$$E(\overline{X}) = E(X), \text{ that is, } \mu_{\overline{X}} = \mu_X. \qquad (15.9)$$

Proof.

$$E(\overline{X}) = E\left(\frac{X_1 + X_2 + \cdots + X_N}{N}\right)$$

$$= \frac{1}{N} [E(X_1 + X_2 + \cdots + X_N)]$$

$$= \frac{1}{N} [E(X_1) + E(X_2) + \cdots + E(X_N)].$$

But because the sample is a random one (see Section 6.2),

$$E(X_i) = E(X), \qquad i = 1, 2, , , N.$$

Therefore,

$$E(\overline{X}) = \frac{1}{N} \cdot N \cdot E(X) = E(X).$$

Theorem 15.1b. *The last theorem and its corollary are valid for the* *continuous case where* **P** *is a continuous function of* **N** *variables.* The proof involves calculus.

Theorem 15.2 *If* **X** *and* **Y** *are independent random variables with joint probability function* **P(X,Y)** *defined as in Table* 15-5, *then*

$$E(XY) = E(X)E(Y), \quad \text{that is,} \quad \mu_{XY} = \mu_X \mu_Y. \tag{15.10}$$

Proof.

$$E(XY) = \sum_{j=1}^{n} \sum_{i=1}^{m} P(x_i, y_j)(x_i y_j).$$

Because of the independence,

$$P(X, Y) = f(X)g(Y);$$

hence,

$$E(XY) = \sum_{j=1}^{n} \sum_{i=1}^{m} f(x_i)g(y_j)x_i y_j$$

$$= \sum_{j=1}^{n} g(y_j)y_j \sum_{i=1}^{m} f(x_i)x_i$$

$$= E(X)E(Y).$$

The similarity of formula (15.10) to formula (4.8) $[P(A \cap B) = P(A)P(B)]$, both of which are concerned with independence, should not mislead the reader. The former is concerned with expected values, the latter, with probabilities. Furthermore, Theorem 15.2 does *not* state that the relation (15.10) is a *sufficient* condition for independence. The fact that the converse of this theorem is false is shown in the following example.

EXAMPLE 3. Given the following bivariate probability table, we see that $E(X) = 0$, $E(Y) = \frac{1}{2}$, and $E(XY) = 0$.

TABLE 15-12

x \ y	0	1	f(x)
−1	0	$\frac{1}{4}$	$\frac{1}{4}$
0	$\frac{1}{2}$	0	$\frac{1}{2}$
1	0	$\frac{1}{4}$	$\frac{1}{4}$
	$\frac{1}{2}$	$\frac{1}{2}$	1

It follows that $E(XY) = E(X)E(Y)$; but X and Y are not independent for $Y = X^2$. Each value of X determines Y.

Theorem 15.2 can be generalized to N variables for both the discrete and continuous cases.

15.6. VARIANCE AND COVARIANCE

In Section 7.7, we defined the variance of a random variable X as:

$$\sigma_X^2 = E(X - \mu_X)^2. \tag{15.11}$$

Let us now derive the variance of a sum (or difference) of two random variables X and Y. By the preceding definition,

$$\sigma_{X \pm Y}^2 = E[(X \pm Y) - \mu_{X \pm Y}]^2.$$

By formulas (15.6) and (15.7),

$$\mu_{X+Y} = \mu_X \pm \mu_Y,$$

hence,

$$
\begin{aligned}
\sigma_{X+Y}^2 &= E[(X \pm Y) - (\mu_X \pm \mu_Y)]^2 \\
&= E[(X - \mu_X) \pm (Y - \mu_Y)]^2 \\
&= E[(X - \mu_X)^2 \pm 2(X - \mu_X)(Y - \mu_Y) + (Y - \mu_Y)^2] \\
&= E(X - \mu_X)^2 \pm 2E(X - \mu_X)(Y - \mu_Y) + E(Y - \mu_Y)^2
\end{aligned}
$$

$$\tag{15.12}$$

The middle term of the right member of the last equation is twice the covariance as defined in Section 14.2.

We may rewrite Eq. (15.12) as

$$\sigma_{X \pm Y}^2 = \sigma_X^2 + 2\sigma_{XY} + \sigma_Y^2. \tag{15.12a}$$

Theorem 15.3. The covariance of two random variables, X and Y, equals the mean of XY minus the product of the mean of X and the mean of Y; in symbols,

$$\sigma_{XY} = \mu_{XY} - \mu_X \mu_Y. \tag{15.13}$$

Proof.

$$
\begin{aligned}
\sigma_{XY} &= E(X - \mu_X)(Y - \mu_Y) \\
&= E(XY - \mu_X Y - \mu_Y X + \mu_X \mu_Y) \\
&= E(XY) - \mu_X E(Y) - \mu_Y E(X) + \mu_X \mu_Y \\
&= E(XY) - \mu_X \mu_Y - \mu_X \mu_Y + \mu_X \mu_Y \\
&= \mu_{XY} - \mu_X \mu_Y.
\end{aligned}
$$

Theorem 15.4. If X and Y are independent random variables, their covariance is zero.

The proof follows directly from formula 15.13. Because of the independence, $\mu_{XY} = \mu_X \mu_Y$ [formula (15.10)].

Examples. The random variables of Table 15-1 are independent; hence $\sigma_{XY} = 0$. For those of Table 15-4, the situation is different. The student should verify that

$$\mu'_{XY} = \frac{46}{25}, \qquad \mu_X = \frac{4}{5}, \quad \text{and} \quad \mu_Y = \frac{8}{5},$$

whence

$$\sigma_{XY} = \frac{46}{25} - \left(\frac{4}{5}\right)\left(\frac{8}{5}\right) = \frac{14}{25}.$$

Theorem 15.5. *If X and Y are independent random variables,*

$$\sigma^2_{X \pm Y} = \sigma^2_X + \sigma^2_Y. \qquad (15.14)$$

The proof follows immediately from formula (15.12) and Theorem 15.4. Note that the plus sign holds for $X - Y$ as well as $X + Y$.

A generalization of Theorem 15.5 follows:

Theorem 15.5a. *Let X_1, X_2, , , X_N be N independent random variables with probability function $P(X_1, X_2, , , X_N)$. Then the variance of the sum $X_1 + X_2 + \cdots + X_N$ equals the sum of the variances, that is,*

$$\sigma^2_{12 \cdots N} = \sigma^2_1 + \sigma^2_2 + \cdots + \sigma^2_N. \qquad (15.14a)$$

The proof follows by mathematical induction. See exercise 28.

Corollary. *Let $\overline{X}$ be the mean of a random sample of N drawn with replacement from a population with probability function $f(X)$. Then,*

$$\sigma^2_{\overline{X}} = \frac{\sigma^2_X}{N}. \qquad (15.14b)$$

Proof. Since

$$\overline{X} = \frac{1}{N} \sum_{i=1}^{N} X_i,$$

$$\sigma^2_{\overline{X}} = \frac{1}{N^2} \sum_{i=1}^{N} \sigma^2_i,$$

because of the preceding theorem and Theorem 7.5. Then,

$$\sigma^2_{\overline{X}} = \frac{1}{N^2} \cdot N \sigma^2_X, \qquad \text{since } \sigma^2_i = \sigma^2_X, \qquad i = 1, 2, , , N.$$

$$= \frac{\sigma^2_X}{N}.$$

Theorem 15.5b. *The last theorem is also true for the continuous case.*

Let us now consider two random variables X and Y where $Y = a + bX$, a and b being constants. Y is expressed as a linear function of X and is, therefore, completely determined by X. Since one value of X yields only one value of Y, the joint probability table is square in form as shown in Table 15-13. Furthermore, if we arrange the possible outcomes for X in ascending

TABLE 15-13

x \\ y	y_1	y_2	$\cdots$	y_n	$f(x)$
x_1	P_{11}	0	$\cdots$	0	P_{11}
x_2	0	P_{22}	$\cdots$	0	P_{22}
.	.	.	$\cdots$	.	.
.	.	.	$\cdots$	.	.
.	.	.	$\cdots$	.	.
x_n	0	0	$\cdots$	P_{nn}	P_{nn}
$g(y)$	P_{11}	P_{22}	$\cdots$	P_{nn}	1

order, there will be a diagonal of nonzero probabilities with all other probabilities zero. Here we let $P_{ij} = P(x_i, y_j)$.

$$\sigma_{XY} = E(X - \mu_X)(Y - \mu_Y).$$

But for this table, $Y = a + bX$; hence $\mu_Y = a + b\mu_X$ by Theorems 7.1 and 7.2 Thus,

$$\sigma_{XY} = E(X - \mu_X)[(a + bX) - (a + b\mu_X)]$$
$$= bE(X - \mu_X)^2$$
$$= b\sigma_X^2$$
$$= \sigma_X \cdot b\sigma_X.$$

But,

$$\sigma_Y = \sigma_{a+bX} = |b| \, \sigma_X, \qquad \text{by Theorem 7.7;}$$

hence,

$$|\sigma_{XY}| = \sigma_X \sigma_Y.$$

We have thus proved:

Theorem 15.6. If Y is a linear function of the random variable X, the absolute value of the covariance of X and Y equals the product of the standard deviations of X and Y, that is,

$$|\sigma_{XY}| = \sigma_X \sigma_Y. \tag{15.15}$$

15.7. REGRESSION

The degree of dependence of Y on X or X on Y would seem to be a function of the departure of the random variables from a linear relationship. In order to measure this tendency to, or departure from, linearity, we introduce the *regression function* of Y on X, $r(X)$, by means of Table 15-14

TABLE 15-14

x	x_1	x_2	$\cdots$	x_m
$r(x)$	$\mu_{Y|x_1}$	$\mu_{Y|x_2}$	$\cdots$	$\mu_{Y|x_m}$

Here, $\mu_{Y|x_i} = E(Y \mid x_i)$. Each conditional mean is merely the mean of the column of y's for a given x, $i = 1, 2, , , m$. (Table 15-5).

> EXAMPLE 1. Table 15-15 is essentially Table 15-4 with the positions of x and y reversed.

TABLE 15-15

y \ x	0	1	2	$g(y)$
0	$\frac{4}{25}$	0	0	$\frac{4}{25}$
1	$\frac{4}{25}$	$\frac{4}{25}$	0	$\frac{8}{25}$
2	$\frac{2}{25}$	$\frac{4}{25}$	$\frac{2}{25}$	$\frac{8}{25}$
3	0	$\frac{2}{25}$	$\frac{2}{25}$	$\frac{4}{25}$
4	0	0	$\frac{1}{25}$	$\frac{1}{25}$
$f(x)$	$\frac{2}{5}$	$\frac{2}{5}$	$\frac{1}{5}$	1

The regression function of Y on X follows in Table 15-16. Note that

$$E(Y \mid x_i) = E\left(\frac{P(x_i, Y)}{f(x_i)}\right).$$

TABLE 15-16

x	0	1	2
$r(x)$	$\dfrac{4}{5}$	$\dfrac{9}{5}$	$\dfrac{14}{5}$

For example,

$$\mu_{Y|0} = \frac{1}{2/5}\left(\frac{4}{25}\cdot 0 + \frac{4}{25}\cdot 1 + \frac{2}{25}\cdot 2 + 0\cdot 3 + 4\cdot 0\right) = \frac{4}{5}$$

and so on. Furthermore, the values of $r(x)$ are *not* probabilities, but conditional or column means.

In Fig. 15-2, we have plotted the points (x,y) of Table 15-15 with a weighting factor attached to each point, each weight being merely a corresponding probability mutiplied by 25. The straight line of the graph will be

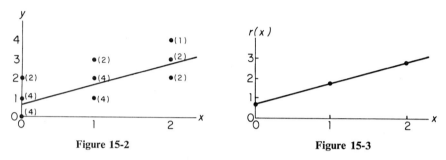

Figure 15-2   **Figure 15-3**

explained later. We shall measure the deviation from linearity as the sum of the column variances:

$$\sum_{i=1}^{m}\sigma^2_{Y|x_i} = \sum_{i=1}^{m} E(Y - \mu_{Y|x_i})^2. \tag{15.16}$$

We return to the geometric aspect of linearity by plotting the graph of the regression function of Table 15-15 in Figs. 15-2 and 15-3. Thus the graph of the regression function, defined by Table 15-14, is the configuration of points whose coordinates are given by the set $\{x_i, \mu_{Y|x_i}\}, i = 1, 2, , , m$. If the points lie on a straight line, we have *linear regression*. When this condition subsists,

$$\mu_{Y|x_i} = a + bx_i. \tag{15.17}$$

It is seen from Fig. 15-3 that linear regression does exist. Even if this condition should not exist, we can find the equation of the straight line that best fits the points of the graph. In other words, we can evaluate a and b of formula (15.17) for any given bivariate table, even if the fit is a bad one. For a perfect fit, the sum of the variances in formula (15.16) is zero, since $y = \mu_{Y|x_i}$; for a bad fit, the sum is relatively large.

The constants of the regression formula (15.17) are found as follows:
(1) Multiply formula (15.17) by $f(x_i)$ and sum from $i = 1$ to m. Then

$$\sum_{i=1}^{m} f(x_i)\mu_{Y|x_i} = a \sum_{i=1}^{m} f(x_i) + b \sum_{i=1}^{m} f(x_i)x_i$$

whence

$$\mu_Y = a + b\mu_X. \tag{15.18}$$

(2) Multiply formula (15.17) by $f(x_i)x_i$ and sum again. Then,

$$\sum_{i=1}^{m} f(x_i)x_i\mu_{Y\,|\,x_i} = a \sum_{i=1}^{m} f(x_i)x_i + b \sum_{i=1}^{m} f(x_i)x_i^2.$$

The left member, L, can be written:

$$L = \sum_{i=1}^{m} f(x_i)x_i \left[\sum_{j=1}^{n} (y_j \mid x_i) \frac{P(x_i, y_j)}{f(x_i)} \right]$$

where $(y_j \mid x_i)$ means y_j for a given x_i.

$$L = \sum_{i=1}^{m} x_i \left[\sum_{j=1}^{n} (y_j \mid x_i)P(x_i, y_j) \right]$$

$$= \sum_{i=1}^{m} \sum_{j=1}^{n} (y_j \mid x_i)x_i P(x_i, y_j)$$

$$= \sum_{i=1}^{m} \sum_{j=1}^{n} (x_i y_j)P(x_i, y_j) = \mu_{XY}.$$

The right member is

$$a\mu_X + b\mu_{X^2}. \tag{15.19}$$

Therefore,

$$\mu_{XY} = a\mu_X + b\mu_{X^2}.$$

Solving Eq. (15.18) and (15.19) for a and b, we obtain:

$$a = \frac{\mu_{X^2}\mu_Y - \mu_{XY}\mu_X}{\sigma_X^2} \tag{15.20a}$$

$$= \frac{E(X^2)E(Y) - E(XY)E(X)}{E(X - \mu_X)^2} \tag{15.20b}$$

and

$$b = \frac{\mu_{XY} - \mu_X\mu_Y}{\sigma_X^2} \tag{15.21a}$$

$$= \frac{E(XY) - E(X)E(Y)}{E(X - \mu_X)^2} \tag{15.21b}$$

$$= \frac{E(X - \mu_X)(Y - \mu_Y)}{E(X - \mu_X)^2}. \tag{15.21c}$$

EXAMPLE 1. Let us find the regression equation for the data of Table 15-15, that is, let us fit a regression line to the points of Fig. 15-2. We know from

Sections 5 and 6 of this chapter that

$$\mu_X = \frac{4}{5}, \qquad \mu_Y = \frac{8}{5}, \qquad \mu_{XY} = \frac{46}{25}$$

$$\sigma_X^2 = \frac{14}{25}, \qquad \sigma_{XY} = \frac{14}{25}, \qquad \mu_{X^2} = \frac{14}{25} + \left(\frac{4}{5}\right)^2 = \frac{6}{5}.$$

Therefore, by Eqs. (15.20a) and (15.21a),

$$a = \frac{4}{5}$$

$$b = 1,$$

and the equation of the regression line is:

$$y = \frac{4}{5} + x.$$

This agrees with the graph of Fig. 15-3.

EXAMPLE 2. Given the bivariate probability function (Table 15-17),

TABLE 15-17

y \ x	0	1	2	3	g(y)
0	0	0	0.1	0.2	0.3
1	0	0.2	0.1	0.2	0.5
2	0.1	0	0	0.1	0.2
f(x)	0.1	0.2	0.2	0.5	1

one can verify (exercise 18) that the regression function is given by Table 15-18, and its graph, by Fig. 15-4.

TABLE 15-18

x	0	1	2	3
r(x)	2	1	0.5	0.8

The graph suggests a curvilinear regression. Nevertheless, one could find the corresponding regression line. The equation of this line is (exercise 18):

$$y = 1.46 - 0.27x.$$

From Fig. 15-4, it appears that the line is a poor fit to the points.

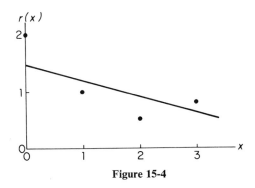

Figure 15-4

15.8. REMARK

Corresponding to the regression function of y on x and its allied concepts is the regression function of x on y, so that one can associate two regression functions and lines with a bivariate table.

15.9. CORRELATION

As in the preceding chapter, we find it advantageous to express the covariance in terms of standardized random variables,

$$Z_X = \frac{X - \mu_X}{\sigma_X} \quad \text{and} \quad Z_Y = \frac{Y - \mu_Y}{\sigma_Y} \tag{15.22}$$

and then to define the resulting expression as the coefficient of correlation, ρ. Then,

$$\rho = \sigma_{Z_X Z_Y} = E\left(\frac{X - \mu_X}{\sigma_X}\right)\left(\frac{Y - \mu_Y}{\sigma_Y}\right). \tag{15.23}$$

Alternative formulas for ρ are:

$$\rho = \frac{\mu_{XY} - \mu_X \mu_Y}{\sigma_X \sigma_Y} \tag{15.24}$$

$$= \frac{E(XY) - E(X)E(Y)}{\sigma_X \sigma_Y}.$$

One advantage of this change of variable becomes clear: the covariance of the nonstandardized variables varies with the magnitudes of X and Y. Now, with standardized variables, the correlation coefficient, ρ, has values independent of the sizes of X and Y.

A second advantage is that, in the case of linear dependence ($y = ax + b$), Eq. (15.23) becomes by virtue of (15.13) and (15.15),

$$\rho = \frac{\pm \sigma_X \sigma_Y}{\sigma_X \sigma_Y} = \pm 1.$$

Theorem 15.7. The possible values of ρ are restricted to the interval $-1 \leq \rho \leq +1$.

Proof.

$$\sigma^2_{Z_X \pm Z_Y} = \sigma^2_{Z_X} + \sigma^2_{Z_Y} + 2\sigma_{Z_X Z_Y}, \qquad \text{by (15.12a)}$$

Since

$$\sigma^2_{Z_X} = \sigma^2_{Z_Y} = 1 \quad \text{and} \quad \rho = \sigma_{Z_X Z_Y},$$

from (15.23),

$$\sigma^2_{Z_X \pm Z_Y} = 2 \pm 2\rho$$
$$= 2(1 \pm \rho).$$

A variance, such as that on the left, cannot be negative; therefore, ρ on the right cannot exceed 1 because of the minus sign, nor be less than -1 because of the plus sign. This proves the theorem.

EXAMPLE 1. From Table 15-4 and the example of Section 15.6, $\sigma_{XY} = \frac{14}{25}$, $\sigma^2_X = \frac{14}{25}$, and $\sigma^2_Y = \frac{28}{25}$; hence,

$$\rho = \frac{\sigma_{XY}}{\sigma_X \sigma_Y} = \frac{14/25}{(\sqrt{14}/5)(\sqrt{28}/5)} = \frac{\sqrt{2}}{2} = 0.707.$$

15.10. CORRELATION AND DEPENDENCE

To explain the manner in which the correlation coefficient measures the degree of dependence of one random variable on another, we shall exhibit three illustrations of a progressive character.

EXAMPLE 1. Let an unbiased coin be tossed twice. Let a tail be designated by 0 and a head by 1. Let X be the outcome on the first toss and Y the sum of the outcomes on the first and second tosses. The probability function appears in Table 15-19.

TABLE 15-19

x \ y	0	1	2	$f(x)$
0	$\frac{1}{4}$	$\frac{1}{4}$	0	$\frac{1}{2}$
1	0	$\frac{1}{4}$	$\frac{1}{4}$	$\frac{1}{2}$
$g(y)$	$\frac{1}{4}$	$\frac{1}{2}$	$\frac{1}{4}$	1

It may be verified that $\mu_X = \frac{1}{2}$, $\mu_Y = 1$, $\mu_{XY} = \frac{3}{4}$, $E(X^2) = \frac{1}{2}$, $E(Y^2) = \frac{3}{2}$, $\sigma_X = \frac{1}{2}$, and $\sigma_Y = \sqrt{2}/2$. It follows that:

$$\rho = \frac{3/4 - 1/2}{(1/2)(\sqrt{2}/2)} = \sqrt{2}/2 = 0.707.$$

EXAMPLE 2. Let the unbiased coin be tossed three times. Let X be the sum on the first two tosses and Y be the sum on all three tosses. From the sample space,

$$S = \{HHH, HHT, HTH, THH, HTT, THT, TTH, TTT\},$$

we obtain the pairs (x,y), namely,

$$(2,3),\ (2,2),\ (1,2),\ (1,2),\ (1,1),\ (1,1),\ (0,1),\ (0,0).$$

From this we construct Table 15-20.

TABLE 15-20

x \ y	0	1	2	3	$f(x)$
0	$\frac{1}{8}$	$\frac{1}{8}$	0	0	$\frac{1}{4}$
1	0	$\frac{1}{4}$	$\frac{1}{4}$	0	$\frac{1}{2}$
2	0	0	$\frac{1}{8}$	$\frac{1}{8}$	$\frac{1}{4}$
$g(y)$	$\frac{1}{8}$	$\frac{3}{8}$	$\frac{3}{8}$	$\frac{1}{8}$	1

The reader may verify (exercise 29) that $\mu_X = 1$, $\mu_Y = \frac{3}{2}$, $\mu_{XY} = 2$, $E(X^2) = \frac{3}{2}$, $E(Y^2) = 3$, $\sigma_X = \sqrt{2}/2$, and $\sigma_Y = \sqrt{3}/2$; whence,

$$\rho = \frac{2 - 3/2}{(\sqrt{2}/2)(\sqrt{3}/2)} = \sqrt{2/3} = 0.817.$$

EXAMPLE 3. We now assume that the coin is tossed four times. Let X be the sum on the first three tosses, and let Y be the sum on all four tosses. This leads to the sample space of 16 elements:

$$S = \{HHHH, HHHT, HHTH, HTHH, THHH, HHTT, HTHT, THHT,$$
$$HTTH, THTH, TTHH, TTTH, TTHT, THTT, HTTT, TTTT\}$$

and to Table 15-21.

TABLE 15-21

x \ y	0	1	2	3	4	$f(x)$
0	$\frac{1}{16}$	$\frac{1}{16}$	0	0	0	$\frac{1}{8}$
1	0	$\frac{3}{16}$	$\frac{3}{16}$	0	0	$\frac{3}{8}$
2	0	0	$\frac{3}{16}$	$\frac{3}{16}$	0	$\frac{3}{8}$
3	0	0	0	$\frac{1}{16}$	$\frac{1}{16}$	$\frac{1}{8}$
$g(y)$	$\frac{1}{16}$	$\frac{1}{4}$	$\frac{3}{8}$	$\frac{1}{4}$	$\frac{1}{16}$	1

$\mu_X = \frac{3}{2}$, $\mu_Y = 2$, $\mu_{XY} = \frac{15}{4}$, $E(X^2) = 3$, $E(Y^2) = 5$, $\sigma_X = \sqrt{3}/2$, and $\sigma_Y = 1$; whence $\rho = \sqrt{3}/2 = 0.866$.

It should be clear from these three examples that the sum y, produced by all the tosses, 2, 3, and 4 in number, is increasingly influenced by the first 1, 2, and 3 tosses, respectively. Accordingly, the value of ρ increases from 0.707 to 0.817 and then to 0.866. Moreover, the table shows an increasing diagonal trend of the probabilities. We recall that in Table 15-13, a single diagonal of nonzero probabilities produced a value of $\rho = \pm 1$.

The remarks following Theorem 15.2 called attention to the fact that, although independence of two random variables X and Y implies that $\mu_{XY} = \mu_X \mu_Y$, the converse is not necessarily true. Similarly, if $\mu_{XY} = \mu_X \mu_Y$, then in Eq. (15.24), $\rho = 0$; but this does not mean that uncorrelated variables are necessarily independent. Table 15-2 defines two random variables for which $\mu_{XY} = \mu_X \mu_Y$, that is, for which $\rho = 0$; and yet they are dependent variables since $Y = X^2$.

In statistics, as we shall see later, one is often interested in measuring the degree of association that exists between two (or more) variables. The weights of human beings seem to be associated in some degree with their heights; the size of a potato crop is dependent, at least partially on the amount of fertilizer used. This degree of association is measured often by the correlation coefficient ρ. It would seem that a bivariate population for which $\rho = 0$ indicates that no association or dependence exists between the two variables; but this is not necessarily true. If a linear relationship $Y = a + bX$ exists, then $\rho = 0$ does imply independence of X and Y. But for nonlinear relationships, it is possible to have $\rho = 0$ and yet have an intimate relationship exist between X and Y.

15.11. χ^2 AND ρ^2

The bivariate binomial table was conceived as a model for 2×2 tables to be subjected to a χ^2 test. In a similar manner, Table 15-5 may be thought of as a model for the $p \times q$ contingency table (Section 11.11). Table 15-5 is reproduced with a more suggestive notation as Table 15-22.

TABLE 15-22

	y_1	y_2	$\cdots$	y_n	
x_1	p_{11}	p_{12}	$\cdots$	p_{1n}	p_1
x_2	p_{21}	p_{22}	$\cdots$	p_{2n}	p_2
.	.	.	$\cdots$	.	.
.	.	.	$\cdots$	.	.
.	.	.	$\cdots$	.	.
x_m	p_{m1}	p_{m2}	$\cdots$	p_{mn}	p_m
	q_1	q_2	$\cdots$	q_n	1

An $m \times n$ table may be typified as Table 15-23.

TABLE 15-23

	y_1	y_2	$\cdots$	y_n	
x_1	a_{11}	a_{12}	$\cdots$	a_{1n}	a_{10}
x_2	a_{21}	a_{22}	$\cdots$	a_{2n}	a_{20}
.	.	.	$\cdots$	.	.
.	.	.	$\cdots$	.	.
.	.	.	$\cdots$	.	.
x_m	a_{m1}	a_{m2}	$\cdots$	a_{mn}	a_{m0}
	a_{01}	a_{02}	$\cdots$	a_{0n}	N

The estimates $a'_{ij} = \left(\dfrac{a_{i0}}{N}\right) a_{0j}$ $\qquad\qquad i = 1, 2, , , m$

$$j = 1, 2, , , n$$

so that

$$\chi^2 = \sum_{j=1}^{n} \sum_{i=1}^{m} \frac{(a_{ij} - a_{i0}a_{0j}/N)^2}{a_{i0}a_{0j}/N} \qquad \text{(Section 11.11)}$$

$$= N \sum_{j=1}^{n} \sum_{i=1}^{m} \frac{[a_{ij}/N - (a_{i0}/N)(a_{0j}/N)]^2}{(a_{i0}/N)(a_{0j}/N)}$$

$$= N \sum_{j=1}^{n} \sum_{i=1}^{m} \frac{(p'_{ij} - p'_i q'_j)^2}{p'_i q'_j}, \tag{15.25}$$

where the prime superscripts denote estimates.

Let us compare this value of χ^2 with ρ^2. In Eq. (15.24), we defined:

$$\rho = \frac{\mu_{XY} - \mu_X \mu_Y}{\sigma_X \sigma_Y}.$$

Assuming the variables to be numerically valued and standardized so that $\sigma_X = \sigma_Y = 1$,

$$\rho = \sum_{j=1}^{n} \sum_{i=1}^{m} p_{ij} x_i' y_j' - \left(\sum_{i=1}^{m} p_i x_i' \right) \left(\sum_{j=1}^{n} q_j' y_j' \right),$$

where x' and y' denote standardized variables. Then,

$$\rho = \sum_{j=1}^{n} \sum_{i=1}^{m} p_{ij} x_i' y_j' - \Sigma \Sigma \, p_i q_j x_i' y_j'$$

$$= \sum_{j=1}^{n} \sum_{i=1}^{m} (p_{ij} - p_i q_j) x_i' y_j'. \tag{15.26}$$

We cannot prove that χ^2 is approximately equal to ρ^2 as in the 2×2 table, but we do note the important similar factors $p_{ij}' - p_i' q_j'$ in Eq. (15.25) and $p_{ij} - p_i q_j$ in Eq. (15.26).

If we knew the probabilities p_{ij} for obtaining $x_i y_j$, we could employ the multinomial theorem (Section 11.1) to compute the probability for the mn $x_i y_j$'s to occur with the respective frequencies a_{ij} shown in Table 15-23, or with more unusual frequencies. Because such a computation would be exceedingly onerous, as stated in Section 11.2, we use the χ^2 distribution as an approximation. An example was given in Section 11.11.

In the 2×2 table discussed in the previous chapter, we defined (Section 14.2 and exercise 14.5):

$$\rho = \frac{p_{11} - p_1 p_2}{\sqrt{p_1 p_2 q_1 q_2}}.$$

If the variables were completely independent, then $p_{11} - p_1 p_2 = 0$ and $\rho = 0$. It follows, then, that the extent of dependence could be measured by the discrepancy between p_{11} and $p_1 p_2$. If we extend this inference to the $m \times n$ Table 15-22, it would seem that one (not necessarily the only one) measure of dependence would take account of the discrepancies between p_{ij} and $p_i p_j$; $i = 1, 2, , , m$; $j = 1, 2, , , n$. Since the positive and negative discrepancies cancel each other, $\Sigma \Sigma \, (p_{ij} - p_i p_j) = 0$ always (see exercise 30). For this reason, we use

$$N \, \Sigma \Sigma \, \frac{(p_{ij} - p_i p_j)^2}{p_i p_j} \tag{15.27}$$

as a measure of dependence or association, and designate it as a *coefficient of dependence*. It does not, however, have the desirable limits, -1 to $+1$, that ρ possesses. Various measures of association have been devised which make use of $\Sigma\Sigma(p_{ij} - p_ip_j)^2$. See, for example, Goodman, L. A., and Kruskal, W. H., *Measures of Association for Cross Classifications*, Journal of the American Statistical Association, Vol. 49, No. 268, Dec. 1954, pp. 732–764. Note that in formula (15.25) we have *estimated* probabilities, whereas in formula (15.27), we have *true* probabilities. Thus the latter formula is a model for the former.

EXERCISES

1. Given the bivariate probability function, $P(X, Y)$, defined by the following table:

x \ y	0	1	3	4
1	0.1	0.1	0	0.2
2	0.3	0	0.2	0.1

(a) Define the marginal probability functions.
(b) Find $P(Y = 3 \mid X = 2)$ and $P(X = 1 \mid Y = 0)$.
(c) Construct $g(Y \mid 1)$ and $f(X \mid 4)$.

2. Given the bivariate probability function, $P(X, Y)$, defined by the following table:

x \ y	0	5	10	15
5	$\frac{1}{24}$	$\frac{1}{8}$	$\frac{1}{12}$	$\frac{1}{12}$
10	$\frac{1}{12}$	$\frac{1}{4}$	$\frac{1}{6}$	$\frac{1}{6}$

(a) Define the marginal probability functions.
(b) Find $P(Y = 10 \mid X = 5)$ and $P(X = 5 \mid Y = 15)$.
(c) Construct $f(X \mid Y = 10)$ and $g(Y \mid X = 5)$.

3. An instructor gives only two types of grades in his quizzes: 2 (pass) and 0 (fail). In his nine o'clock class of 20 students, 15 pass and five fail; in his 2 o'clock class of 25 students, 20 pass and five fail. One student is chosen at random from each of the classes. Let X be the grade of the student chosen from the 9 o'clock class and Y, the sum of the grades of the two students chosen. (a) Make a joint probability table for X and Y together with the marginal probabilities. (b) Are X and Y independent? Why?

4. A die with four faces numbered 1 and two faces numbered 2, is rolled twice. Let X be the number showing on the first roll and let Y be the product of

the numbers showing on the two rolls. (a) Make a joint probability table for X and Y. (b) Determine the marginal probability functions. (c) Determine the conditional probability function of Y, given $X = 2$. (d) Are X and Y independent? Why?

5. Two pennies and a dime are tossed. Let a tail be denoted by 0 and a head by 1. Let X be the sum appearing on the two pennies, and let Y be the sum appearing on all three coins. (a) Make a joint probability table for the function $P(X,Y)$. (b) Define the marginal probability functions. (c) Find $g(Y\mid 1)$ and $f(X\mid 2)$. (d) Are X and Y independent? Why?

6. A club consists of three married couples, two spinsters, and two bachelors. A committee of two is to be chosen by lot. Let X be the number of women chosen, and Y be the number of single persons chosen. (a) Make a joint probability table. (b) Find the probability that just one woman who is also a spinster is included. (c) Find the probability that if just one woman is chosen, two single persons are chosen. (d) Find the probability that if no single person is selected, two women are.

7. Given the table of exercise 1, find the probability function of U when (a) $U = X + Y$; (b) $U = Y - X$.

8. Given the table of exercise 2, find the probability function of U when (a) $U = XY/5$; (b) $U = X + Y$.

9. Are X and Y independent in exercise 1? exercise 2? Why?

10. Find $E(XY)$ from the table of exercise 1.

11. Find $E(X + Y)$ from the table of exercise 2, in two different ways.

12. Find the covariance for Table 15-12.

13. Find the covariance from the table of exercise 1.

14. Find the covariance from the table of exercise 2.

15. Given the joint probability table:

x \ y	1	3	5
-1	$\frac{1}{4}$	0	0
0	0	$\frac{1}{2}$	0
1	0	0	$\frac{1}{4}$

Show that the covariance equals 1. Note that $Y = 2X + 3$.

16. Find the regression function of Y on X for (a) Table 15-12; (b) the table of exercise 1.

17. Find the equation of the regression line of Y on X for (a) Table 15-12; (b) the table of exercise 1.

18. Verify (a) the regression function, and (b) the equation of the regression line given in example 2 of Section 15.7.

19. Given the table:

y \ x	0	1	2	3
1	0.1	0	0.1	0
2	0	0.2	0	0.1
3	0.2	0	0.3	0

(a) Find the regression function of Y on X. (b) Find the equation of the regression line of Y on X. (c) Plot the graph of the bivariate function. (d) Construct the regression line found in (b) on the graph of (c). (e) Compute ρ.

20. Verify Theorem 15.5 by applying it to the variables of exercise 2.

Compute ρ for the following:

21. Exercise 1.   22. Exercise 2.   23. Exercise 4.

24. Exercise 6.   25. Exercise 15.   26. Exercise 19.

27. Complete the proof of Theorem 15.1a.

28. Prove Theorem 15.5a by following the suggestions given in the outline of the proof of Theorem 15.1a.

29. Verify the results given in example 2 of Section 15.10.

30. Prove that $\sum_{j=1}^{n} \sum_{i=1}^{m} (p_{ij} - p_i p_j) = 0.$

16

Estimation

16.1. INTRODUCTION

A professor of statistics who wished to introduce the material of this chapter used to begin by inquiring of his class, "How old do you think I am?" Before receiving their replies he assured the students that no reprisals would ensue if their guesses exceeded his age. The replies were invariably in the form "52 years," "49 years;" "58 years;" and so on. Each guess was always an "all or nothing" guess, that is to say, each answer was always given as an exact number of years and was either right or wrong. If it was wrong, there was no way of knowing how much it was in error. Such "all or nothing" estimates are called *point estimates* in statistics.

The professor next asked his students if there wasn't some other way of guessing his age so that limits could be placed on his probable age. Usually this type of response followed. "You are between 50 and 55;" "You are between 45 and 55;" "You are between 40 and 60;" and so forth. Now the estimates of his age took the form of intervals. In the case of the teacher and the guess of 40 to 60 years, the answer was felt to be almost surely correct and the students were willing to place heavy odds on a bet that this was a correct statement. As for the first guess, 50 to 55, there was a distinct drop in the degree of confidence in the estimate—appearances are deceptive and young people are not usually expert in estimating the ages of older people. This second type of estimate is called an *interval estimate*. In statistics, it has the advantage that the interval can be adjusted, that is, widened or narrowed, with a corresponding increase or reduction in the confidence of being correct. For this reason, we shall speak of the *confidence interval* as a method of statistical estimation. Both types of estimates are in common use and each has its special advantages.

16.2. THE POINT ESTIMATE

We shall first consider point estimates that are *unbiased*. More precisely, we state the following definition:

The statistic $\hat{\theta}$ is an unbiased estimator of the parameter θ if $E(\hat{\theta}) = \theta$.

Briefly, this means that if repeated samplings of the same population took place and the statistic $\hat{\theta}$ were computed each time, the mean of the $\hat{\theta}$'s would tend toward the parameter θ. Some estimates have a tendency to be biased—to be either too large or too small. There are estimates other than unbiased ones, and these are mentioned briefly in Section 16.11.

The word *estimator* refers to the function, and *estimate*, to a particular value of the function. To designate an estimator of a parameter, we place a circumflex accent above the symbol for the parameter.

16.3. THE EXPECTED VALUE OF A
   SAMPLE MEAN

Given a sample mean $\bar{x}$, what is the best estimate one can make of the mean, μ, of the population from which the sample is drawn? Since we lack other information, our intuition leads us to conclude that $\bar{x}$ is the best estimator of μ. Furthermore, the larger the sample size is, the greater our faith in the accuracy of this estimate.

Theorem 16.1. *Let x_1, x_2, , , x_N, be N values randomly drawn with replacement from a population characterized by a probability function, $f(X)$, of a discrete variable, and let $\bar{x} = 1/N \sum_{i=1}^{N} x_i$. Then*

$$E(\bar{X}) = E(X), \quad \text{that is,} \quad \mu_{\bar{X}} = \mu_X. \tag{16.1}$$

This is the same as the corollary to Theorem 15.1a. See also Theorem 15.1b.

16.4. THE EXPECTED VALUE OF p

Let p be the proportion of individuals having a given characteristic in a finite population, and let a random sample of N be drawn with replacement from it. If x individuals out of N are found to possess the given characteristic, then x/N would seem to be the best estimate that we could make of p. This intuition can be proved to be correct.

Theorem 16.2. If X is the number of individuals possessing a given characteristic in a random sample of N drawn with replacement from a finite population in which p is the proportion of individuals possessing this characteristic, then X/N is an unbiased estimator of p.

Proof.

$$E(X/N) = \left(\frac{1}{N}\right) E(X)$$

$$= \left(\frac{1}{N}\right) \cdot Np = p \qquad \text{by Eq. (8.6)}$$

hence,

$$\hat{p} = \frac{X}{N} . \tag{16.2}$$

In the case of a continuously distributed random variable with probability density function $f(t)$ (Section 9.6), the true proportion of individuals having values lying between t_1 and t_2 is given by $\int_{t_1}^{t_2} f(t)\, dt$. We use the variable t here to distinguish it from the X of the theorem which has positive integral values only. For example, p might be the proportion of adult American males with statures between 70 and 72 inches.

16.5. THE UNBIASED ESTIMATE OF σ^2

Following the discussion of the preceding two sections, one might guess that an unbiased estimator of the population variance σ^2, is s^2, where $s^2 = (1/N) \Sigma (X - \bar{X})^2$. If N is large, this guess is close to the truth; but if N is small, a serious error might be committed. The explanation is not difficult to follow. By Exercise 26, the sum of the squares of the deviations of the sample values from their own mean, $\bar{x}$, will be smaller than the sum of the squares of the deviations from the true mean, μ. Thus s^2 tends to be smaller than σ^2. If N is large, $\bar{x}$ is probably very close to μ so that the bias is negligibly small.

Theorem 16.3. *An unbiased estimator of the population variance* σ^2, *is given by the formula:*

$$\hat{\sigma}^2 = \frac{1}{N-1} \Sigma (X - \overline{X})^2 \qquad (16.3)$$

or

$$= \frac{Ns^2}{N-1} \qquad (16.4)$$

Proof. Since

$$s^2 = \frac{1}{N} \sum_{i=1}^{N} x_i^2 - \bar{x}^2,$$

$$E(s^2) = E\left[\frac{1}{N} \sum_{i=1}^{N} X_i^2\right] - E(\overline{X}^2).$$

Note that the *i*th variate, x_i, arising in a sample may be treated as a random variable, X_i, and that

$$E(X_i) = E(X_j) = E(X)$$

Also,

$$E(X_i^2) = E(X_j^2) = E(X^2).$$

In what follows, we shall use ΣX_i in place of $\sum_{i=1}^{N} X_i$. Then

$$E(s^2) = \frac{1}{N} N \cdot E(X^2) - E\left(\frac{1}{N} \Sigma X_i\right)^2$$

$$= E(X^2) - \frac{1}{N^2} E\left[\Sigma X_i^2 + \sum_{i \neq j} X_i X_j\right]$$

$$= E(X^2) - \frac{1}{N^2} \Sigma (X_i^2) - \frac{1}{N^2} \sum_{i \neq j} [E(X_i X_j)].$$

Since X_i and X_j are independent, $E(X_i X_j) = E(X_i)E(X_j) = \mu^2$; therefore,

$$E(s^2) = E(X^2) - \frac{N}{N^2} E(X^2) - \frac{N(N-1)}{N^2} E(X_i)E(X_j),$$

since there are N terms of the form $E(X_i^2)$ and $N!/(N-2)!$ of the form $E(X_i X_j)$, $i \neq j$. Then

$$E(s^2) = E(X^2) - \frac{1}{N} E(X^2) - \frac{N-1}{N} \mu^2$$

But

$$E(X^2) = \sigma^2 + \mu^2, \qquad \text{(by Eq. 7.14b)}$$

therefore,

$$E(s^2) = \frac{N-1}{N}(\sigma^2 + \mu^2) - \frac{N-1}{N}\mu^2$$

$$= \frac{N-1}{N}\sigma^2.$$

It follows that

$$E\left(\frac{Ns^2}{N-1}\right) = \sigma^2,$$

that is

$$\hat{\sigma}^2 = \frac{Ns^2}{N-1}$$

$$= \frac{1}{N-1}\Sigma(X_i - \bar{X})^2.$$

Since s^2 tends to be too small, the replacement of N by $N-1$ in the denominator of the formula for s^2 offsets this bias. Because of the foregoing facts, some statisticians prefer to define the sample variance as in Eq. (16.3). In consulting other books and papers in statistics, the reader should take care to note what definition of s^2 is used.

We may also prove by formula (16.4) that an unbiased estimator of the variance of the mean:

$$\hat{\sigma}_{\bar{x}}^2 = \frac{\hat{\sigma}_x^2}{N} \tag{16.5}$$

$$= \frac{s^2}{N-1}. \tag{16.6}$$

If N is large, the replacement by $N-1$ is a negligible improvement. If N is small, this replacement is important. Small-sample theory and large-sample theory are generally different.

The symbol, $\hat{\sigma}^2$, is not to be construed as $(\hat{\sigma})^2$, because it does not follow from Eq. (16.3) that an unbiased estimator of the standard deviation,

$$\hat{\sigma} = \left[\frac{1}{N-1}\Sigma(X - \bar{X})^2\right]^{1/2},$$

although it is frequently used as such. Unfortunately, the reason for this seeming paradox cannot be stated here. Suffice it to say that the probability density functions of s^2 and s are unlike.

If two samples of N_x and N_y are assumed to be drawn from the same population and yield variances s_x^2 and s_y^2, respectively, it can also be proved that a useful unbiased estimator of the population variance, σ^2, is obtained by pooling the two sample variances. The formula is in fact the following:

$$\hat{\sigma}^2 = \frac{N_x s_x^2 + N_y s_y^2}{N_x + N_y - 2} . \tag{16.7}$$

This result can be generalized for k samples, so that

$$\hat{\sigma}^2 = \frac{\sum\limits_{i=1}^{k} N_i s_i^2}{\sum\limits_{i=1}^{k} N_i - k} . \tag{16.8}$$

The results of this section also hold for the continuous case.

16.6. CONFIDENCE LIMITS FOR μ

Suppose that a random sample of N has been drawn from a normal population with unknown mean, μ, and unknown variance, σ^2. From the information, N, $\bar{x}$, and s, contained in the sample, we wish to estimate the value of μ. If we made a point estimate of this value, we should choose $\bar{x}$; but we should have no way of knowing how good this estimate might be. Instead, we shall calculate a *confidence interval* within which, it will be stated, μ lies. A measurable degree of confidence will be associated with this statement. The reason that we cannot make a probability statement about μ is that μ is not a chance variable; it is a constant, fixed, but unknown. Probability statements are always associated with chance or random variables.

To illustrate the method, let us suppose that a random sample of 26 electric light bulbs shows a mean length of life of 1000 hours and a standard deviation of 200 hours. We seek the 95% confidence limits for μ, the mean life of the lot of bulbs from which this sample was drawn.

If the lives of bulbs are assumed to be normally distributed, we may employ the Student-Fisher t-variable defined in formula (13.11). From Table F, when $n = 25$ and $P = 0.025$, $t = +2.06$ (Fig. 16-1). Thus we may determine 95% confidence limits for μ as follows:

For $t = +2.06$ and the given data, formula (13.11) becomes

$$\pm 2.06 = \frac{(1000 - \mu)\sqrt{25}}{200} .$$

Solving for μ, we have for the plus sign $\mu = 918$ and for the minus sign $\mu = 1082$. We now make the following statement: $918 < \mu < 1082$. This statement may be wrong, because the sample might be unusual in its mean or in its standard deviation or in both. In such a case, the value of t would deviate abnormally from its mean, $\mu_t = 0$, and the limits for μ based upon

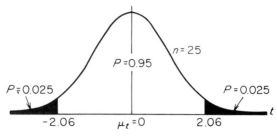

Figure 16-1

this value would be incorrect. On the other hand, if the sample exhibits only the usual fluctuations (say those occurring 95% of the time), then the double inequality will be correct. We now assert the following (see Fig. 16-1):

(1) For a sample of 26, there is a probability of 0.95 that

$$-2.06 < t < 2.06,$$

(2) and there is a probability of 0.95 that

$$-2.06 < \frac{(\bar{x} - \mu)\sqrt{25}}{s} < 2.06$$

or that

(3) $$-0.412s < \bar{x} - \mu < 0.412s.$$

This implies that 95% of the time,

(4) $$\mu - 0.412s < \bar{x} < \mu + 0.412s.$$

If a given $\bar{x}$ does lie in such an interval (lower portion of Fig. 16-2), then by virtue of (4), μ lies in the interval

$$\bar{x} - 0.412s \quad \text{to} \quad x + 0.412s,$$

(upper portion of Fig. 16-2). But if a given $\bar{x}$ does *not* lie in this interval

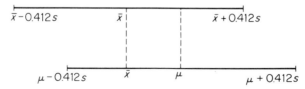

Figure 16-2

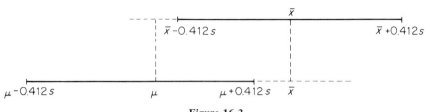

Figure 16-3

(Fig. 16-3) and this happens in 5% of the samples, then μ does not lie in the interval defined above.

In the illustrative problem, $N = 26$, $\bar{x} = 1000$, and $s = 200$; hence μ lies in the interval

$$1000 - (0.412 \times 200) \quad \text{to} \quad 1000 + (0.412 \times 200)$$

that is,

$$918 < \mu < 1082.$$

In words, then, we state that the mean length of life of the entire lot of bulbs lies between 918 and 1082 hours. Statements such as this will be correct 95% of the time and incorrect 5% of the time. This means that, under the same conditions, repeated samplings of 26, leading to repeated inequality statements, would produce 95% correct statements because 95% of the time the sample means would lie within $0.412s$ of the population mean. Of course, any confidence interval other than one for 95% may be used. Clearly, the higher the confidence level, the wider the confidence interval, and the lower the confidence level, the narrower the interval.

A general formula for confidence limits for μ is

$$\bar{x} - \frac{s}{\sqrt{N-1}}\, t_{\alpha/2} < \mu < \bar{x} + \frac{s}{\sqrt{N-1}}\, t_{\alpha/2}, \tag{16.9}$$

where $t_{\alpha/2}$ is the right-tail value of t corresponding to $100(1 - \alpha)\%$ of confidence.

16.7. CONFIDENCE LIMITS FOR $\mu_x - \mu_y$

Given two normal populations from which samples of N_x and N_y have been drawn, with means $\bar{x}$ and $\bar{y}$ and variances s_x^2 and s_y^2 respectively, confidence limits can be computed for $\mu_x - \mu_y$ in the following manner. In formula (16.9), replace $\bar{x}$ by $\bar{x} - \bar{y}$, $(s/\sqrt{N-1})$ by the denominator of formula (13.13), and μ by $\mu_x - \mu_y$.

16.8. CONFIDENCE INTERVALS AND TESTS OF HYPOTHESES

One advantage derived from the use of confidence intervals is that, in addition to making estimates, they can be used to test hypotheses concerning unknown parameters. A confidence interval can be treated as an acceptance region for the hypothesis.

> EXAMPLE 1. Let us refer to the data of Section 16.6 and test the hypothesis that the mean length of life of the lot of bulbs is 950 hours, against the alternative that it is not. Using $\alpha = 0.05$ to correspond to 95% limits, we note that $\mu = 950$ lies within the interval $918 < \mu < 1082$ already found. The hypothetical value, 950, is, therefore, consistent with this interval estimate based on the sample data.

> EXAMPLE 2. (A one-sided confidence interval). A random sample of 17 pieces of thread is selected from a shipment and has a mean breaking strength of 17.4 ounces and a standard deviation of 2.13 ounces. With $\alpha = 0.05$, test the hypothesis that μ for the shipment is at least 18 ounces.
> Here $N - 1 = 16$, $\bar{x} = 17.4$, $s = 2.13$, and $t = -1.746$. Therefore
>
> $$-1.746 = \frac{(17.4 - \mu)\sqrt{16}}{2.13}$$

whence $\mu = 18.3$. Thus the upper limit for μ is estimated to be 18.3 ounces. Our hypothesis that μ is at least 18 is consistent with this estimate.

16.9. CONFIDENCE LIMITS FOR p

Example. A pre-election poll is taken in a town by means of a carefully selected sample of 50 voters. Of these, 40% declare that they will vote for Bill Jones to be Mayor. Find the 90% confidence interval for the proportion in the town who will vote for Jones.

From Eq. (12.5),

$$\pm z = \frac{p_1 \mp \dfrac{1}{2N} - p}{\left[\dfrac{p(1-p)}{N}\right]^{1/2}} \; ; \qquad \textbf{(16.10)}$$

Hence,

$$\pm 1.645 = \frac{0.4 \mp 0.01 - p}{\left[\dfrac{p(1-p)}{50}\right]^{1/2}} \qquad \textbf{(16.11)}$$

where the upper signs are used for the lower confidence limit and the lower signs are used for the upper one. By squaring and simplifying Eq. (16.11), we obtain the quadratic equations:

$$1.0541p^2 - 0.8341p + 0.1521 = 0, \quad \text{(upper signs)} \qquad \textbf{(16.12)}$$

$$1.0541p^2 - 0.8741p + 0.1681 = 0, \quad \text{(lower signs)} \qquad \textbf{(16.13)}$$

with roots 0.505 and 0.285 for the first equation and 0.526 and 0.302 for the second. Since Eq. (16.12) is not equivalent to Eq. (16.11) with the upper sign, we find that only the root, 0.285, satisfies the latter. Similarly, only the root, 0.526, satisfies Eq. (16.11) with the lower sign. Then the 90% confidence interval is defined by the double inequality $0.285 < p < 0.526$.

A simplification of the computational labor can be obtained by following this working rule:

When N is large or when $0.3 < p_1 < 0.7$, we may derive a good approximation to the confidence limits by replacing $p(1 - p)$ in the denominator of Eq. (16.10) by $p_1(1 - p_1)$.

If we use this approximation, we have:

$$\pm 1.645 = \frac{0.40 \mp 0.01 - p}{\left[\dfrac{(0.40 \times 0.60)}{50} \right]^{1/2}},$$

whence for the upper signs, $p = 0.276$, and for the lower signs $p = 0.524$. Then $0.276 < p < 0.524$.

There is no practical difference between the answers obtained by these two methods; hence, the shorter one is recommended when the appropriate conditions are met. Observe also that, even if we have unbounded faith in the representativeness of the sample and the veracity of the sampled voters, a prediction that the vote for Jones will be between 0.28 and 0.52 of the total vote cast will not enable us to decide, with 90% confidence, the outcome of the election. If, however, we reduce our confidence level to 80% ($z = \pm 1.282$), then we may state that $0.30 < p < 0.50$. Thus our prediction is that Jones will be defeated; but our confidence in this prediction is at a lower level.

The calculations of this section can be avoided if we refer to charts showing "Confidence Belts for p." These appear in a paper by C. J. Clopper and E. S. Pearson, "The Use of Confidence or Fiducial Limits Illustrated in the Case of the Binomial," *Biometrika*, Volume 26 (1934), pages 410 and 411. Table H in the Appendix reproduces such a chart for a confidence coefficient of 0.95. From this chart, one can find readily the 95% confidence interval for the Jones vote to be $0.27 < p < 0.55$. One may also find confidence limits for p from the tables of Mainland, Herrera, and Sutcliffe (Reference 19).

16.10. CONFIDENCE LIMITS FOR σ^2

Given a sample of N with variance s^2, one can establish confidence limits for the population variance σ^2. This is done by means of the Chi-square distribution (Section 11.12).

16.11. PROPERTIES OF POINT ESTIMATES

In Section 16.2 we defined an unbiased estimate of a parameter. An unbiased estimator, $\hat{\theta}$, may occasionally deviate considerably from θ. therefore, we take into consideration its variability with respect to θ measured in terms of the variance. A desirable property, then, of an estimator, $\hat{\theta}$, is that its variance should be as small as possible; in other words, it should be *efficient*.

The statistic $\hat{\theta}$ is an efficient estimator of the parameter θ if the variance of $\hat{\theta}$ is not greater than the variance of any other estimator of θ.

The concept of the *relative efficiency* of two estimates is an important one, especially in many practical applications.

The efficiency of an unbiased estimate $\hat{\theta}'$ relative to some other unbiased estimate $\hat{\theta}$ is defined as the ratio of $\sigma_{\hat{\theta}}^2$ to $\sigma_{\hat{\theta}'}^2$.

For example, the mean $\bar{x}$ and the median x_m are both measures of central tendency. To compare their efficiencies as estimates of the population mean μ, we divide $\sigma_{\bar{x}}^2$ by $\sigma_{x_m}^2$. In the case of a normal population and a sample of 10, it has been shown that this quotient is about 0.72. Thus the efficiency of the median x_m, is 0.72 relative to that of the mean $\bar{x}$, for samples of 10. This means that the accuracy of the estimate of μ from the median of a sample of 100 is approximately the same as that from the mean of a sample of 72. Thus fewer observations are necessary for efficient estimators than for less efficient ones.

It can be proved that the sample mean, $\bar{x}$, is an unbiased and efficient estimator, of μ, and that the sample variance,

$$s^2 = \frac{1}{N} \sum_{i=1}^{N} (x_i - \bar{x})^2,$$

provides a biased estimate of σ^2.

However,

$$\frac{N}{N-1} s^2 \quad \text{or} \quad \frac{1}{N-1} \sum_{i=1}^{N} (x_i - \bar{x})^2$$

is unbiased. The latter is an efficient but not exactly the "most efficient" estimate of σ^2, for its efficiency can be shown to be $(N-1)/N$, which approaches 1 (100%) as N becomes larger and larger. The estimate $\frac{1}{N} \Sigma (x - \mu)^2$ has a smaller variance than $\frac{1}{N-1} \Sigma (x - \bar{x})^2$, but it is biased.

EXERCISES

1. In exercise 9.2, the mean blood pressure of the 278 males is 130.7. In exercise 9.3, the mean weight of the 100 aspirin tablets is 4.90 gr. What is an unbiased estimate of (a) the mean blood pressure of the population of healthy adult males? (b) the mean weight of all aspirin tablets manufactured by the same source. (c) Which of these two estimates is likely to be more accurate? Why?

2. The reading rates (story-book reading) of ten junior high school pupils before and after remedial work showed means of 218 and 257 words per minute, respectively. Make a point estimate of the mean gain in rate to be expected from similar work in the future.

3. Assume that random samples of 80 men voters and 60 women voters in a village showed 50 men and 40 women registered as Republicans. Make a point estimate of the percentage in the village of (a) male Republicans; (b) female Republicans; (c) Republicans.

4. The mean mileage obtained from a sample of 17 automobile tires of a taxicab company was 28,000 with $s = 1800$. Find the 90% confidence interval for the mean life of tires used by this company.

5. Twenty-six typical army recruits have a mean pulse rate of 71.2 beats per minute with a variance of 83.4. Find the 95% confidence limits for the mean pulse rate of recruits in general. What does your answer mean?

6. If the mean age at death of 64 men engaged in a somewhat hazardous occupation is 52.4 years with a standard deviation of 10.2 years, what are the 98% confidence limits for the mean age of all men so engaged?

7. A random sample of 15 capsules of a halibut liver oil product was tested for Vitamin A content. The mean amount (in 1000 international units per gram) was found to be 23.4 with a standard deviation of 8.50. Find the 90% confidence interval for μ.

8. A sample of 17 shows a product to have a mean per cent of purity of 91.3 with $s = 1.43$. What are the 95% confidence limits for the mean per cent of purity of the population?

9. A special aptitude test was given to 26 law school freshmen. The results showed a mean score of 82.0 and a variance of 49.00. Set up the 90% confidence interval for the mean score of all law school freshmen.

10. After a fixed dose of a certain drug had been administered to 17 selected students, it was found that their pulse rates increased by the following amounts:

13, 15, 14, 10, 8, 12, 15, 9, 18, 10, 16, 11, 7, 15, 13, 16, 11.

In general, pulse rates of students increase by 10 for the same dose. Is the mean increase in this group significantly greater than the mean for all students in general? Solve by two methods, one of which requires finding 95% confidence limits for μ.

11. In exercise 13.24, find the one-sided 95% confidence interval for the mean time required when *all* workers are given the special training. Does the given population mean, 36 seconds, lie above the upper limit of this interval? What does your answer indicate?

12. In exercise 13.25, find the 95% confidence interval for μ and use it to test the hypothesis stated.

13. In exercise 13.33, calculate the 95% confidence limits for $\mu_x - \mu_y$, where μ_x is the population mean I.Q. of the second school, and μ_y, that of the first school.

14. In exercise 13.35, construct a 90% confidence interval for $\mu_y - \mu_x$ based on the data given for the two samples. By means of it, test the hypothesis H_0: $\mu_y - \mu_x = 0$.

15. The scores, x, of 63 seniors on a Graduate Record Examination showed $\Sigma x = 34,540$ and $\Sigma x^2 = 19,480,000$. Calculate the unbiased estimate of the population variance of scores. What is your estimate of σ?

16. (a) A sample of 26 has a variance, $s^2 = 2.50$. What is an unbiased estimate of σ^2? (b) If two samples, sized 10 and 15, are drawn from the same population and have variances of 2.40 and 2.70 respectively, what is an unbiased estimate of the population variance?

17. Three samples, sized 10, 20, and 30, are drawn from populations having the same variance, σ^2, and show variances of 12.3, 14.5, and 11.2, respectively. Find an unbiased estimate of σ^2.

18. We know that the variable, Z, where $Z = (\bar{X} - \mu)/\sqrt{N}/\sigma$, has, in general, a normal distribution. If you did not know σ but did know s, and replaced σ by its approximate point estimate $\sqrt{\hat{\sigma}^2}$, what kind of a variable would Z become?

19. Assume that, in testing the hypothesis, $\mu_x = \mu_y$, we did not know anything about σ_x^2 and σ_y^2 except that they were equal. Replace the numerators of the denominator of Eq. (13.10) by the unbiased estimate of the common variance σ^2. What familiar formula do you obtain?

20. Prove that when the N's are large, say $N_x + N_y - 2 > 100$, so that $N_x + N_y - 2 = N_x + N_y$ approximately, the estimated variance of the difference of two means given by the denominator of formula (13.13) may be expressed approximately by

$$\sigma^2_{\bar{x} - \bar{y}} = \frac{s_x^2}{N_y} + \frac{s_y^2}{N_x}.$$

21. The percentage of purity of a medical preparation was tested by means of five samples of ten vials each and produced the following data. Estimate the standard deviation of the population.

Sample	s^2
1	2.72
2	2.13
3	2.45
4	3.06
5	2.31

22. From a lot of capsules the contents of five samples of four each were weighed in milligrams. The results follow:

Sample No.	1	2	3	4	5
	62.3	61.9	63.1	62.5	62.5
	62.0	61.8	61.9	62.3	62.1
	62.9	62.0	61.9	62.5	61.8
	62.8	62.2	62.6	61.6	62.9

Calculate the variance of each sample and from these variances estimate the population (lot) variance.

23. If 180 manufactured items were found to have 40 defective, what are the 95% confidence limits for the percentage defective in the population from which the 180 were selected? Use the tables described in Reference 19.

24. In a group of 28 patients, 19 reported immediate improvement upon use of a given drug. Find the 95% confidence limits for the percentage of such patients expected to improve. Use the tables described in Reference 19.

25. It has been proved that $\sigma_p^2 = pq/N$ (Section 12.1). If we replace p by X/N and q by $(N - X)/N$, would $s_p^2 = X(N - X)/N^2$ be an unbiased estimator of σ_p^2? Prove that $\hat{\sigma}_p^2 = (N/N - 1)s_p^2$.

26. Write $\Sigma (x - x_0)^2 = \Sigma [(x - \bar{x}) + (\bar{x} - x_0)]^2$. Expand the right member as a binomial, apply Theorem 6.4, and show that

$$\Sigma (x - x_0)^2 = \Sigma (x - \bar{x}^2) + \Sigma (\bar{x} - x_0)^2.$$

Thus a single sum of squares has been expressed as the sum of two sums of squares. Now show that $\Sigma (x - x_0)^2$ is a minimum when $x_0 = \bar{x}$.

17

Line Fitting: Regression

An equation is the most serious and important thing in mathematics.

Sir Oliver Lodge
Easy Mathematics, 1906

17.1. INTRODUCTION

The accompanying graphs exhibit markedly different configurations of plotted points. In Fig. 17-1, the points appear to lie fairly well along a straight line; in Fig. 17-2, they appear to lie on or near a curve known as a parabola; and in Fig. 17-3, they do not appear to lie along any recognizable curve. Configurations of plotted points may or may not indicate trends or relationships in the data from which they arise. It is often the duty of the statistician to discover and to measure such trends or relationships when they exist. This means that he must solve a problem in curve fitting.

In this chapter, we are concerned with the limited but important problem of fitting a straight line to data involving a finite number of paired values. Statistical problems centered about curve fitting may be resolved into three parts.

(1) *The statistician must decide what kind of curve to fit to the data.*
(2) *The statistician must calculate the constants involved in the equation of the curve selected to fit the data.* This equation is usually written in the form $y = f(x)$, where $f(x)$ is some function of x.

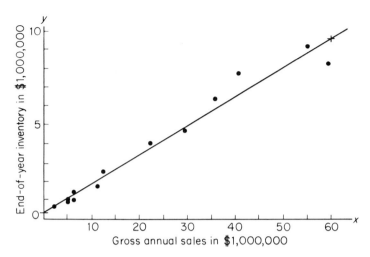

Fig. 17-1. End-of-year inventory and gross annual sales of 13 U.S. drug store chains for 1954. (*American Druggist*, May 9, 1955, p. 12.)

For example, the first-degree equation:

$$y = a + bx \qquad\qquad (17.1)$$

defines a straight line. If we selected this equation as the one best fitting the data of Fig. 17-1, it would be necessary to calculate the values of the parameters a and b which characterize the particular straight line we seek.

(3) *The statistician may interpret the results by means of explanations, estimates, and predictions.*

17.2. THE STRAIGHT LINE

Equation (17.1) is an equation of the first degree in x and y. It can be proved to define a straight line. For this reason it is called a *linear equation*. The point (x_i, y_i) lies on the line, (17.1) if, and only if, its coordinates satisfy the equation of the line, that is, if

$$y_i = a + bx_i,$$

or

$$y_i - (a + bx_i) = 0.$$

When $x = 0$, $y = a$; hence, the line crosses the y-axis at a units from the origin, O (Fig. 17-4). a is called the *y-intercept* of the line (17.1).

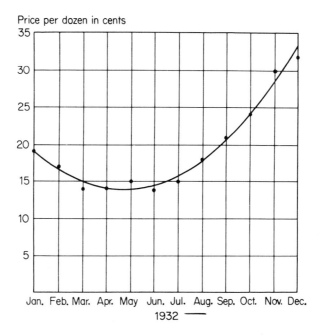

Fig. 17-2. Average wholesale price per dozen of eggs, Boston, 1932.

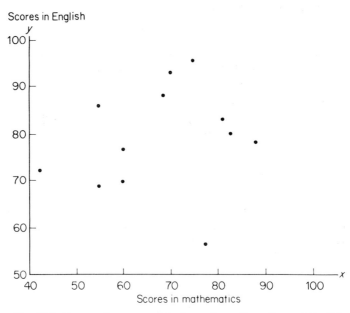

Fig. 17-3. Scores of a group of freshmen in mathematics and English.

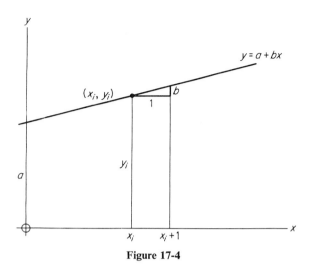

Figure 17-4

From Fig. 17-4, we can find a simple but significant meaning for the parameter b. For every unit increase in x, y changes by b units; thus b measures the steepness of the line and, for this reason, is called its *slope*. b is also termed the *regression coefficient*. When b is positive, the line ascends from left to right; when b is negative, the line descends from left to right.

17.3. THE METHOD OF LEAST SQUARES

The selection of a straight line rather than some other curve to fit a set of points is usually made upon the basis of the appearance of the plotted points themselves. One would not hesitate to select a straight line for those of Fig. 17-1. There are, however, occasions when we desire to find best-fitting straight lines for points such as those of Fig. 17-3.

"Fitting a straight line" usually means finding the values of the parameters a and b of the straight line (17.1) as well as actually constructing the line itself. The *least squares* method assumes that the best-fitting line is the one for which the sum of the squares of the vertical distances of the points (x_i, y_i) from the line is a minimum. It is in very common use and possesses the advantage that it is applicable to more general cases.

If

$$y = a + bx \tag{17.2}$$

is the equation of this line, we can find the ordinate of any point, Q_i, on the line vertically above or below a given point, P_i, by substituting the abscissa, x_i, in the right-hand member. The two coordinates of Q_i will be $(x_i, a + bx_i)$

(Fig. 17-5). The vertical distance, e_i from the line of any point P_i with coordinates (x_i, y_i) will therefore be given by the equation:

$$e_i = y_i - (a + bx_i). \qquad (17.3)$$

We may say that e_i represents the difference between the *actual* ordinate, y_i, of a point and its *theoretical* ordinate, $a + bx_i$. The quantity e_i is often called a *residual* or *error*. It may be positive or negative.

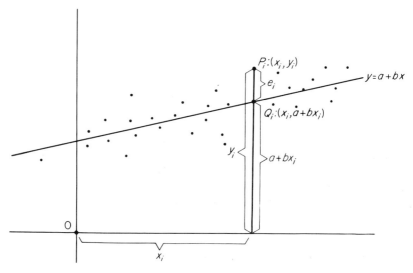

Figure 17-5

The best-fitting line is that line for which the sum of the squares, $\Sigma\, e_i^2$, is a minimum. Our problem is to find the values of a and b which make $\Sigma\, e_i^2$ a minimum. It will be shown in Section 17.5 that these values are given by the formulas,

$$a = \frac{\Sigma\, x_i^2\, \Sigma\, y_i - \Sigma\, x_i\, \Sigma\, x_i y_i}{N\, \Sigma\, x_i^2 - (\Sigma\, x_i)^2} \qquad (17.4)$$

$$= \bar{y} - b\bar{x}, \qquad (17.5)$$

$$b = \frac{N\, \Sigma\, x_i y_i - \Sigma\, x_i\, \Sigma\, y_i}{N\, \Sigma\, x_i^2 - (\Sigma\, x_i)^2}, \qquad (17.6)$$

where N is the number of points (x_i, y_i). Note the analogy between formulas (17.4), (17.6), and (15.20b), (15.21b).

It will be useful here to prove that formula (17.4) is equivalent to formula (17.5). To do this let us substitute $\bar{x}$ for x in Eq. (17.2) and see what the corresponding value of y is. First let us note that the common denominator of formulas (17.4) and (17.6) is

$$N \sum x^2 - (\sum x)^2 = N^2 s_x^2. \qquad (17.7)$$

If

$$y = a + b\bar{x}$$

then by formulas (17.4) and (17.6),

$$y = \frac{\sum x^2 \sum y - \sum x \sum xy}{N^2 s_x^2} + \frac{N \sum xy - \sum x \sum y}{N^2 s_x^2} \bar{x}.$$

But since $\bar{x} = 1/N \sum x$,

$$y = \frac{\sum x^2 \sum y - \sum x \sum xy + \sum xy \sum x - \dfrac{1}{N}(\sum x)^2 \sum y}{N^2 s_x^2}$$

$$= \frac{\sum y \left[\sum x^2 - \dfrac{1}{N}(\sum x)^2 \right]}{N^2 s_x^2}$$

$$= \frac{\sum y \cdot N s_x^2}{N^2 s_x^2} = \bar{y}.$$

Thus the means $(\bar{x}, \bar{y})$ determine a point that lies on the fitted line, $y = a + bx$, so that

$$\bar{y} = a + b\bar{x} \qquad (17.8)$$

always, and this is equivalent to formula (17.4).

17.4. AN EXAMPLE

The tabulation in Table 17-1 shows the data from which Fig. 17-1 was constructed.

Formula (17.6) requires the calculation of $\sum x$, $\sum y$, $\sum x^2$, and $\sum xy$. These are found as column totals in Table 17-1. From formula (17.6) we find that

$$b = \frac{(13 \times 1849.70) - (295.0 \times 50.0)}{(13 \times 11{,}305.30) - (295.0)^2} = \frac{9296}{59{,}944} = 0.155,$$

and from formula (12.5), that

$$a = \frac{50.0}{13} - 0.155 \times \frac{295.0}{13} = 0.33,$$

whence the equation of the least squares line becomes:

$$y = 0.33 + 0.155x. \qquad \text{(17.9)}$$

Thus we have fitted, *algebraically*, Eq. (17.9) to the data. To construct the line, that is, to fit it *geometrically* to the points of Fig. 17-1, we locate two convenient points on the line. For example, if $x = 0$, $y = 0.33$, and if

TABLE 17-1

Drug Store Chain	Sales in $1,000,000 x	Inventory in $1,000,000 y	x^2	y^2	xy
Crown	12.2	1.8	148.84	3.24	21.96
Cunningham	41.0	7.8	1681.00	60.84	319.80
Dow	5.4	0.9	29.16	0.81	4.86
Gallagher	13.0	2.6	169.00	6.76	33.80
Gray	22.6	4.1	510.76	16.81	92.64
Katz	35.9	6.4	1288.81	40.96	229.76
Kinsel	7.2	1.3	51.84	1.69	9.36
Parkview	5.2	0.9	27.04	0.81	4.68
Peoples	55.0	9.1	3025.00	82.81	500.50
Reed	2.4	0.7	5.76	0.49	1.68
Sommers	6.8	1.5	46.24	2.25	10.20
Sun Ray	29.6	4.7	876.16	22.09	139.12
Whelan	58.7	8.2	3445.69	67.24	481.34
Totals	295.0	50.0	11,305.30	306.80	1849.70

$x = 60$, $y = 0.33$, $+ (0.155 \times 60) = 9.63$. The two points $(0, 0.33)$ and $(60, 9.63)$ are marked with crosses in Fig. 17-1 and determine the line shown there.

If we may consider this fitted line to be representative of the population of drug store chains, then we may draw inferences like the following:

(1) The slope of the line is 0.155; hence, for every $1,000,000 increase in annual gross sales, there is, on an average, an increase of approximately $155,000 in end-of-the-year inventory.
(2) If a chain has annual sales of $60,000,000, its end-of-year inventory is estimated to be close to $9,630,000, as seen above.

As another illustration of the use of a fitted line, consider the equation

$$y = 58.0 - 1.50x, \qquad \text{(17.10)}$$

where y represents the yearly infant mortality rate (number of deaths per

1000) in New York City and $x = 0, 1, 2, \ldots$, correspond to the years 1930, 1931, 1932, $\ldots$, respectively. We may make statements like the following:

(1) There was an average yearly *decrease* of 1.50 deaths per 1000 among infants.
(2) In 1935 ($x = 5$) the rate is estimated to have been $y = 58 - (1.50 \times 5)$, or 50.5 per 1000.
(3) To find, for example, the year in which the rate was 43.0, we set $43.0 = 58.0 - 1.50x$, whence $x = 10$; and this corresponds to the year 1940.

All of these conclusions assume that the trend indicated by the line Eq. (17.10) continues through the range of prediction.

17.5. THE DERIVATION OF THE LEAST SQUARES FORMULAS

Students familiar with calculus should find the following derivation of formulas (17.4) and (17.6) not difficult. Let

$$S = \Sigma\, e_i^2 = \Sigma\, [y_i - (a + bx_i)]^2.$$

[See formula (17.3).] To find the values a and b that minimize this sum, we set the partial derivatives with respect to a and b, equal to zero, that is, we differentiate S, first, with respect to a only, and then with respect to b only. Note that x_i and y_i are constants, the data given.

$$\left.\begin{aligned}
\frac{\partial S}{\partial a} &= 2\, \Sigma\, (y_i - a - bx_i)(-1) = 0, \\[2mm]
\frac{\partial S}{\partial b} &= 2\, \Sigma\, (y_i - a - bx_i)(-x_i) = 0.
\end{aligned}\right\}$$

These two equations reduce to:

$$\left.\begin{aligned}
\Sigma\, y_i - Na - b\, \Sigma\, x_i &= 0, \\
\Sigma\, x_i y_i - a\, \Sigma\, x_i - b\, \Sigma\, x_i^2 &= 0.
\end{aligned}\right\}$$

The values that satisfy this pair of linear equations in a and b is found by elementary algebra to be given by formulas (17.4) and (17.6).

17.6. REGRESSION

The word "regression" came into statistical use when Sir Francis Galton (1822–1911), in investigations into heredity, found that "the sons of fathers who deviate x inches from the mean height of all fathers, themselves deviate from the mean height of all sons by less than x inches." Galton termed this a "regression to mediocrity." Today the word is used in a broader sense to connote many functional relationships. In studying the simplest kind of relation between two statistical variables, x and y, we make use of the dot diagram and a least squares line. Such a line can be termed a *regression line*. In less simple cases, we make use of *regression curves*, as, for example, polynomials, or we may study the interrelations among three or more variables by means of regression equations involving these variables.

In many regression problems, we know or suspect that one variable x, is the cause, partially at least, of the variation in the other variable y. For example, we note that an increase in gross annual sales increases the end-of-year inventory (Fig. 17-1); a change in the concentration of an insecticide produces a change in the per cent of insects killed; an increase in the time spent on remedial reading results in an increase in reading speed, and so on. The line of regression of y on x, the causal variable, affords a method of making estimates or predictions of y for a given x.

17.7. EXPLAINED AND UNEXPLAINED VARIANCE

The scatter diagram of Fig. 17-6 exhibits no upward or downward trend or regression. Obviously, the value of y is not influenced by the value

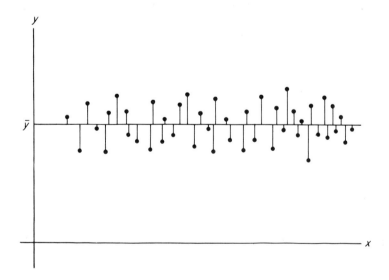

Figure 17-6

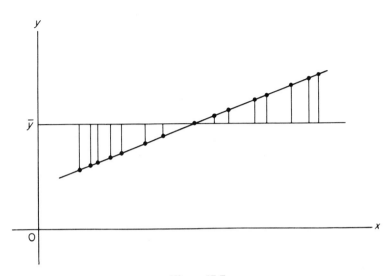

Figure 17-7

of x. The over-all variance of the y's, designated as usual by s_y^2, is the mean of the squares of the lengths of the vertical line segments shown in the figure.

In Fig. 17-7, *all* the points lie on the line of regression; hence, the variability of the y's can be completely explained as due to the regression. In fact, each y is defined by means of the linear equation:

$$y = a + bx.$$

The variance s_y^2 is again the mean of the squares of the lengths of the vertical line segments shown in Fig. 17-7. In Fig. 17-6, none of the variance can be thus explained.

The configuration of points shown in Fig. 17-8 indicates that some but not all of the variability among the y's can be explained by regression. If the points all lay on the line as in Fig. 17-7, we could account for all of the variance. We measure the failure of the points to lie on the line by means of the distances, e_i, of the points from the line of regression. These afford a measure of the variability that regression does not explain.

We distinguish between two values of y corresponding to x_i: (1) the observed y_i, given by the data, and (2) the estimated y_i' calculated from the equation of the regression line, so that

$$y_i' = a + bx_i. \tag{17.11}$$

Thus (x_i, y_i') defines a point lying on the line. By Eq. (17.3)

$$e_i = y_i - (a + bx_i)$$
$$= y_i - y_i'. \tag{17.12}$$

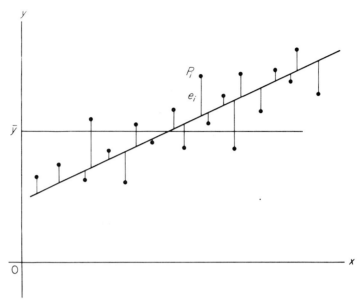

Figure 17-8

The mean of the estimated y's is:

$$\bar{y}' = \frac{1}{N} \Sigma\, y_i'$$

$$= \frac{1}{N} \Sigma\, (a + bx_i)$$

$$= \frac{1}{N} \Sigma\, a + b \cdot \frac{1}{N} \Sigma\, x_i$$

$$= a + b\bar{x},$$

hence, by formula (17.8),

$$\bar{y}' = \bar{y}. \tag{17.13}$$

Thus the mean of the estimated y's equals the mean of the observed y's.

Next,

$$\Sigma\, e_i = \Sigma\, (y_i - y_i')$$

$$= \Sigma\, y_i - \Sigma\, y_i'$$

$$= N\bar{y} - N\bar{y}'$$

so that by formula (17.13),

$$\Sigma\, e_i = 0. \tag{17.14}$$

Thus

$$\bar{e} = \frac{1}{N} \Sigma\, e_i = 0.$$

It follows that the sum of the vertical distances of the points (x_i, y_i) *above* the line (taken as positive) must equal the corresponding sum for the points *below* the line (taken as negative). This fact is useful in fitting a straight line to data visually, rather than by the method of least squares. Frequently, a set of points lies close to a straight line as in Fig. 17-1, and a line fitted visually may be accurate enough for many purposes. A taut string, a transparent ruler, or a thin ruler placed on edge is located so that the sums mentioned above appear to be equal, and then a line is drawn. The co-ordinates of (x_1, y_1) and (x_2, y_2) of two convenient, widely spaced points on the line are estimated and substituted in the equation $y = a + bx$. This operation produces two equations in the two unknowns, a and b, which can be readily solved for these parameters.

The mean of the squares of the vertical distances e_i, is called the *variance of the errors of estimate* and is designated by s_e^2. Thus,

$$s_e^2 = \frac{1}{N} \Sigma e_i^2. \qquad (17.15)$$

The quantity, s_e, is called the *standard error of estimate*.

The variance of the estimated y's is:

$$s_{y'}^2 = \frac{1}{N} \Sigma (y_i' - \bar{y}')^2$$

$$= \frac{1}{N} \Sigma (y_i' - \bar{y})^2. \qquad (17.16)$$

$s_{y'}$ is called the *standard error of the estimated values*.

The following interesting and important relation will now be proved

$$s_y^2 = s_e^2 + s_{y'}^2. \qquad (17.17)$$

$$s_e^2 = \frac{1}{N} \Sigma [y_i - (a + bx_i)]^2.$$

From (17.5),

$$s_e^2 = \frac{1}{N} \Sigma [(y_i - \bar{y}) - (bx_i - b\bar{x})]^2$$

$$= \frac{1}{N} \Sigma [(y_i - \bar{y})^2 - 2b(y_i - \bar{y})(x_i - \bar{x}) + b^2(x_i - \bar{x})^2]$$

$$= \frac{1}{N} \Sigma (y_i - \bar{y})^2 - \frac{2b}{N} \Sigma (x_i - \bar{x})(y_i - \bar{y}) + \frac{b^2}{N} \Sigma (x_i - \bar{x})^2$$

$$= s_y^2 - 2b \cdot \frac{1}{N} \Sigma (x_i - \bar{x})(y_i - \bar{y}) + b^2 s_x^2. \qquad (17.18)$$

Let us examine the middle term of the expression on the right.

$$\frac{1}{N} \Sigma (x_i - \bar{x})(y_i - \bar{y}) = \frac{1}{N} \Sigma (x_i y_i - x_i \bar{y} - \bar{x} y_i + \bar{x}\bar{y})$$

$$= \frac{1}{N} \Sigma x_i y_i - \bar{y} \cdot \frac{1}{N} \Sigma x_i - \bar{x} \cdot \frac{1}{N} \Sigma y_i + \frac{1}{N} \Sigma \bar{x}\bar{y}$$

$$= \frac{1}{N} \Sigma x_i y_i - \bar{y}\bar{x} - \bar{x}\bar{y} + \bar{x}\bar{y}$$

$$= \frac{1}{N} \Sigma x_i y_i - \bar{x}\bar{y}$$

$$= \frac{1}{N} \Sigma x_i y_i - \frac{\Sigma x_i}{N} \frac{\Sigma y_i}{N}$$

$$= \frac{N \Sigma x_i y_i - \Sigma x_i \Sigma y_i}{N^2}. \qquad (17.19)$$

But from (17.6) and (17.7),

$$b = \frac{N \Sigma x_i y_i - \Sigma x_i \Sigma y_i}{N^2 s_x^2} \qquad (17.20)$$

therefore,

$$b s_x^2 = \frac{N \Sigma x_i y_i - \Sigma x_i \Sigma y_i}{N^2}$$

hence, by (17.19),

$$b s_x^2 = \frac{1}{N} \Sigma (x_i - \bar{x})(y_i - \bar{y}). \qquad (17.21)$$

Thus, (17.18) becomes:

$$s_e^2 = s_y^2 - 2b^2 s_x^2 + b^2 s_x^2$$

or

$$s_e^2 = s_y^2 - b^2 s_x^2. \qquad (17.22)$$

Next

$$s_{y'}^2 = \frac{1}{N} \Sigma (y_i' - \bar{y})^2.$$

By (17.11) and (17.8),

$$s_{y'}^2 = \frac{1}{N} \Sigma [(a + bx_i) - (a + b\bar{x})]^2$$

$$= \frac{1}{N} \Sigma b^2 (x_i - \bar{x})^2$$

$$s_{y'}^2 = b^2 s_x^2. \qquad (17.23)$$

If, then, we add (17.22) to (17.23), we obtain (17.17)

It is now evident that the over-all variance, s_y^2, may be decomposed into two parts, the *explained variance*, $s_{y'}^2$ and the *unexplained variance*, s_e^2. The first part is also called the *variance of the estimated values*; the second, the *error* or *residual variance*. Formulas (17.22) and (17.23) are useful in computing these component variances.

17.8. TESTING HYPOTHESES CONCERNING SLOPES

It is often desirable to determine if the difference between the sample regression coefficient, b, and an assumed population regression coefficient, β, is such as to be interpreted as ordinary sampling variation or as a denial of such variation. Frequently we may prefer to find a confidence interval for β.

If we assume that the $x_1, x_2, \ldots, x_N$, of the sample are fixed, but that the corresponding $y_1, y_2, \ldots, y_N$, are random variables normally distributed about the population regression line

$$y = \alpha + \beta x$$

with a common variance, σ_e^2, then the variable t defined by the formula

$$t = (b - \beta)\sqrt{\frac{(N - 2)s_x^2}{s_e^2}} \qquad (17.24)$$

will have a Student t-distribution with $N - 2$ degrees of freedom. The assumption implies that the values of x are selected in advance by the experimenter as those best suited or most convenient for his investigation and that replications of the experiment would always involve the same set of values of x. The most common form of test arises when we assume $\beta = 0$.

Example. For the sales and inventory data of Section 17.4, let us find the 90 per cent confidence interval for β.

One can verify that $N = 13$, $b = 0.155$, $s_x^2 = 354$, and $s_e^2 = 0.35$. Then for 11 degrees of freedom, $t_{0.05} = 1.80$, so

$$\pm 1.80 = (0.155 - \beta)\sqrt{\frac{11 \times 354}{0.35}}$$

whence

$$0.14 < \beta < 0.17.$$

Obviously this is inconsistent with the hypothesis that $\beta = 0$. Thus there is some positive regression.

Given two regression coefficients, b_1 and b_2, and assuming that the population residual variances $\sigma_{e_1}^2$ and $\sigma_{e_1}^2$, are the same, we may test the hypothesis $\beta_1 = \beta_2$, by means of the statistic

$$t = \frac{b_1 - b_2}{\left[\dfrac{N_1 s_{e1}^2 + N_2 s_{e2}^2}{N_1 + N_2 - 4}\left(\dfrac{1}{N_1 s_{x1}^2} + \dfrac{1}{N_2 s_{x2}^2}\right)\right]^{\frac{1}{2}}} \qquad (17.25)$$

which has a Student t-distribution with $N_1 + N_2 - 4$ degrees of freedom.

EXERCISES

1. Given the following set of points: (1,2), (4,5), (7,7), (10,12), (13,13), (a) Construct a scatter diagram. (b) Find the equation of the least squares line fitting these points. (c) Construct the line.

2. A group of five students took tests before and after training and obtained the following scores:

Before, x:	8	10	10	15	20
After, y:	10	12	15	20	20

Find by the method of least squares, the equation of the line fitting these data. Plot the points and the line.

3. When the temperatures, y, in Fahrenheit degrees were plotted against the number, x, of chirps per minute of crickets, the plotted points were found to lie very close to a straight line. The equation of the best fitting line was found to be $y = 40 + 0.25x$. (a) What would you estimate the temperature to be when a cricket is making 120 chirps per minute? (b) How much faster would a cricket chirp if the temperature increased $1°F$?

4. (a) Fit a least squares line to the points (3,5), (5,7), (1,1), (6,9), $(-2,-3)$, (3,4), (4,6), $(-1,-1)$, (1,2), (2,3). (b) Calculate the explained and unexplained variances of the y's. What percentage of the total variance is explained by regression?

5. Systematic efforts to reduce the percentage of defective articles produced by one manufacturing unit of a certain plant showed the following results for the first 12 weeks.

Week	1	2	3	4	5	6
Per cent defective	7	6.5	7	6	6	5.5

Week	7	8	9	10	11	12
Per cent defective	6	5	5.5	4	5	4.5

Fit a least squares line to the data and from its equation estimate the average weekly reduction in the percentage of defectives.

6. The temperature readings (y) at regular time intervals (x) were as follows:

Time (minutes)	0	1	2	3	4	5	6
Temperature	70	77	92	118	136	143	155

Find the equation of the regression line and plot this line on a dot diagram of the data. Interpret b.

7. The scores, x, of 22 students in a calculus class on the first hour-quiz and on their final examination, y, yielded $\Sigma x = 1717$, $\Sigma y = 1408$, $\Sigma xy = 112{,}854$, $\Sigma x^2 = 138{,}341$, $\Sigma y^2 = 98{,}818$. Find the equation of the least squares line fitting these data.

8. The mental ages, x, and the scores on a test, y, of a group of 12 boys were as follows:

(5,0), (5,5), (7,8), (8,10), (8,18), (9,20), (10,30), (11,40), (12,35), (13,43), (14,50), (15,50).

(a) Find the slope of the least squares line. What information about ages and scores does the value of the slope give you? (b) What percentage of the variance of the test scores can be explained by the regression?

9. Given the number of mice dying per group of ten from various doses of a drug:

Dosage (x):	50	56	62	70	80
No. dying (y):	0	4	5	6	9

From the equation of the least squares line, estimate the *median lethal dose* (MLD), that is, the dose that will kill just half of the mice.

10. Various doses of a drug are administered to groups of ten mice and the number dying per dose recorded. The equation of the least squares line was found to be $y = -12.1 + 0.265x$, where x is the dose and y, the number dying. A fixed unknown dose of the same drug is administered to five groups of ten mice each and shows the following numbers dead: 4, 5, 7, 5, 6. Estimate the strength of the dose.

11. In a laboratory, the times in minutes, x, required by a group of girls to perform a certain operation were recorded. The girls were then retrained to perform the same operation differently and the times, y, required were noted. Points were plotted to correspond to the two times for each girl and a straight line fitted to them. Its equation is $y = -2.3 + 0.84x$. State two important conclusions that one may draw from this equation.

12. In exercise 8, find the 95% confidence interval for β. By means of it, test the hypothesis that $\beta = 3$.

13. In exercise 7, test the hypothesis that $\beta = 0$.

14. The following data were obtained on the hardness, x, and the tensile strength, y, of five specimens of castings:

x:	53	70	55	53	69
y:	29	34	30	31	36

Find the 90% confidence limits for the regression coefficient, β, of the population regression line. Test the hypothesis that $\beta = 0.80$.

15. In exercise 4, find the 95% confidence interval for β.

16. In a study on the gain in weight in grams (y), for different types of rations in 100 calorie units (x), made with samples of ten rats each, the following results were obtained:

Ration A. Line of regression: $y = 40.6 + 0.396x$;

$$\Sigma x = 1500, \qquad \Sigma x^2 = 230{,}000$$
$$\Sigma y = 1000, \qquad \Sigma y^2 = 102{,}000$$

Ration B. Line of regression: $y = 14.1 + 0.677x$;

$$\Sigma x = 1120, \qquad \Sigma x^2 = 128{,}000$$
$$\Sigma y = 859, \qquad \Sigma y^2 = 76{,}000.$$

Test the hypothesis that $\beta_1 = \beta_2$.

18

Correlation

It is evident that the understanding of
relations is a major concern of all men
and women.

CASSIUS J. KEYSER
Mole Philosophy

18.1. INTRODUCTION

Simple correlation may be defined as "the amount of similarity, in direction and degree, of variations in corresponding pairs of observations of two variables." The principal problem of simple correlation is that of determining the degree of association between these pairs of observations. Thus we may inquire concerning the correlation between the weights and heights of American soldiers, between end-of-year inventories and yearly sales of drug stores, between birth rates and per capita property values of states, and so on.

Regression and correlation are intimately connected as the subsequent sections will demonstrate; but there are essential differences. In what may be termed a pure regression problem, there is an independent or causal variable, x, and a dependent variable, y. The values of x are assumed to be selected in advance and held fixed (see Section 17.8); then the corresponding values of y are observed. For example, we may choose a set of varying doses, x, of a drug to be administered to groups of animals, and then note the numbers, y, succumbing to the doses; or we may select intervals of time at whose end-points, x, we observe instrument readings, y. In a pure correlation problem, we choose a sample of pairs of observations from a bivariate population as, by way of illustration, a company of soldiers whose heights and weights we record, or a group of states of the Union whose birth rates and per capita property values we ascertain. In this latter case, we cannot say that the birth rate depends upon the per capita value any more than we can say that the per capita value depends upon the birth rate. Do people have more children when they possess less, or do people possess less when they have more children? Here the functional relationship, assuming that such exists, is, from the statistical standpoint, a reversible one.

18.2. TWO LINES OF REGRESSION

In a correlation problem, it is sometimes useful to consider two lines of regression, that of y on x which was treated in the previous chapter, and that of x on y. In the former case, we used a least squares line that minimized the sum of the squares of the *vertical* or y-distances of the points from the line; in the latter case we minimize the sum of the squares of the *horizontal* or x-distances of the points from the line.

The problem of finding the equation of this companion line involves nothing new. It requires merely an exchange in the roles of the x- and y-axes. Hence we may obtain the desired equations by replacing x by y and y by x in Eqs. (17.4), (17.5), and (17.6). The equation of the regression line of x on y will then be:

$$x = a' + b'y \qquad (18.1)$$

where

$$a' = \bar{x} - b'\bar{y} \qquad (18.2)$$

$$b' = \frac{N \Sigma\, xy - \Sigma\, x\, \Sigma\, y}{N \Sigma\, y^2 - (\Sigma\, y)^2} \qquad (18.3)$$

Equation (18.1) is more appropriate for estimating an x from a given y.

18.3. THE COEFFICIENT OF CORRELATION

Let

$$r^2 = \frac{s_{y'}^2}{s_y^2}, \qquad (18.4)$$

be the ratio of the explained variance to the total variance; it represents the fraction of the over-all variance that is explained by regression. If the points of a dot diagram lie exactly on the regression line, as in Fig. 17-7, $s_{y'}^2 = s_y^2$; all of the variance is attributable to regression and $r^2 = 1$. If no regression whatsoever exists, as in Fig. 17-6, $s_{y'}^2 = 0$; none of the variability is explained and $r^2 = 0$. The quantity

$$r = \pm \frac{s_{y'}}{s_y}$$

is called the *coefficient of correlation*. Since by formula (17.17)

$$s_{y'}^2 = s_y^2 - s_e^2$$

then,

$$r^2 = \frac{s_y^2 - s_e^2}{s_y^2} = 1 - \frac{s_e^2}{s_y^2} . \tag{18.5}$$

It is obvious from the preceding discussion that r numerically never exceeds 1. The sign of r is always taken as that of the slope of the regression line. Thus, a positive value of r indicates that y tends to increase with x; a negative value, that y tends to decrease as x increases.

A more practical formula for r is obtained in the following manner.

$$r^2 = \frac{s_{y'}^2}{s_y^2}$$

$$= \frac{b^2 s_x^2}{s_y^2} , \qquad \text{by formula (17.23);}$$

then

$$r = \frac{bs_x}{s_y} . \tag{18.6}$$

This formula is useful in converting the regression coefficient, b, into the correlation coefficient, r, and vice versa. For the line of regression of x on y,

$$r = \frac{b's_y}{s_x} . \tag{18.6a}$$

By means of (17.20) Eq. (18.6) becomes:

$$r = \frac{N \Sigma xy - \Sigma x \Sigma y}{N^2 s_x s_y} , \tag{18.7}$$

and from the well-known formula for variance,

$$r = \frac{N \Sigma xy - \Sigma x \Sigma y}{\sqrt{[N \Sigma x^2 - (\Sigma x)^2][N \Sigma y^2 - (\Sigma y)^2]}} . \tag{18.8}$$

This formula involves five basic sums, Σx, Σy, Σx^2, Σy^2, and Σxy, which are readily obtained from an automatic desk calculator. It may also be proved (See exercise 18.17) that (18.7) can be converted into a formula useful in theoretical work

$$r = \frac{1}{N} \Sigma \left(\frac{x - \bar{x}}{s_x} \right) \left(\frac{y - \bar{y}}{s_y} \right) . \tag{18.9}$$

The expression on the right is called the *product-moment* or the *covariance* as in Section 15.6; *r* is often termed the *Pearson product-moment coefficient of correlation* after the English statistician, *Karl Pearson* (1857–1936), who devised it. In formula (18.9), *r* is the arithmetic mean of the products of the corresponding values of the two sets of variates expressed as standard deviates.

18.4. PROPERTIES RELATED TO *r*

From (18.5) one can easily show that

$$s_e^2 = s_y^2(1 - r^2). \tag{18.10}$$

Also, for the line of regression of *x* on *y*,

$$s_e^2 = s_x^2(1 - r^2), \tag{18.10a}$$

and since variances are always positive, this means that r^2 can never exceed 1 and is obviously non-negative.

$$0 \leq r^2 \leq 1.$$

From this, it follows that the possible values of *r* range from -1 to $+1$:

$$-1 \leq r \leq +1.$$

When $r = 0$, also $b = b' = 0$ [see formulas (18.6) and (18.6a)] and the regression lines

$$\left. \begin{array}{l} y = a + bx \\ x = a' + b'y \end{array} \right\}$$

become

$$\left. \begin{array}{l} y = a \\ x = a' \end{array} \right\}.$$

Since the regression lines always pass through the point $(\bar{x},\bar{y})$, then $a = \bar{y}$ and $a' = \bar{x}$ and the equations become:

$$y = \bar{y} \quad \text{and} \quad x = \bar{x}.$$

When $r = \pm 1$, the sum of the squares in both Eqs. (18.10) and (18.10a) is zero, a minimum; hence, all points must lie on both lines of regression. The only way in which this can happen is to have the lines coincide.

The slopes *b* and *b'* depend upon *r*, as we see by formulas (18.6) and (18.16a). When *r* is positive, the slope is also, and the lines of regression ascend from left to right (Fig. 18-1a and b). When *r* is negative, the slope is also, and the lines of regression descend from left to right (Fig. 18-1c). When *r* is numerically very small, the line of regression of *y* on *x* is close to the line $y = \bar{y}$. Similarly the line of regression of *x* on *y* is close to the line

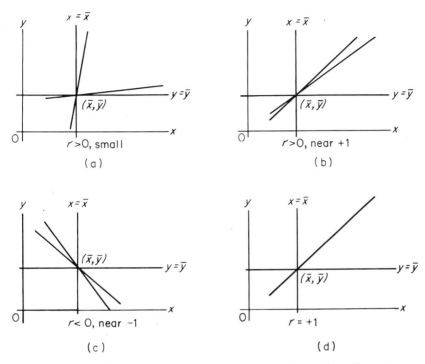

Figure 18-1. Positions of regression lines for various values of r.

$x = \bar{x}$ (Fig. 18-1a). When r is near ± 1, the lines very nearly coincide (Fig. 18-1c) and when $r = \pm 1$, the lines do coincide (Fig. 18-1cd).

Thus, as r varies from 0 to either $+1$ or -1, the lines of regression rotate from positions on the lines $x = \bar{x}$ and $y = \bar{y}$ toward each other until they coincide. Consequently, the amount of divergence between the two lines of regression gives a simple visual estimate of the degree of correlation.

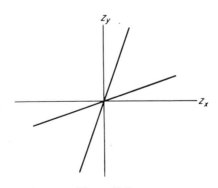

Figure 18-2

It can be shown, when standard variables are used, $z_x = (x - \bar{x})/s_x$, $z_y = (y - \bar{y})/s_y$, that the two regression lines always have symmetrical positions with respect to the line bisecting the quadrants through which they pass. This means that the line of regression of z_y on z_x makes the same angle with the positive z_x-axis that the line of regression of z_x on z_y makes with the positive z_y-axis. (Fig. 18-2.)

From the preceding paragraphs, it appears that the closer the points lie to a line of regression, the more nearly does a simple linear equation express the association between the values of x and y. Thus, a correlation coefficient of nearly 1 (or -1) would seem to indicate a definite relationship between two given sets of values; a coefficient near zero would seem to indicate practically no such relationship.

18.5. THE COMPUTATION OF r FOR UNGROUPED DATA

The widespread use of computing machines has diminished but not eliminated the necessity for shortcut methods of pencil calculation such as coding. When coding is unnecessary, formula (18.8) is an excellent one to use. The method of coding is illustrated in detail in Reference 8, pp. 66 and 67.

Let us compute the coefficient of correlation for the birth rates and per property values of Table 18-1. The steps in the computation appear in this table. The squares were found in Table A.

$$\Sigma x = 1074 \qquad \Sigma x^2 = 50,144 \qquad \Sigma xy = 31,314$$
$$\Sigma y = 723 \qquad \Sigma y^2 = 23,161$$

From formula (18.8),

$$r = \frac{(24 \times 31,314) - (1074 \times 723)}{\sqrt{(24 \times 50,144 - 1074^2)(24 \times 23,161 - 723^2)}}$$
$$= -0.614.$$

This sample consists of 24 pairs of variates drawn from a finite population, 48 states plus the District of Columbia (in 1920). There is no large or potentially infinite population from which this sample can be conceived to be drawn. The computed value of r would seem to indicate a fairly high degree of correlation, the negative sign implying that high per capita property values go, in general, with low birth rates. A question somewhat beyond the scope of this book is the following: Are birth rates and property values directly related to the extent measured by the value, $r = -0.61$, or are both attributes really dependent upon other variables, or latent factors, not

TABLE 18-1

<small>Birth Rates of Native-born Whites per 1000 Enumerated Female Population, 1920, and per Capita Estimated Value of All Property, 1922, by States.* Computation of *r* for Birth Rate and per Capita Property Value</small>

State	Birth Rate x	Per Capita Value of All Property in $100 y	x^2	y^2	xy
Conn	31	36	961	1296	1116
Mass	33	32	1089	1024	1056
N.Y.	34	34	1156	1156	1156
D.C.	34	39	1156	1521	1326
Cal	35	40	1225	1600	1400
N.H.	37	31	1369	961	1147
Vt	39	24	1521	576	936
Ore	40	42	1600	1764	1680
Ohio	40	30	1600	900	1200
Wash	41	36	1681	1296	1476
Me	41	26	1681	676	1066
Penn	42	32	1764	1024	1344
Ind	44	29	1936	841	1276
Wis	45	29	2025	841	1305
Kan	46	35	2116	1225	1610
Md	47	27	2209	729	1269
Mich	48	29	2304	841	1392
Minn	48	34	2304	1156	1632
Neb	50	40	2500	1600	2000
Ky	55	15	3025	225	825
Va	57	20	3249	400	1140
S.C.	59	14	3481	196	826
N.C.	64	17	4096	289	1088
Utah	64	32	4096	1024	2048
Totals	1074	723	50,144	23,161	31,314

* (Adapted from Raymond Pearl, *The Biology of Population Growth*, Knopf, 1925, p. 160.)

revealed by the bare data of Table 18-1? The discussion of this question may be found in the source of this table.

The equations of the lines of regression have been found to be:

$$\begin{cases} y = 5252 - 50.0x \\ x = 67.5 - 0.00754y. \end{cases}$$

Here, since we calculated *r* first, we computed $b(-50.0)$ from formula (18.6),

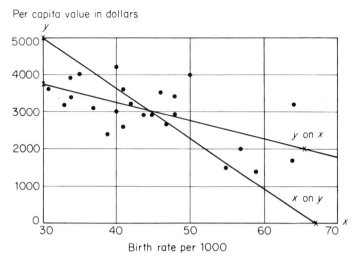

Per capita value in dollars

Fig. 18-3. Scatter diagram for birth rates and per capita property value. (Data of Table 18-1.)

$b = r(s_y/s_x)$. Similarly $b' = r(s_x/s_y)$. The regression lines are plotted in Fig. 18-3, where the crosses indicate convenient points used to determine the lines. To check on the work, we estimate the coordinates of the point of intersection of the lines. These should be $(\bar{x},\bar{y})$ or approximately (45, 3000).

18.6. TESTING THE HYPOTHESIS
THAT $\rho = 0$

For samples of N pairs (x,y) each assumed to be drawn from a normal bivariate population (Section 18.10) with means μ_x and μ_y, standard deviations σ_x and σ_y, and correlation coefficient ρ, the distribution of r has been determined. This distribution has a complicated form; but when $\rho = 0$, its equation for a given N defines a curve symmetrical about $\rho = 0$ with a range from -1 to $+1$. See the figure accompanying Table I, of the Appendix.

A sample value of r may be most easily tested without computation by means of Table I. In that table, the sign of r is ignored. The number of degrees of freedom, $n = N - 2$.

Example. A sample of 15 shows $r = 0.53$. Test $H_0:\rho = 0$ against the alternative $H_1:\rho \neq 0$.

From Table I with $n = 15 - 2 = 13$, we find that at the 5 per cent level (two-tail probability), $r = 0.514$; hence, r is significantly different from $\rho = 0$, and we cannot accept H_0. Thus for $\alpha = 0.05$, we should concede that a positive correlation exists in the population.

18.7. THE USE OF THE *t*-DISTRIBUTION

For the hypothesis $\rho = 0$,

$$t = r\left(\frac{N-2}{1-r^2}\right)^{1/2} \tag{18.11}$$

is known to have a *t*-distribution with $N - 2$ degrees of freedom; hence, we may test t with the aid of Table F. Formula (18.11) can be shown to be equivalent to formula (17.24) with $\beta = 0$.

18.8. THE FISHER *z*-TRANSFORMATION

When $\rho \neq 0$, the distribution of r is skew and the skewness increases with the numerical value of ρ. However, the variable,

$$z = \frac{1}{2}\log_e\frac{1+r}{1-r}, \tag{18.12}$$

devised by R. A. Fisher, has approximately a normal distribution which changes little in form with ρ. For this distribution we use

$$\mu_z = \frac{1}{2}\log_e\frac{1+\rho}{1-\rho}. \tag{18.13}$$

and

$$\sigma_z = \frac{1}{\sqrt{N-3}}. \tag{18.14}$$

For a discussion of the limitations of this method and a useful table for converting r to z, see pp. 246–247 of Reference 8.

Given ρ and N, the probability that a sample correlation coefficient does not numerically exceed a given value, r, for samples of $N = 3$ to 25 principally, may be found in *David's Tables* (Reference 14). Useful charts showing confidence belts for ρ corresponding to $P = 0.90, 0.95, 0.98,$ and 0.99 are also found there. One such chart is reproduced as Table J in the Appendix.

Example. Suppose that for $N = 25, r = 0.45$. Find the 95 % confidence limits for ρ.

From Table J, we find that $0.66 < \rho < 0.71$.

18.9. THE CORRELATION TABLE

When the total number, N, of paired values is large, a preliminary analysis of the data may be made by means of a double frequency distribution or correlation table. This has as its theoretical basis the bivariate probability function of Table 15-5. The table consists of a rectangular array of squares or *cells* containing frequencies. The frequency recorded in a given cell represents the number of items belonging to a certain x-class and to a certain y-class simultaneously. In Table 18-2, each cell frequency represents the number of women students having, simultaneously, a certain weight and a certain height. For example, there were twelve students weighing from 110

TABLE 18-2

CORRELATION TABLE FOR THE WEIGHTS AND HEIGHTS OF 285 BOSTON
UNIVERSITY WOMEN STUDENTS
(*Original Data—Weights in Pounds*)

$x \rightarrow$ $y \downarrow$	85	95	105	115	125	135	145	155	165	175	185	195	205	f_v
57										1				1
58														0
59	1		4	2										7
60		3	8	1				1						13
61	1	3	2	4	5	3								18
62		3	7	8	11	3	2							34
63			7	12	13	6	1	1				1		41
64			8	8	14	10	6	2			1			49
65			1	10	15	11	4			1				42
66		1	2	9	10	6	5	2		1				36
67			2	4	8	5	3			1			1	24
68				1	2	2	2	1	1					9
69						4	1	1	1					7
70										1				1
71				1							1			2
72					1									1
f_x	2	10	39	57	75	54	26	11	2	5	2	1	1	285

Heights in Inches

to 120 pounds (class mark, 115), and ranging in height from 62.5 to 63.5 inches (class mark, 63). If each cell frequency is replaced by an appropriate number of dots, a scatter diagram results. Whether we do this or not (and it's usually unnecessary), it is generally possible to decide whether or not the Pearson coefficient, r, is an appropriate measure of correlation to use. In the example under discussion, it appears that increasing height is associated with fairly steadily increasing weight; so we may safely assume that we may use "lines" of regression rather than "curves" of regression.

For a detailed explanation of the method of calculating r from a correlation table, see pp. 249–252 of Reference 8.

18.10. THE CORRELATION SURFACE

The graphical representation of a frequency distribution by means of a histogram or frequency polygon (Section 9.1) and the idealization of the latter into a frequency curve are already familiar. Similar processes are employed in the case of a *bivariate* distribution represented by a correlation table. Let each cell in the table be the base of a solid rectangular column whose height is proportional to the frequency of the cell. The aggregate of columns thus constructed forms a solid histogram, a sort of modernistic building (Fig. 18-4). If the dimensions of each cell are k_x and k_y (the class

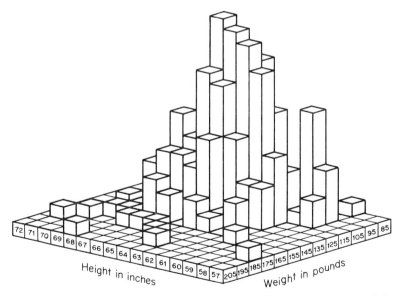

Fig. 18-4. Solid histogram for the correlation Table 18-2 of heights and weights of 285 Boston University women students.

intervals for x and y, respectively) and if the total frequency is N, then the volume of this solid histogram will be Nk_xk_y. If the class intervals are reduced to unity, the volume becomes equal to N.

The concept of the solid histogram is not without its practical applications. For example a certain shoe store in Boston uses an effective form of it. The lengths of men's shoes from 4 to 12 and the widths from AAA to E constitute a double array of sizes. Upon each cell, for example, that for size $7\frac{1}{2}$ C, is erected a vertical rod upon which uniform washers of constant thickness can be strung. For each pair of shoes sold, a washer is dropped upon the appropriate rod. The number of washers built up on each rod represents the frequency. After a period of time, say a week, the aggregate of cylindrical columns formed by the washers on the rods yields a form of solid histogram that records the distributions of shoe sales by lengths and widths. Orders for new stocks of shoes can be constructed accordingly.

Returning to the discussion of the first paragraph, if we assume the class intervals, k_x and k_y, each to approach zero while the total frequency, N, becomes infinite, in such a way that the product Nk_xk_y remains finite, the rectangular columns will become infinitely slender and infinitely numerous. We assume that their upper bases will approach, as a limiting form, a certain curved surface called a *frequency surface* (see Section 14.3). In the case of a so-called *normal bivariate distribution*, this surface will be bell-shaped (Fig. 18-5). Any cross section parallel to the (x,y)-plane upon which the array of cells is situated will be an ellipse or circle. The centers of all such ellipses will lie upon the vertical line throughout the "mean point," (μ_x,μ_y); the axes of these ellipses will lie in two vertical planes perpendicular each to each. We shall call these the *axial planes* of the frequency surface. If ρ, the correlation

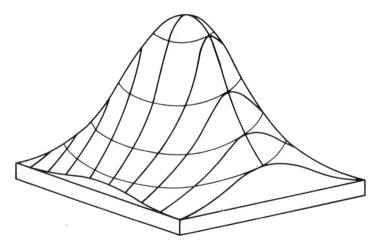

Fig. 18-5. A normal frequency surface.

coefficient of the population, is numerically near 1, the ellipses will be slender ones, that is, the *major axis* will be much greater than the *minor axis*. If ρ is numerically near 0, the ellipses will be nearly circular, that is, the major and minor axes will be nearly equal. Any vertical cross section parallel to an axis or to any direction whatsoever will yield a normal curve. The surface will be asymptotic to the base, that is, it will approach infinitely near the base as it extends to infinity in all directions.

The equation of the surface corresponding to a normal bivariate population with means μ_x and μ_y, standard deviations, σ_x and σ_y, and correlation coefficient, ρ, can be shown to be

$$f(x, y) = \frac{1}{2\pi\sigma_x\sigma_y(1 - \rho^2)^{\frac{1}{2}}} e^{-\frac{1}{2(1-\rho^2)}\left[\left(\frac{x-\mu_x}{\sigma_x}\right)^2 - 2\rho\left(\frac{x-\mu_x}{\sigma_x}\right)\left(\frac{y-\mu_y}{\sigma_y}\right) + \left(\frac{y-\mu_y}{\sigma_y}\right)^2\right]} \quad (18.15)$$

This equation arises as a limiting form of the binomial probability function as stated in Section 14.4. The detailed study of the normal frequency surface defined by Eq. (18.15) must be left to a more advanced course. At this point, however, we call attention to two important aspects of the correlation table and its associated surface. These are best explained by referring to correlation Table 18-2.

In the first place, we observe that the main body of this table may be enclosed in an ellipse whose longer axis slopes diagonally downward from the upper left-hand region of the table, and whose shorter axis slopes diagonally upward. The nearer we approach these axes, the greater, generally, do the frequencies become. These axes lie close to the axes associated with the ideal frequency surface. (Fig. 18-5.)

In the second place, it is possible to find, for each column representing a weight class, the average height of students belonging to that class. Similarly, for each row representing a height class, one may compute the average weight of students belonging to that class. For example, the average height of the 54 students belonging to the 135-pound class is 65.1 inches, and the average weight of the 13 students in the 60-inch class is 107.3 pounds. Let us denote the average of the y's, the heights, corresponding to a given weight class, x_i, by the symbol $\bar{y}_i$, and the average of the x's, the weights, corresponding to a given height class, y_j, by the symbol, $\bar{x}_j$. In what follows, the variable subscript i will refer always to the x's and the variable subscript j to the y's. Let us plot $\bar{y}_i$, against x_i, and then $\bar{x}_j$ against y_j, as in Fig. 18-6. The crosses represent the points $(x_i, \bar{y}_i)$, and the circles, the points $(\bar{x}_j, y_j)$. It can be shown that the line best fitting the set of crosses is precisely the line of regression of y on x; the line best fitting the set of circles is the line of regression of x on y. Note the similarity to the regression function of Table 15-14. For the best fit, we weight the means according to the frequencies they represent, and employ vertical distances in the former case and horizontal distances in the latter. Passing to the ideal double-frequency distribution as

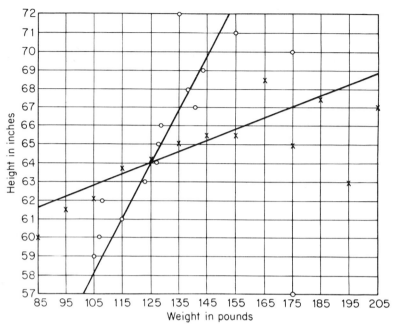

Figure 18-6

represented by a frequency surface, it can be proved that if the surface is normal, the crosses and circles will lie precisely on straight lines, the *ideal* lines of regression. These facts are important in certain phases of the work on correlation.

18.11. REMARKS

The theory of correlation as discussed up to this point has been based upon the notion of a straight line best fitting an array of points in a plane. As long as the data given exhibit a fairly linear trend, no serious difficulties ensue. However, if the points seem to lie along a curve, other methods should be used. A bivariate universe that is not normal is represented by a frequency surface that is not normal. It can be shown that the two ideal "lines" of regression associated with non-normal distributions are not ordinarily both straight lines; one or both may be curved lines. Grossly misleading results may be obtained if we compute r upon the hypothesis of a linear trend when the trend is curvilinear. The *correlation ratio* and the *correlation index* are two measures used when nonlinear regression exists. (See pp. 259 and 260 of Reference 8.)

Simple correlation deals with the degree of association between two variables, such as weight and height. *Multiple correlation* deals with the degree of interrelationship among three or more variables. Weight may depend not only upon height but upon age as well in the case of growing children. General intelligence in school may be related to grades in mathematics and grades in English. The yield of a potato planting may depend upon the rainfall, the temperature, the amount of fertilizer, and the spacing of the plants.

In the case of a three-way distribution, it is, of course, possible to study the correlation between x and y for a given value of z. For example, we may measure the correlation between the heights and weights of American schoolboys of age 16, or the correlation between grades in mathematics and grades in English for high school boys having intelligence quotients of 110. These are examples of *partial correlation*.

The general subject of correlation is a vast one, and one that cannot be comprehensively treated here. For further discussions of multiple and partial correlation involving not only three but more than three variables, the reader should consult other works (see for example, Reference 7).

EXERCISES

Compute r by means of formula (18.8) for the following:

1. The pairs of values in exercise 17.1.

2. The test scores in exercise 17.2.

3. The pairs of values in exercise 17.4.

4. The calculus scores in exercise 17.7.

5. Convert any slope, b, that you found in the preceding exercises into r by means of formula (18.6). Use your result to check your answer in exercises 1–4.

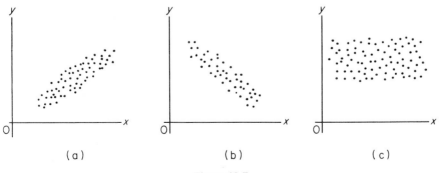

(a)   (b)   (c)

Figure 18-7

6. From the dot diagrams (Fig. 18-7), estimate the value of r associated with each.

7. From the graphs of the regression lines shown below (Fig. 18-8), estimate the value of r in each case.

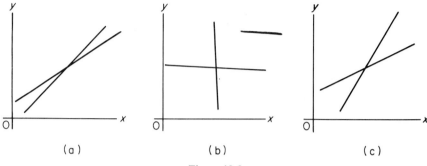

(a)   (b)   (c)

Figure 18-8

8. Examine the scatter diagram shown in Fig. 18-9. What is wrong with the following statements? (a) $r = 0.95$. (b) The line of regression of y on x has the equation $y = 11 + 2x$.

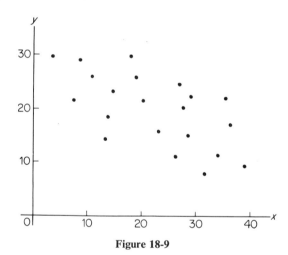

Figure 18-9

9. For 563 students majoring in literature, the correlation coefficient for verbal scores and literature scores on a Graduate Record Examination was 0.59. For 343 students majoring in chemistry, the correlation coefficient for verbal scores and chemistry was 0.43. Interpret each of these statements.

10. Five specimens of castings showed a correlation coefficient of 0.95 for hardness and tensile strength. Test $H_0 : \rho = 0$ against the alternative $H_1 : \rho \neq 0$ with $\alpha = 0.05$.

11. In a study of the relation between the average daily prescription sales and other sales, 19 drug stores showed $r = 0.45$. Make two different statements about the information that this value gives you.

12. By means of Table I, test the hypothesis that $\rho = 0$ for each of the following sample correlation coefficients, with type I errors and alternative hypotheses as indicated.

(a) $r = 0.29$, $N = 42$; $H_1:\rho \neq 0$, $\alpha = 0.05$.

(b) $r = 0.67$, $N = 18$; $H_1:\rho > 0$, $\alpha = 0.01$.

(c) $r = -0.44$, $N = 27$; $H_1:\rho < 0$, $\alpha = 0.025$.

(d) $r = -0.87$, $N = 10$; $H_1:\rho \neq 0$, $\alpha = 0.05$.

13. Find 95% confidence intervals for ρ as indicated. Use Table J.

(a) $r = 0.48$, $N = 16$.

(b) $r = -0.32$, $N = 23$.

(c) $r = 0.71$, $N = 8$.

14. A person claims that a value of $r = -0.50$ from a sample of 20 indicates moderately good correlation (say $\rho < -0.40$) in the population from which the sample was drawn. Do you agree? To answer this question find the 95% confidence interval for ρ.

15. In investigating the effects of a certain drug on a group of 19 patients, it was found that $r = 0.43$. Find 95% confidence limits for ρ.

16. The following correlation coefficients have been obtained from actual data. Assuming the samples involved to be large, how would you interpret each result?

(a) The weights and lengths of babies: $r = 0.62$ to 0.64.
(b) Right and left first joint of the ring finger: $r = 0.93$.
(c) Strength of pull and stature: $r = 0.22$ to 0.30.
(d) Number of children and per cent of desertions: $r = -0.92$.

17. Prove that formula (18.9) is equivalent to formula (18.7).

18. Compute r for the data of Table 17-1. Check your answer by means of the value of b given in formulas (17.9) and (18.6).

19

Markov Chains

A chain of proofs must have their com-
mencement somewhere.

JEREMY BENTHAM
An Introduction to the Principles of
Morals and Legislation

19.1. MATRICES AND VECTORS

Many branches of mathematics and many fields of science make extensive use of vectors and matrices. In particular, they are extremely useful
in studying Markov processes. We begin with a brief study of these entities.

A *matrix* is a rectangular array of m rows and n columns of numbers and
is written thus:

$$M = \begin{pmatrix} e_{11} & e_{12} & \cdots & e_{1n} \\ e_{21} & e_{22} & \cdots & e_{2n} \\ \cdot & \cdot & \cdots & \cdot \\ \cdot & \cdot & \cdots & \cdot \\ \cdot & \cdot & \cdots & \cdot \\ e_{m1} & e_{m2} & \cdots & e_{mn} \end{pmatrix}. \tag{19.1}$$

A *row vector* is a matrix consisting of a single row, and a *column vector*
is a matrix consisting of a single column. We illustrate these definitions with

the following examples.

(a) $\begin{pmatrix} 1 & 2 \\ 0 & 1 \\ -2 & 3 \end{pmatrix}$ (b) $\begin{pmatrix} \frac{1}{2} & \frac{1}{3} & \frac{1}{6} \\ 0 & \frac{1}{2} & \frac{1}{2} \\ \frac{1}{4} & \frac{1}{4} & \frac{1}{2} \end{pmatrix}$ (c) $\begin{pmatrix} 1 & 2 & 2 \\ -2 & -1 & 5 \\ 1 & 0 & -1 \\ 3 & 1 & 2 \end{pmatrix}$

(d) $(2,-1,3)$ (e) $\begin{pmatrix} 1 \\ 2 \\ -2 \\ 3 \end{pmatrix}$ (f) $(\frac{2}{5},\frac{3}{5},0)$

(a) is a 3×2 matrix, (b) is a 3×3 *square matrix*, (c) is a 4×3 matrix, (d) is a row vector having three components, (e) is a column vector with four components, and (f) is a special kind of row vector called a *probability vector* because its components are non-negative and have a sum of 1. (b) is also called a *stochastic matrix* since each row is a probability vector.

If two matrices, A and B, are such that the number of columns in A equals the number of rows in B, their product $A \times B$ is defined as the matrix for which the element in the ith row and jth column consists of the sum of the products obtained when each element of the ith row of A is multiplied by the corresponding element in the jth column of B. Thus an $m \times r$ matrix, A, multiplied into an $r \times n$ matrix, B, yields an $m \times n$ matrix.

EXAMPLE 1. Let $A = \begin{pmatrix} a_{11} & a_{12} & a_{13} \\ a_{21} & a_{22} & a_{23} \end{pmatrix}$ and $B = \begin{pmatrix} b_{11} & b_{12} \\ b_{21} & b_{22} \\ b_{31} & b_{32} \end{pmatrix}$.

Then

$$A \times B = \begin{pmatrix} a_{11}b_{11} + a_{12}b_{21} + a_{13}b_{31} & a_{11}b_{12} + a_{12}b_{22} + a_{13}b_{32} \\ a_{21}b_{11} + a_{22}b_{21} + a_{23}b_{31} & a_{21}b_{12} + a_{22}b_{22} + a_{23}b_{32} \end{pmatrix}.$$

Note that A is a 2×3 matrix and B is a 3×2 matrix; hence, $A \times B$ is a 2×2 matrix.

EXAMPLE 2. Let

$$A = \begin{pmatrix} 1 & 2 & 3 \\ 0 & 1 & 0 \end{pmatrix} \text{ and } B = \begin{pmatrix} 1 & 2 & 3 & 2 \\ -1 & 3 & 1 & 0 \\ 0 & -2 & -3 & 2 \end{pmatrix}.$$

Then

$$A \times B = \begin{pmatrix} -1 & 2 & -4 & 8 \\ -1 & 3 & 1 & 0 \end{pmatrix}.$$

Note that in example 2, $B \times A$ is not defined. Why? If A and B are square matrices, that is, matrices in which there are the same number of rows as columns, $A \times B \neq B \times A$ generally, for matrix multiplication is not commutative. For example, let

$$A = \begin{pmatrix} 1 & 2 \\ 2 & 1 \end{pmatrix} \quad \text{and } B = \begin{pmatrix} 0 & 1 \\ 2 & 0 \end{pmatrix}$$

then

$$A \times B = \begin{pmatrix} 4 & 1 \\ 2 & 2 \end{pmatrix} \neq B \times A = \begin{pmatrix} 2 & 1 \\ 2 & 4 \end{pmatrix},$$

for two matrices are equal if, and only if, their corresponding elements are equal.

Square matrices can be raised to the nth power $n = 2, 3, , ,$ by successive multiplications.

19.2. AN EXAMPLE

Let us assume that we possess two honest dice; one which we designate by I has four white faces and two black ones; the other, designated by II, has one white face and five black ones. We select a die at random by tossing an unbiased coin. If it shows head, we roll die I; if it shows tail, we roll die II. If the die rolled shows a white face, we roll I; if it shows a black face, we roll II. We continue this process where the choice of the die to be rolled depends on the previous outcome. This series of rolls or trials illustrates a simple type of Markov chain or, more precisely, a series of *Markov dependent binomial trials*.

In what follows, we designate by $P(W_k)$ and $P(B_k)$ the respective probabilities of W and B showing on the kth trial. Also, we let $P(W_k \mid W_{k-1})$ be the probability for W to appear on the kth trial, provided W has appeared on the $(k-1)$th trial, with similar meanings for $P(B_k \mid W_{k-1})$, $P(W_k \mid B_{k-1})$, and $P(B_k \mid B_{k-1})$.

$$P(W_1) = \frac{1}{2}\left(\frac{2}{3} + \frac{1}{6}\right) = \frac{5}{12}$$

$$P(B_1) = \frac{1}{2}\left(\frac{1}{3} + \frac{5}{6}\right) = \frac{7}{12}.$$

Then

$$P(W_2) = P(W_1)P(W_2 \mid W_1) + P(B_1)P(W_2 \mid B_1)$$
$$= \frac{5}{12} \cdot \frac{2}{3} + \frac{7}{12} \cdot \frac{1}{6} = \frac{3}{8}$$

$$P(B_2) = P(W_1)P(B_2 \mid W_1) + P(B_1)P(B_2 \mid B_1)$$
$$= \frac{5}{12} \cdot \frac{1}{3} + \frac{7}{12} \cdot \frac{5}{6} = \frac{5}{8}.$$

Also

$$P(W_3) = P(W_2)P(W_3 \mid W_2) + P(B_2)P(W_3 \mid B_2)$$

$$= \frac{3}{8} \cdot \frac{2}{3} + \frac{5}{8} \cdot \frac{1}{6} = \frac{17}{48}$$

$$P(B_3) = P(W_2)P(B_3 \mid W_2) + P(B_2)P(B_3 \mid B_2)$$

$$= \frac{3}{8} \cdot \frac{1}{3} + \frac{5}{8} \cdot \frac{5}{6} = \frac{31}{48}$$

This process may be continued indefinitely. We observe that at each step of the series $P(W_i) + P(B_i) = 1$, $i = 1, 2, , ,$. The possible outcomes and their respective probabilities may also be obtained with the aid of a tree diagram. Figure 19-1 shows such a diagram for the eventuality that die I is

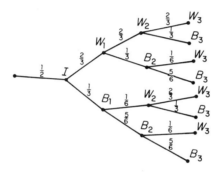

Figure 19-1

selected for the first throw. A similar diagram for the alternative eventuality can be constructed (exercise 9). For example, $P(B_3 \mid I)$, the probability for black to show on the third trial provided die I was selected for the first trial, is obtained as the sum of the products of three probabilities noted on the branches of the tree ending at B_3, ($\frac{1}{2}$ is not included).

$$P(B_3 \mid I) = \frac{4}{27} + \frac{5}{27} + \frac{1}{54} + \frac{25}{108} = \frac{7}{12}.$$

We shall now formalize the ideas contained in this example and obtain some general results.

19.3. MARKOV DEPENDENT BINOMIAL TRIALS

In the study of the binomial probability function, we were concerned with N *independent* trials of an experiment with a constant probability of success. In what follows, we are interested in a succession of *dependent* trials, where the probability of success on a given trial depends upon the outcome of the preceding trial.

Let there be N trials of an experiment, each of which has only two possible outcomes denoted by S and F. Assume that the outcome on any trial depends only on that of the preceding trial. There will then be four probabilities associated with the $(k + 1)$th trial, $k = 1, 2, , ,$ namely:

$$P(S_{k+1} \mid S_k), \quad P(S_{k+1} \mid F_k), \quad P(F_{k+1} \mid S_k), \quad \text{and} \quad P(F_{k+1} \mid F_k).$$

Thus we have defined a series of Markov dependent binomial trials. It is customary to call the outcomes *states*, and the probabilities for these outcomes, *transition probabilities*. We shall call S, state 1, and F, state 2. We speak, then, of a Markov chain with two states. Note that the probability of a given outcome on the $(k + 1)$th trial is a conditional one, depending only on the outcome on the kth trial and not on any earlier outcomes. If the four probabilities just given are independent of k, then we may write:

$$p_{11} = P(S \mid S), \quad p_{21} = P(S \mid F), \quad p_{12} = P(F \mid S), \quad \text{and} \quad p_{22} = P(F \mid F).$$

Let

$$P = \begin{pmatrix} p_{11} & p_{12} \\ p_{21} & p_{22} \end{pmatrix}. \tag{19.2}$$

It should be evident that

$$\left. \begin{aligned} p_{11} + p_{12} &= 1 \\ p_{21} + p_{22} &= 1 \end{aligned} \right\}. \tag{19.3}$$

Since each row of P is a probability vector, P is a stochastic matrix.

It is desirable to calculate $p_1^{(n)}$ and $p_2^{(n)}$, the respective probabilities for state 1 and state 2, for the $(n + 1)$th trial, that is, after n steps. It is important to note that a step in the Markov process means a transition from one trial to the next. Thus, the nth step implies $n + 1$ trials. In particular, the third trial involves two steps; from the first trial to the second, and from the second to the third. The first trial is step number zero. The equations,

$$\left. \begin{aligned} p_1^{(n)} &= p_1^{(n-1)} p_{11} + p_2^{(n-1)} p_{21} \\ p_2^{(n)} &= p_1^{(n-1)} p_{12} + p_2^{(n-1)} p_{22} \end{aligned} \right\}, \tag{19.4}$$

hold since the first right-hand member represents the probability for state 1 at the nth step, provided either state 1 or state 2 occurred at the previous step, and the second right-hand member is the probability for state 2 at the nth step, provided either state 1 or state 2 occurred at the previous step.

We may write Eq. (19.4) as the product:

$$(p_1^{(n-1)}, p_2^{(n-1)}) \begin{pmatrix} p_{11} & p_{12} \\ p_{21} & p_{22} \end{pmatrix}$$

which becomes the row vector:

$$p^{(n)} = (p_1^{(n-1)}p_{11} + p_2^{(n-1)}p_{21}, \; p_1^{(n-1)}p_{12} + p_2^{(n-1)}p_{22}). \qquad (19.5)$$

Consequently,

$$p^{(n)} = p^{(n-1)}P, \qquad (19.6)$$

which is a *recursion formula* for obtaining $p^{(n)}$ from $p^{(n-1)}$.

Since

$$p^{(1)} = p^{(0)}P$$

$$p^{(2)} = p^{(1)}P$$

$$\cdot \quad \cdot \quad \cdot$$
$$\cdot \quad \cdot \quad \cdot$$
$$\cdot \quad \cdot \quad \cdot$$

$$p^{(n)} = p^{(n-1)}P,$$

it follows that

$$p^{(n)} = p^{(0)}P^n. \qquad (19.7)$$

This means that the product of the initial probability vector $p^{(0)}$ and the nth power of the matrix of transition probabilities, P, yields the row vector $p^{(n)}$ of probabilities of being in each of the two states after n steps.

EXAMPLE 1. Let us refer to the example of Section 19.2. Let W be state 1, and B, state 2.

$$P = \begin{pmatrix} \frac{2}{3} & \frac{1}{3} \\ \frac{1}{6} & \frac{5}{6} \end{pmatrix}.$$

By Eq. (19.4)

$$\left. \begin{array}{l} p_1^{(1)} = p_1^{(0)}p_{11} + p_2^{(0)}p_{21} \\ p_2^{(1)} = p_1^{(0)}p_{12} + p_2^{(0)}p_{22} \end{array} \right\}.$$

We have previously shown that

$$P(W_1) = p_1^{(0)} = \frac{5}{12}$$

and

$$P(B_1) = p_2^{(0)} = \frac{7}{12}.$$

Then

$$p_1^{(1)} = \frac{5}{12} \cdot \frac{2}{3} + \frac{7}{12} \cdot \frac{1}{6} = \frac{3}{8}$$

$$p_2^{(1)} = \frac{5}{12} \cdot \frac{1}{3} + \frac{7}{12} \cdot \frac{5}{6} = \frac{5}{8}.$$

EXAMPLE 2. Suppose that we compute the probabilities of states 1 and 2 after three trials for the example of Section 2. Then by Eq. (19.7),

$$p^{(2)} = p^{(0)}P^2$$

$$= (\tfrac{5}{12}, \quad \tfrac{7}{12}) \begin{pmatrix} \tfrac{2}{3} & \tfrac{1}{3} \\ \tfrac{1}{6} & \tfrac{5}{6} \end{pmatrix}^2$$

$$= (\tfrac{5}{12}, \quad \tfrac{7}{12}) \begin{pmatrix} \tfrac{1}{2} & \tfrac{1}{2} \\ \tfrac{1}{4} & \tfrac{3}{4} \end{pmatrix}$$

$$= \left(\frac{17}{48}, \quad \frac{31}{48} \right).$$

It will be seen that these results agree with those obtained in Section 3.

19.4. ANOTHER METHOD

The probabilities for states 1 and 2 after n steps are given by Eq. (19.4).

$$\left.\begin{aligned} p_1^{(n)} &= p_1^{(n-1)}p_{11} + p_2^{(n-1)}p_{21} \\ p_2^{(n)} &= p_1^{(n-1)}p_{12} + p_2^{(n-1)}p_{22} \end{aligned}\right\}.$$

But

$$p_2^{(n-1)} = 1 - p_1^{(n-1)}$$

and

$$p_{21} = 1 - p_{22}.$$

Therefore,

$$p_1^{(n)} = p_1^{(n-1)}p_{11} + [1 - p_1^{(n-1)}][1 - p_{22}]$$

$$= p_1^{(n-1)}(p_{11} + p_{22} - 1) + (1 - p_{22}). \qquad \textbf{(19.8)}$$

It will be convenient to let

$$R_1 = 1 - p_{11}$$

$$R_2 = 1 - p_{22}$$

and

$$Q = p_{11} + p_{22} - 1,$$

so that Eq. (19.8) becomes:

$$p_1^{(n)} = p_1^{(n-1)}Q + R_2. \qquad \textbf{(19.9a)}$$

This is a recursion formula that enables us to compute $p_1^{(n)}$ from $p_1^{(n-1)}$. Similarly,

$$p_2^{(n)} = p_2^{(n-1)}Q + R_1. \qquad \textbf{(19.9b)}$$

Let us apply it to the example of Section 2:

$$p_{11} = \frac{2}{3} \quad p_{22} = \frac{5}{6}; \quad \text{hence} \quad R_1 = \frac{1}{3}, \quad R_2 = \frac{1}{6}, \quad \text{and} \quad Q = \frac{1}{2}.$$

For state 1 on the second trial,

$$p_1^{(1)} = p_1^{(0)}Q + R_2$$

$$= \frac{5}{12} \cdot \frac{1}{2} + \frac{1}{6} = \frac{3}{8}.$$

On the third trial,

$$p_1^{(2)} = p_1^{(1)}Q + R_2$$

$$= \frac{3}{8} \cdot \frac{1}{2} + \frac{1}{6} = \frac{17}{48},$$

and so on.

Since any $0 \leq p \leq 1$, it follows that $|Q| \leq 1$. However, we shall assume that $|Q| < 1$ in order to rule out the cases in which $p_{11} = p_{22} = 0$ or $p_{11} = p_{22} = 1$. By mathematical induction (exercise 17), it can be proved that:

$$p_1^{(n)} = \left(p_1^{(0)} - \frac{R_2}{1-Q}\right)Q^n + \frac{R_2}{1-Q}. \tag{19.10}$$

If we interchange states 1 and 2 in Eq. (19.10), the resulting equation is:

$$p_2^{(n)} = \left(p_2^{(0)} - \frac{R_1}{1-Q}\right)Q^n + \frac{R_1}{1-Q}. \tag{19.11}$$

Thus Eqs. (19.10) and (19.11) enable one to find the probabilities for states 1 and 2 after n steps without resorting to a recursion formula.

19.5. UNKNOWN INITIAL PROBABILITIES

Although the probability for state 1 at the initial trial may be unknown, one can, nevertheless, compute the probabilities for state 1 or state 2 after n steps, given states 1 or 2 at the first trial. These probabilities will be denoted by $p_{11}^{(n)}$, $p_{21}^{(n)}$, $p_{12}^{(n)}$, and $p_{22}^{(n)}$. Since

and

$$\left.\begin{aligned} p_{12}^{(n)} &= 1 - p_{11}^{(n)} \\ p_{21}^{(n)} &= 1 - p_{22}^{(n)} \end{aligned}\right\} \tag{19.12}$$

we need only to obtain $p_{11}^{(n)}$ and $p_{22}^{(n)}$. By the same method used to derive formula (19.9a), we find (exercise 20) that:

$$p_{11}^{(n)} = p_{11}^{(n-1)}Q + R_2. \tag{19.13}$$

Again we resort to mathematical induction (exercise 21) to derive:

$$p_{11}^{(n)} = \left[p_{11}^{(0)} - \frac{R_2}{1-Q}\right]Q^n + \frac{R_2}{1-Q}. \tag{19.14}$$

Because $p_{11}^{(0)} = p_{11}$, this equation becomes

$$p_{11}^{(n)} = \frac{R_1}{1 - Q} Q^n + \frac{R_2}{1 - Q}. \qquad (19.15)$$

Interchanging 1 and 2, we obtain:

$$p_{22}^{(n)} = \frac{R_2}{1 - Q} Q^n + \frac{R_1}{1 - Q}. \qquad (19.16)$$

From Eqs. (19.12) and (19.14), we find that:

$$p_{12}^{(n)} = \frac{R_1}{1 - Q} (1 - Q^n). \qquad (19.17)$$

Similarly,

$$p_{21}^{(n)} = \frac{R_2}{1 - Q} (1 - Q^n). \qquad (19.18)$$

EXAMPLE 1. In the example of Section 2, let us assume that the coin tossed at the outset of the experiment is biased, and that we do not know the probability for head. It follows that $p_1^{(0)}$ and $p_2^{(0)}$ are unknown. We can, however, compute the probabilities for the four possible conditional outcomes, $p_{11}^{(n)}$, $p_{12}^{(n)}$, $p_{21}^{(n)}$, and $p_{22}^{(n)}$, by means of Eqs. (19.15) to (19.18). For example, the probability for white (state 1) to show on the sixth roll of the die, provided the first roll showed black (state 2), is given by Eq. (19.18). $R_2 = \frac{1}{6}$ and $Q = \frac{2}{3} + \frac{5}{6} - 1 = \frac{1}{2}$. The number of steps is $n = 5$.

$$p_{21}^{(5)} = \frac{1/6}{1/2}\left[1 - \left(\frac{1}{2}\right)^5\right] = \frac{31}{96}.$$

EXAMPLE 2. The Problem of the Four Liars. The reader should refer back to Section 5.6 where this problem was stated and then solved for the three-liar case by elementary methods. We shall now consider the given succession of statements as a Markov process, where a truth is designated as state 1 and a lie as state 2; but it will not be a series of Markov dependent binomial trials unless we assume that the statements of C, B, and A are made knowing only the utterance of the previous speaker. The observed state is 1 or 2 depending on whether the corresponding statement implies that D is telling the truth or lying.

Because of the independence of the utterances,

$$p_1^{(n)} = \frac{1}{3} \quad \text{and} \quad p_2^{(n)} = \frac{2}{3} \quad \text{where } n = 0, 1, 2, 3.$$

Recalling that an even number of lies results in a truth, we can write $p_{11} = p_{22} = \frac{1}{3}$. Then $R_1 = R_2 = \frac{2}{3}$, $Q = -\frac{1}{3}$, and $1 - Q = \frac{4}{3}$.

The initial state is that of D. If A affirms that B denies that C declares that D is a liar, then for the alternatives "D told the truth," (T), and "D lied," (L), we have for the statements of A B C D, the respective combinations, $T\,T\,L\,T$ and $T\,T\,L\,L$, in each of which A implies that D told the truth. We seek, then, the probability—call it $p_{11}^{(0)}$—that D told the truth on the condition that A implied that he did. The steps, 0, 1, 2, 3, in the process correspond to the statements of D, C, B, and A, respectively.

The probability that D spoke the truth and that A implied that he did, by the multiplication theorem [formula (4.6)], may be written in these two equivalent ways:

$$p_1^{(3)} p_{11}^{(0)} = p_1^{(0)} p_{11}^{(3)}$$

whence

$$p_{11}^{(0)} = \frac{p_1^{(0)} p_{11}^{(3)}}{p_1^{(3)}}$$

Now

$$p_1^{(n)} = \tfrac{1}{3}.$$

Also by Eq. (19.15),

$$p_{11}^{(3)} = \frac{2/3}{4/3} \left(-\frac{1}{3} \right)^3 + \frac{2/3}{4/3} = \frac{13}{27}.$$

By Eq. (19.10),

$$p_1^{(3)} = \left(\frac{1}{3} - \frac{2/3}{4/3} \right) \left(-\frac{1}{3} \right)^3 + \frac{2/3}{4/3} = \frac{41}{81},$$

whence

$$p_{11}^{(0)} = \frac{(1/3)(13/27)}{41/81} = \frac{13}{41}, \qquad \text{as previously calculated.}$$

19.6. STATISTICAL EQUILIBRIUM

From the fact that $|Q| < 1$, it follows that $\lim\limits_{n \to \infty} Q^n = 0$; hence, from Eqs. (19.15) and (19.18), we find that

$$\lim_{n \to \infty} p_{11}^{(n)} = \lim_{n \to \infty} p_{21}^{(n)} = \frac{R_2}{1 - Q}, \qquad (19.19)$$

and from Eqs. (19.16) and (19.17),

$$\lim_{n \to \infty} p_{22}^{(n)} = \lim_{n \to \infty} p_{12}^{(n)} = \frac{R_1}{1 - Q}. \qquad (19.20)$$

It becomes evident that a large number of Markov dependent binomial trials leads to a state of *statistical equilibrium*. This means that $p_1^{(n)}$ and $p_2^{(n)}$ remain practically constant and independent of the initial outcomes for large n. The largeness of n will depend upon the size of Q and this, in turn, is a function of p_{11} and p_{22}. If state 1 tends to be followed by state 1, and state 2 by state 2, then equilibrium will ensue rapidly. In particular, if $p_{11} = p_{22}$ for all n, then $R_1 = R_2$ and $p_{11}^{(n)} = p_{21}^{(n)} = p_{22}^{(n)} = p_{12}^{(n)} = \tfrac{1}{2}$, approximately. This means that $p_1^{(n)} = p_2^{(n)} = \tfrac{1}{2}$, approximately, for large n. We say, then, that the binomial trials constitute a fair game.

Example. Refer to example 1 of Section 19.5. By Eq. (19.15), since $R_1 = \frac{1}{3}$, $R_2 = \frac{1}{6}$, and $Q = \frac{1}{2}$,

$$p_{11}^{(10)} = \frac{1/3}{1/2}\left(\frac{1}{2}\right)^{10} + \frac{1/6}{1/2} = \frac{1}{1536} + \frac{1}{3}.$$

By Eq. (19.19),

$$p_{21}^{(10)} = \frac{1/6}{1/2}\left[1 - \left(\frac{1}{2}\right)^{10}\right] = \frac{1}{3} - \frac{1}{3072}.$$

Each of these probabilities is approximately $\frac{1}{3}$, the value given by Eq. (19.19), regardless of the outcome on the first trial.

19.7. A MORE GENERAL MARKOV CHAIN

In the preceding sections, we discussed a sequence of experiments where each had only two states. We now consider the case where each experiment may have a finite number, r, of possible states denoted by $\{e_1, e_2, , , e_r\}$. Again we assume that the probability of an outcome depends only on the outcome immediately preceding it. Let $P(e_j \mid e_i) = p_{ij}$. It is convenient to represent the transition probabilities by means of a square matrix. Such a matrix for a 3-state Markov process is:

$$P = \begin{pmatrix} p_{11} & p_{12} & p_{13} \\ p_{21} & p_{22} & p_{23} \\ p_{31} & p_{32} & p_{33} \end{pmatrix}. \tag{19.21}$$

When a transition is impossible, its probability is defined to be 0. P is a stochastic matrix.

EXAMPLE 1. Suppose that we possess three dice: the first has three red faces, two white, and one blue; the second has two red faces, three white, and one blue; and the third has one red, two white, and three blue faces. Then an ordinary die is rolled. If it shows 1 or 4, the first colored die is rolled; if it shows 2 or 5, the second colored die is rolled; if it shows 3 or 6, the third colored die is rolled. If the colored die shows red, the first die is rolled; if white, the second die is rolled; if blue, the third die is used, and so on. Thus we have a Markov chain with three states: $e_1 = R$, $e_2 = W$, $e_3 = B$.

$$p_1^{(0)} = \frac{1}{3}\left(\frac{1}{2} + \frac{1}{3} + \frac{1}{6}\right) = \frac{1}{3}$$

$$p_2^{(0)} = \frac{1}{3}\left(\frac{1}{3} + \frac{1}{2} + \frac{1}{3}\right) = \frac{7}{18}$$

$$p_3^{(0)} = \frac{1}{3}\left(\frac{1}{6} + \frac{1}{6} + \frac{1}{2}\right) = \frac{5}{18}.$$

The transition matrix can be verified to be:

$$P = \begin{pmatrix} \frac{1}{2} & \frac{1}{3} & \frac{1}{6} \\ \frac{1}{3} & \frac{1}{2} & \frac{1}{6} \\ \frac{1}{6} & \frac{1}{3} & \frac{1}{2} \end{pmatrix}.$$

This Markov chain may be represented by a tree diagram as in Fig. 19-2.

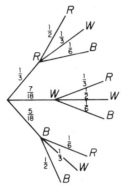

Figure 19-2

An important type of problem arises when we seek the probability $p_{ij}^{(n)}$ that a process assumed to begin in state i is in state j after n steps. The probabilities involved can be arrayed in a matrix:

$$\boldsymbol{P}^{(n)} = \begin{pmatrix} p_{11}^{(n)} & p_{12}^{(n)} & p_{13}^{(n)} \\ p_{21}^{(n)} & p_{22}^{(n)} & p_{23}^{(n)} \\ p_{31}^{(n)} & p_{32}^{(n)} & p_{33}^{(n)} \end{pmatrix}. \tag{19.22}$$

For the condition stated in the preceding example, let us ask: "What is the probability that a die shows red after two tosses following the appearance of blue?" The probabilities in the matrix (19.22) can be obtained from a tree diagram, Fig. 19-3.

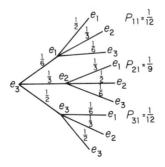

Figure 19-3

The desired probability $p_{31}^{(2)}$ is derived as the sum of the probabilities taken from all branches of the tree beginning at e_3, and ending at e_1; hence,

$$p_{31}^{(2)} = p_{11} + p_{21} + p_{31}$$

$$= \frac{1}{12} + \frac{1}{9} + \frac{1}{12} = \frac{5}{18}.$$

Similarly, $p_{32}^{(2)}$ and $p_{33}^{(2)}$ are derived. These probabilities constitute the third row of the matrix:

$$P^{(2)} = \begin{pmatrix} \frac{7}{18} & \frac{7}{18} & \frac{2}{9} \\ \frac{13}{36} & \frac{5}{12} & \frac{2}{9} \\ \frac{5}{18} & \frac{7}{18} & \frac{1}{3} \end{pmatrix}.$$

To find the first and second rows, we construct trees stemming from e_1 and e_2 (exercise 23). Note, for example, that the probabilities in row three add to 1 because, beginning at state e_3, we must arrive at some one of the three possible states after two steps.

EXAMPLE 2. Assume that in a certain region of the United States, 50% of the voters are Republicans, (e_1); 40% are Democrats, (e_2); and 10% are Independents, (e_3). Assume that in succeeding generations, 70% of the children of Republicans become Republicans; 10%, Democrats; and 20%, Independents. For the Democrats, 80% of the children become Democrats; 10%, Republicans; and 10%, Independents. For the Independents, 30%

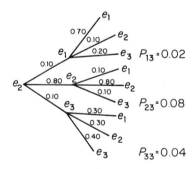

Figure 19-4

of the children become Republicans; 30%, Democrats, and 40%, Independents. What is the probability that (a) a Democrat has a grandchild who becomes an Independent? (b) a voter chosen at random has a grandchild who becomes an Independent? Assume that all voters have children who become voters.

By means of the tree diagram of Fig. 19-4, we find that

$$p_{23}^{(2)} = 0.02 + 0.08 + 0.04 = 0.14.$$

Similarly, we find that

$$p_{13}^{(2)} = 0.14 + 0.01 + 0.08 = 0.23$$

and

$$p_{33}^{(2)} = 0.06 + 0.03 + 0.16 = 0.25.$$

It follows that, for (b)

$$p_{3}^{(2)} = (0.5 \times 0.23) + (0.4 \times 0.14) + (0.1 \times 0.25) = 0.196.$$

19.8. SOME INTERESTING RELATIONSHIPS

It is possible to show that Eq. (19.6),

$$p^{(n)} = p^{(n-1)}P,$$

and Eq. (19.7),

$$p^{(n)} = p^{(0)}P^n,$$

which were derived for a 2-state Markov chain, hold also for an r-state chain (exercise 24). However, in this book, we have restricted ourselves to the 3-state case. Recalling that:

$$P = \begin{pmatrix} p_{11} & p_{12} & p_{13} \\ p_{21} & p_{22} & p_{23} \\ p_{31} & p_{32} & p_{33} \end{pmatrix}$$

and

$$P^{(n)} = \begin{pmatrix} p_{11}^{(n)} & p_{12}^{(n)} & p_{13}^{(n)} \\ p_{21}^{(n)} & p_{22}^{(n)} & p_{23}^{(n)} \\ p_{31}^{(n)} & p_{32}^{(n)} & p_{33}^{(n)} \end{pmatrix}, \tag{19.23}$$

one can show that:

$$P^{(n)} = P^n. \tag{19.24}$$

Thus the probabilities contained in $P^{(n)}$ can be obtained from matrix P by successive multiplications. Except for simple cases, these multiplications can become so laborious that the aid of a computing machine must be sought.

An interesting result is the following:

If some power of a stochastic matrix contains no zero probabilities, then

$$\lim_{n \to \infty} P^n = T, \tag{19.25}$$

where T is a stochastic matrix with identical rows.

Let us prove this result for a 2-state Markov chain. From Eqs. (19.16) and (19.17),

$$p_{22}^{(n)} = \frac{R_2}{1 - Q} Q^n + \frac{R_1}{1 - Q}$$

$$p_{12}^{(n)} = \frac{R_1}{1 - Q} (1 - Q^n).$$

Again, since $|Q| < 1$,

$$\lim_{n \to \infty} p_{22}^{(n)} = \frac{R_1}{1 - Q},$$

$$\lim_{n \to \infty} p_{12}^{(n)} = \frac{R_1}{1 - Q},$$

hence

$$p_{22}^{(n)} = p_{12}^{(n)} \quad \text{approximately, for large } n.$$

Similarly, we can prove that

$$p_{11}^{(n)} = p_{21}^{(n)} = \frac{R_2}{1 - Q} \quad \text{approximately, for large } n.$$

Since

$$P^{(n)} = \begin{pmatrix} p_{11}^{(n)} & p_{12}^{(n)} \\ p_{21}^{(n)} & p_{22}^{(n)} \end{pmatrix},$$

if we let n become infinite,

$$\lim_{n \to \infty} P^{(n)} = \begin{pmatrix} \dfrac{R_2}{1 - Q} & \dfrac{R_1}{1 - Q} \\ \dfrac{R_2}{1 - Q} & \dfrac{R_1}{1 - Q} \end{pmatrix} = T,$$

which is a stochastic matrix having identical rows (exercise 25).

By virtue of Eq. (19.24), the theorem summarized in Equation (19.25) follows.

Example. Let

$$P = \begin{pmatrix} \frac{2}{5} & \frac{3}{5} \\ \frac{2}{3} & \frac{1}{3} \end{pmatrix}.$$

Then

$$P^2 = \begin{pmatrix} 0.56 & 0.44 \\ 0.489 & 0.511 \end{pmatrix}$$

$$P^3 = \begin{pmatrix} 0.529 & 0.471 \\ 0.523 & 0.477 \end{pmatrix}$$

$$P^4 = \begin{pmatrix} 0.526 & 0.474 \\ 0.526 & 0.474 \end{pmatrix}.$$

It appears that the limit matrix T will have entries approximately equal to those in P^4.

The probability vector t, defined by the identical rows of T, is called a *fixed point* of the *transformation P* because

$$tP = t. \tag{19.26}$$

The reason for this terminology is as follows. By Eq. (19.6), the probability vector $p^{(n-1)}$, when multiplied by P, is transformed into the probability vector $p^{(n)}$. Hence, the "fixed" vector t is transformed into itself when multiplied by P.

19.9. APPLICATIONS

The theory of Markov chains has a large variety of applications. Illustrations of some of these follow.

Genetics. Characteristics of an animal are known to be determined by the genes transmitted by its parents. A given trait stems from two inherited genes, one from each parent. In a very simple type of inheritance, each gene of a transmitted pair may be either one of two types, which we shall symbolize by D and d. Thus there arise three possible combinations of genes in an individual: the genotypes DD, Dd, and dd. If an individual has inherited two D genes, one from each parent, it is said to be *dominant*, DD; if it has inherited two d genes, it is said to be *recessive*, dd; if it inherits a D gene from one parent and a d gene from the other, it is a *hybrid, Dd*.

If a dominant individual mates with another dominant, this mating can produce only dominants (Table A). An analogous conclusion results from the mating of two recessives. If a dominant mates with a hybrid, offspring of two genotypes are produced, DD and Dd, each with probability $\frac{1}{2}$ (Table B). A similar result follows when a recessive mates with a hybrid. For the mating of two hybrids, a dominant is produced with probability $\frac{1}{4}$, a hybrid with probability $\frac{1}{2}$, and a recessive with probability $\frac{1}{4}$ (Table C).

(A)			(B)			(C)		
$DD \times DD$			$DD \times Dd$			$Dd \times Dd$		
	D	D		D	d		D	d
D	DD	DD	D	DD	Dd	D	DD	Dd
D	DD	DD	D	DD	Dd	d	Dd	dd

The probability of occurrence of the three different types in the offspring of successive generations may be studied in terms of a Markov chain. The states are dominant (e_1), hybrid (e_2), and recessive (e_3). Suppose that we cross a dominant with a hybrid and then cross all succeeding generations with a hybrid. What is the probability, $p_{13}^{(3)}$, that an individual in the third generation is a recessive? We shall employ tree diagrams again to solve this problem. The two that follow (Fig. 19-5) are for the events that the individual in the

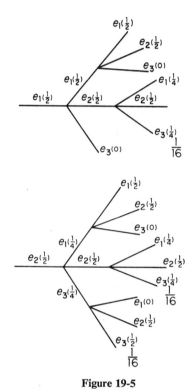

Figure 19-5

first generation is in state e_1 or in state e_2 (Table B). From these trees, it follows that the answer to our question is:

$$p_{13}^{(3)} = \frac{1}{16} + \frac{1}{16} + \frac{1}{16} = \frac{3}{16}.$$

Assume now that we begin, not necessarily with a dominant, but with an individual of unknown genotype crossed with a hybrid. The stochastic matrix for this problem can be verified to be:

$$P = \begin{pmatrix} \frac{1}{2} & \frac{1}{2} & 0 \\ \frac{1}{4} & \frac{1}{2} & \frac{1}{4} \\ 0 & \frac{1}{2} & \frac{1}{2} \end{pmatrix}.$$

Now

$$P^2 = \begin{pmatrix} \frac{3}{8} & \frac{1}{2} & \frac{1}{8} \\ \frac{1}{4} & \frac{1}{2} & \frac{1}{4} \\ \frac{1}{8} & \frac{1}{2} & \frac{3}{8} \end{pmatrix}$$

which is a matrix containing no zero probabilities. By Eq. (19.24), $P^{(n)} = P^n$.

It is possible to show that, according to Eq. (19.25),

$$\lim_{n \to \infty} P^n = T = \begin{pmatrix} \frac{1}{4} & \frac{1}{2} & \frac{1}{4} \\ \frac{1}{4} & \frac{1}{2} & \frac{1}{4} \\ \frac{1}{4} & \frac{1}{2} & \frac{1}{4} \end{pmatrix}$$

which means that after a number of generations, the offspring have approximately the probabilities $\frac{1}{4}$, $\frac{1}{2}$, and $\frac{1}{4}$ of being a dominant, a hybrid, and a recessive, respectively.

It is interesting to note that if the situation discussed in the preceding paragraphs were altered so that the animal of unknown genotype were crossed with a dominant instead of a recessive, and all succeeding offspring were similarly crossed, we could not obtain a recessive offspring at any time even for the first generation. A hybrid is, of course, possible, but the chance of having a hybrid n times in succession is $(\frac{1}{2})^n$. (Note that for P, all the probabilities of the second column equal $\frac{1}{2}$). Since $\lim_{n \to \infty} (\frac{1}{2})^n = 0$, we shall eventually have a dominant. Since it will be mated with a dominant, all succeeding animals will be dominant. Unfortunately, relation Eq. (19.25) is not valid since no power of P is devoid of zero probabilities. The proofs of these facts are omitted.

Random Walk. The phenomenon known as random walk is studied in many branches of physics. We shall discuss briefly one of its simplest forms.

Let there be equally spaced points on a straight line, numbered 1, 2, , , n. (See Fig. 19.6). A particle, initially at point i, $0 < i < n$, moves with prob-

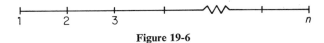

Figure 19-6

ability, p, a step of one unit toward n, and with probability, q, one step toward 1; $p + q = 1$. Whenever the particle reaches 1 or n, its motion is terminated. The succession of movements gives rise to a finite Markov chain with *absorbing barriers* 1 and n. Each position is called a state so that we have an n-state chain.

The stochastic matrix for the case $n = 4$ is:

$$P = \begin{pmatrix} 1 & 0 & 0 & 0 \\ q & 0 & p & 0 \\ 0 & q & 0 & p \\ 0 & 0 & 0 & 1 \end{pmatrix}.$$

For clarification, let us interpret row 2 of this matrix. It contains the probabilities $p_{21} = q$, $p_{22} = 0$, $p_{23} = p$, and $p_{24} = 0$. Thus, if the particle is initially at point 2, $p_{21} = q$ tells us that it moves to 1 with probability q; $p_{22} = 0$ since the particle cannot remain stationary at 2; it must move either forward or backward; $p_{23} = p$ means that it moves from 2 to 3 with probability p; $p_{24} = 0$ means that it cannot move two steps at a time—from 2 to 4.

Among many interesting questions which one may ask concerning random walk are the following:

(1) If a particle starts at position i, what is the probability that after a given number of steps it will be absorbed at n? At 1?
(2) What is the most probable path of the particle?

Let us consider the case for $n = 4$ with $i = 3$, $p = \frac{3}{5}$, and $q = \frac{2}{5}$, with the aid of a tree (Fig. 19-7). Assume five steps. Clearly, the probability for being absorbed at 4 after five steps is given by:

$$p_{34}^{(5)} = \frac{108}{3125} = 0.0346.$$

The most probable path turns out to be the shortest, from 3 to 4 with probability $\frac{3}{5}$. We may note that, if the walk continued indefinitely, there is a possibility that the particle would oscillate between 2 and 3. For $2n$ steps, in this eventuality the probability is $(\frac{2}{5} \cdot \frac{3}{5})^n$ which has the limit 0 as n increases without limit. Clearly, it is unlikely that such an oscillation would continue without end.

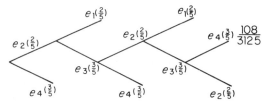

Figure 19-7

The random walk may be studied under various other conditions. Instead of absorption at the boundaries, there may be reflection back to an interior position or to the opposite boundary. Reflection is a condition present when the molecules of a gas are confined within a closed vessel. The various cases for large n must be handled with more complex techniques than we can present in this brief chapter, and the computations necessitate the use of modern computing machines.

Gambler's Ruin. A famous problem involving a game of chance has an intimate relation with the problem of random walk. Suppose that two gamblers, A and B, play a game. A has i dollars and B, j dollars. At each play, A has a probability, p, of winning and q of losing a dollar. The gamblers' play continues for n plays or until one of them has lost all his money. What is the probability that A is ruined, that is, that he loses all of his i dollars? In a fair game, $p = q = \frac{1}{2}$.

In this problem, the number of dollars possessed by A corresponds to position i in the random walk. A step toward n means a winning play for A; a step toward 1 means a winning play for B. Arrival at position 1 means ruin for A; at position n, ruin for B.

EXERCISES

1. Which of the following are probability vectors? Why?
(a) $(\frac{1}{2}, \frac{5}{12}, \frac{1}{12})$
(b) $(\frac{1}{2}, -\frac{1}{2}, 0)$
(c) $(2, 3, 5)$
(d) $(\frac{1}{7}, \frac{2}{7}, \frac{4}{7})$

2. Which of the following are stochastic matrices? Why?

(a) $\begin{pmatrix} 1 & 0 \\ \frac{1}{6} & \frac{5}{6} \end{pmatrix}$ (b) $\begin{pmatrix} \frac{2}{7} & \frac{5}{7} \\ \frac{1}{2} & \frac{1}{2} \end{pmatrix}$

(c) $\begin{pmatrix} 1 & 0 & 0 \\ 0 & 1 & 0 \\ \frac{1}{2} & 0 & \frac{1}{2} \end{pmatrix}$ (d) $\begin{pmatrix} \frac{1}{3} & -\frac{2}{3} & 0 \\ \frac{1}{2} & \frac{1}{2} & 0 \\ \frac{1}{5} & \frac{1}{5} & \frac{3}{5} \end{pmatrix}$

Find the indicated products in exercises 3–7.

3. (a) $\begin{pmatrix} 1 & 2 \\ 0 & 1 \end{pmatrix} \times \begin{pmatrix} 2 & 3 \\ -1 & 2 \end{pmatrix}$

(b) $\begin{pmatrix} \frac{1}{2} & \frac{1}{2} \\ \frac{2}{5} & \frac{3}{5} \end{pmatrix} \times \begin{pmatrix} \frac{1}{3} & \frac{2}{3} \\ \frac{1}{4} & \frac{3}{4} \end{pmatrix}$

4. (a) $\begin{pmatrix} 1 & 2 & 3 \\ 1 & 0 & 1 \\ -1 & -1 & 0 \end{pmatrix} \times \begin{pmatrix} 1 & -1 & 0 \\ 2 & 3 & 1 \\ 1 & 2 & -1 \end{pmatrix}$

(b) $\begin{pmatrix} -1 & 1 & 0 \\ 0 & 0 & 1 \\ 2 & 3 & 2 \end{pmatrix} \times \begin{pmatrix} 3 & 4 & 5 \\ 1 & 2 & 3 \\ 2 & 3 & 4 \end{pmatrix}$

5. (a) $(1,2)\begin{pmatrix} 1 & -1 \\ 2 & 2 \end{pmatrix}$ (b) $(\frac{1}{4}, \frac{1}{4}, \frac{1}{2})\begin{pmatrix} \frac{1}{3} & \frac{2}{3} \\ \frac{3}{5} & \frac{2}{5} \\ \frac{1}{2} & \frac{1}{2} \end{pmatrix}$

6. (a) $\begin{pmatrix} a_{11} & a_{12} \\ a_{21} & a_{22} \end{pmatrix} \times \begin{pmatrix} c_{11} & c_{12} \\ c_{21} & c_{22} \end{pmatrix}$ (b) $\begin{pmatrix} a & b \\ c & d \end{pmatrix} \times \begin{pmatrix} e & f \\ g & h \end{pmatrix}$

7. $\begin{pmatrix} 1 & -1 \\ 0 & 2 \\ 2 & 1 \end{pmatrix}\begin{pmatrix} 0 & 2 & 3 \\ 1 & 0 & -1 \end{pmatrix}$

8. Given $A = \begin{pmatrix} \frac{1}{2} & \frac{1}{2} \\ \frac{2}{3} & \frac{1}{3} \end{pmatrix}$, find A^2 and A^3.

9. Construct a tree diagram for the eventuality that die II is selected for the first toss in the example of Section 19.2. Extend this diagram to three trials as in Fig. 19-1.

10. From the diagram of the preceding exercise where die II is chosen for the first toss, find the probability (a) for black to show on the second trial; (b) for white to show on the third trial; (c) for black to show on the third trial.

11. Refer to the results in examples 1 and 2 of Section 19.3 and apply formula (19.7) to obtain $p_1^{(3)}$ and $p_2^{(3)}$.

12. Imagine a series of electric switches in a mechanism. Denote an open switch by 1 and a closed switch by 2. At any random instant that the mechanism is in operation, assume $p_1^{(0)} = \frac{1}{5}$ and $p_2^{(0)} = \frac{4}{5}$. Also, $p_{11} = \frac{1}{10}$, $p_{12} = \frac{9}{10}$, $p_{21} = \frac{3}{5}$, and $p_{22} = \frac{2}{5}$ for all switches except the first. What is the probability that the fourth switch is open?

13. Assume a series of electric switches where the probability is $\frac{3}{5}$ that a switch is open if the preceding one is, and $\frac{2}{5}$ that a switch is closed if the preceding one is open. The probability is $\frac{2}{3}$ that a switch is open if the preceding is closed and $\frac{1}{3}$ that it is closed if the preceding one is closed. Find the probability (a) that the third switch is open, and (b) that the third is open if the first is. Assume that the probability for the first switch to be open is $\frac{1}{2}$.

14. Solve exercise 13, part (b), by means of a tree diagram.

15. In the example of Section 19.2, compute $p_{11}^{(4)}$, $p_{12}^{(4)}$, and $p_{22}^{(4)}$. Verify that

$$p_{11}^{(4)} + p_{12}^{(4)} = 1 \quad \text{and} \quad p_{21}^{(4)} + p_{22}^{(4)} = 1,$$

where state 1 is white and state 2 is black.

16. Given the equation, $p_n = ap_{n-1} + b$, where a and b are constants and $n = 1, 2, , ,$. If a sequence of numbers $p_0, p_1, p_2, , ,$ satisfies this equation, prove that

$$p_n = \left(p_0 - \frac{b}{1-a} \right) a^n + \frac{b}{1-a}, \text{ provided } a \neq 1.$$

Use mathematical induction.

17. Derive formula (19.10) by mathematical induction. Note that Eq. (19.9) is an equation of the form $p_n = ap_{n-1} + b$. (See exercise 16.)

18. Prove that $p_1^{(n)} + p_2^{(n)} = 1$.

19. Derive formula (19.9b): $p_2^{(n)} = p_2^{(n-1)}Q + R_1$.

20. Derive formula (19.13): $p_{11}^{(n)} = p_{11}^{(n-1)}Q + R_2$.

21. Derive formula (19.14):

$$p_{11}^{(n)} = \left[p_{11}^{(0)} - \frac{R_2}{1-Q} \right] Q^n + \frac{R_2}{1-Q}.$$

22. In the town of Graumark, there are only two political parties, the Hokes and the Dokes. Every year an election for mayor is held, and the mayor serves only one year. The probability that a Hoke succeeds a Hoke as mayor is $\frac{3}{5}$, and that a Doke succeeds a Doke is $\frac{1}{2}$. If a Hoke is elected mayor in 1965, what is the probability that (a) another Hoke will be elected in 1968? (b) a Doke will be elected in 1967?

23. For the data of example 1 of Section 19.7, verify the values given in (a) the first row, and (b) the second row of the matrix $P^{(2)}$.

24. Prove that Eqs. (19.6) and (19.7) hold for an r-state chain, $r > 2$.

25. Prove that
$$\begin{pmatrix} \dfrac{R_1}{1-Q} & \dfrac{R_2}{1-Q} \\ \dfrac{R_1}{1-Q} & \dfrac{R_2}{1-Q} \end{pmatrix}$$
is a stochastic matrix.

26. If $P = \begin{pmatrix} 0.3 & 0.7 \\ 0.6 & 0.4 \end{pmatrix}$; find (a) P^2, P^3, and P^4, (b) the approximate values of the entries in the limit matrix T. Round off each entry to the second decimal place. (c) What is the fixed vector?

27. Verify by means of a tree diagram the values of $p_{13}^{(2)}$ and $p_{33}^{(2)}$ given at the end of Section 19.7.

28. From Fig. 19-5, find the probability that an animal in the third generation is (a) a dominant; (b) a hybrid.

29. Construct a tree for two generations when a hybrid is crossed with a hybrid, and then these offspring are crossed with a hybrid. What is the probability that an offspring of the second generation is a hybrid?

30. From Fig. 19-7, find the probability that the particle reaches position 2 after (a) three steps; (b) five steps; (c) $2m$ steps.

31. From Fig. 19-7, extended if necessary, find the probability that the particle is absorbed after (a) three steps; (b) six steps.

32. A gambles with B in a fair game. Each begins with $3 and they play three times. What is the probability that A (a) goes broke? (b) wins $1?

References

PROBABILITY AND STATISTICS

1. Dixon, W. J., and F. J. Massey, Jr., *Introduction to Statistical Analysis*, 2nd ed., New York: McGraw-Hill Book Co., Inc., 1957.

2. Feller, W., *An Introduction to Probability Theory and Its Applications*, 2nd Ed. Vol. I, New York: John Wiley & Sons, Inc., 1957.

3. Freund, J. E., *Mathematical Statistics*, Englewood Cliffs, N.J.: Prentice-Hall, Inc., 1962.

4. Goldberg, S., *Probability—An Introduction*, Englewood Cliffs, N.J.: Prentice-Hall, Inc., 1960.

5. Hodges, J. L. Jr., and E. L. Lehmann, *Basic Concepts of Probability and Statistics*, San Francisco: Holden-Day, Inc., 1964.

6. Hoel, P. G., *Introduction to Mathematical Statistics*, 3rd Ed., New York: John Wiley & Sons, Inc., 1962.

7. Kenney, J. F., and E. S. Keeping, *Mathematics of Statistics*, 3rd Ed., Part I. 2nd Ed., Part 2. New York D. Van Nostrand Co., Inc., 1951, 1954.

8. Mode, E. B., *Elements of Statistics*, 3rd Ed., Englewood Cliffs, N.J.: Prentice-Hall, Inc., 1961.

9. Mood, A. M., and F. A. Graybill, *Introduction to the Theory of Statistics*, 2nd Ed., New York: McGraw-Hill Book Co., Inc., 1963.

10. Mosteller, F., R. E. K. Rourke, and G. B. Thomas Jr., *Probability with Statistical Applications*, Reading, Mass.: Addison-Wesley Publishing Co., Inc., 1961.

11. Parzen, E., *Modern Probability Theory and Its Applications*, New York: John Wiley & Sons, Inc., 1960.

12. Tucker, H. G., *An Introduction to Probability and Mathematical Statistics*, New York: Academic Press, 1962.

TABLES

13. Burington, R. S., and D. C. May, *Handbook of Probability and Statistics with Tables*, New York: McGraw-Hill Book Co., Inc., 1953.

14. David, F. N., *Tables of the Ordinates and Probability Integral of the Distribution of the Correlation Coefficient in Small Samples*, New York: Cambridge University Press, 1938.

15. Finney, D. J., R. Latscha, B. M. Bennett, and P. Hsu, *Tables for Testing Significance in a 2 × 2 Contingency Table*, New York: Cambridge University Press, 1963.

16. Fisher, R. A., and F. Yates, *Statistical Tables for Biological, Agricultural, and Medical Research*, 6th Ed., New York: Hafner Publishing Co., Inc., 1962.

17. *Tables of the Cumulative Binomial Probability Distribution*, Cambridge: Harvard University Computation Laboratory, 1955.

18. Lieberman, G. J., and D. B. Owen, *Tables of the Hypergeometric Probability Distribution*, Stanford, Cal.: Stanford University Press, 1961.

19. Mainland, D., L. Herrera, and M. I. Sutcliffe, *Statistical Tables for Use with Binomial Samples: Contingency Tests, Confidence Limits, and Samples Size Estimates*, Department of Medical Statistics, New York: New York University College of Medicine, 1956.

20. Molina, E. C., *Poisson's Exponential Binomial Limit*, New York: D. Van Nostrand Co., Inc., 1947.

21. National Bureau of Standards, *Tables of the Binomial Probability Distribution*, Washington, D.C., 1949.

22. Pearson, E. S., and H. O. Hartley, Editors, *Biometrika Tables for Statisticians*, 2nd Ed., (Two Vol.), New York: Cambridge University Press, 1958.

23. Rand Corporation, *A Million Random Digits*, Glencoe, Ill.: The Free Press, 1955.

JOURNALS

24. *The Annals of Mathematical Statistics*, Official Journal of the Institute of Mathematical Statistics, Prof. G. G. Resnikoff, Department of Statistics, California State College, Hayward, Calif.

25. *Biometrics*, published by the American Statistical Association for its Biometric Section, 1757 K St., N.W., Washington, D.C.

26. *Biometrika*, issued by the Biometrika Office, University College, London.

27. *Journal of the American Statistical Association*, 1757 K St., N.W., Washington, D.C.

28. *Psychometrika*, Official Journal of the Psychometric Society, Colorado Springs Colo.

N	0.00	0.01	0.02	0.03	0.04	0.05	0.06	0.07	0.08	0.09
5.0	25.00	25.10	25.20	25.30	25.40	25.50	25.60	25.70	25.81	25.91
5.1	26.01	26.11	26.21	26.32	26.42	26.52	26.63	26.73	26.83	26.94
5.2	27.04	27.14	27.25	27.35	27.46	27.56	27.67	27.77	27.88	27.98
5.3	28.09	28.20	28.30	28.41	28.52	28.62	28.73	28.84	28.94	29.05
5.4	29.16	29.27	29.38	29.48	29.59	29.70	29.81	29.92	30.03	30.14
5.5	30.25	30.36	30.47	30.58	30.69	30.80	30.91	31.02	31.14	31.25
5.6	31.36	31.47	31.58	31.70	31.81	31.92	32.04	32.15	32.26	32.38
5.7	32.49	32.60	32.72	32.83	32.95	33.06	33.18	33.29	33.41	33.52
5.8	33.64	33.76	33.87	33.99	34.11	34.22	34.34	34.46	34.57	34.69
5.9	34.81	34.93	35.05	35.16	35.28	35.40	35.52	35.64	35.76	35.88
6.0	36.00	36.12	36.24	36.36	36.48	36.60	36.72	36.84	36.97	37.09
6.1	37.21	37.33	37.45	37.58	37.70	37.82	37.95	38.07	38.19	38.32
6.2	38.44	38.56	38.69	38.81	38.94	39.06	39.19	39.31	39.44	39.56
6.3	39.69	39.82	39.94	40.07	40.20	40.32	40.45	40.58	40.70	40.83
6.4	40.96	41.09	41.22	41.34	41.47	41.60	41.73	41.86	41.99	42.12
6.5	42.25	42.38	42.51	42.64	42.77	42.90	43.03	43.16	43.30	43.43
6.6	43.56	43.69	43.82	43.96	44.09	44.22	44.36	44.49	44.62	44.76
6.7	44.89	45.02	45.16	45.29	45.43	45.56	45.70	45.83	45.97	46.10
6.8	46.24	46.38	46.51	46.65	46.79	46.92	47.06	47.20	47.33	47.47
6.9	47.61	47.75	47.89	48.02	48.16	48.30	48.44	48.58	48.72	48.86
7.0	49.00	49.14	49.28	49.42	49.56	49.70	49.84	49.98	50.13	50.27
7.1	50.41	50.55	50.69	50.84	50.98	51.12	51.27	51.41	51.55	51.70
7.2	51.84	51.98	52.13	52.27	52.42	52.56	52.71	52.85	53.00	53.14
7.3	53.29	53.44	53.58	53.73	53.88	54.02	54.17	54.32	54.46	54.61
7.4	54.76	54.91	55.06	55.20	55.35	55.50	55.65	55.80	55.95	56.10
7.5	56.25	56.40	56.55	56.70	56.85	57.00	57.15	57.30	57.46	57.61
7.6	57.76	57.91	58.06	58.22	58.37	58.52	58.68	58.83	58.98	59.14
7.7	59.29	59.44	59.60	59.75	59.91	60.06	60.22	60.37	60.53	60.68
7.8	60.84	61.00	61.15	61.31	61.47	61.62	61.78	61.94	62.09	62.25
7.9	62.41	62.57	62.73	62.88	63.04	63.20	63.36	63.52	63.68	63.84
8.0	64.00	64.16	64.32	64.48	64.64	64.80	64.96	65.12	65.29	65.45
8.1	65.61	65.77	65.93	66.10	66.26	66.42	66.59	66.75	66.91	67.08
8.2	67.24	67.40	67.57	67.73	67.90	68.06	68.23	68.39	68.56	68.72
8.3	68.89	69.06	69.22	69.39	69.56	69.72	69.89	70.06	70.22	70.39
8.4	70.56	70.73	70.90	71.06	71.23	71.40	71.57	71.74	71.91	72.08
8.5	72.25	72.42	72.59	72.76	72.93	73.10	73.27	73.44	73.62	73.79
8.6	73.96	74.13	74.30	74.48	74.65	74.82	75.00	75.17	75.34	75.52
8.7	75.69	75.86	76.04	76.21	76.39	76.56	76.74	76.91	77.09	77.26
8.8	77.44	77.62	77.79	77.97	78.15	78.32	78.50	78.68	78.85	79.03
8.9	79.21	79.39	79.57	79.74	79.92	80.10	80.28	80.46	80.64	80.82
9.0	81.00	81.18	81.36	81.54	81.72	81.90	82.08	82.26	82.45	82.63
9.1	82.81	82.99	83.17	83.36	83.54	83.72	83.91	84.09	84.27	84.46
9.2	84.64	84.82	85.01	85.19	85.38	85.56	85.75	85.93	86.12	86.30
9.3	86.49	86.68	86.86	87.05	87.24	87.42	87.61	87.80	87.98	88.17
9.4	88.36	88.55	88.74	88.92	89.11	89.30	89.49	89.68	89.87	90.06
9.5	90.25	90.44	90.63	90.82	91.01	91.20	91.39	91.58	91.78	91.97
9.6	92.16	92.35	92.54	92.74	92.93	93.12	93.32	93.51	93.70	93.90
9.7	94.09	94.28	94.48	94.67	94.87	95.06	95.26	95.45	95.65	95.84
9.8	96.04	96.24	96.43	96.63	96.83	97.02	97.22	97.42	97.61	97.81
9.9	98.01	98.21	98.41	98.60	98.80	99.00	99.20	99.40	99.60	99.80
N	0.00	0.01	0.02	0.03	0.04	0.05	0.06	0.07	0.08	0.09

EXAMPLE 1. The numeral 541.6 is marked thus: 5′41′.6. The first digit on the left of the square root of 541.6 is 2, the first approximation to $\sqrt{5}$. The final square root will then have the form $2x \cdot x$ where the x's are determined from the table as follows: In the N column, we seek the numbers beginning with 2 and then look for the number nearest to 5416 in the table. The decimal point is temporarily neglected. This number in the table is 5429 which corresponds to 233, hence $\sqrt{541.6} = 23.3$.

EXAMPLE 2. $\sqrt{0.00′11′93}$ has the form $0.03xx$ and is nearest to 1190, hence $\sqrt{0.001193} = 0.0345$.

Greater accuracy, if desired, can be obtained by interpolation.

METHODS OF USE OF TABLE B

This is an abbreviated table of cumulative binomial probabilities, that is to say, each value tabulated is the sum of the probabilities from a value of $x = k$ up to and including N. The following examples should clarify this statement.

EXAMPLE 1

If 30% of candidates usually fail a difficult examination, what is the probability that at least half of a group of 20 fail?

The answer is obtained as the cumulative sum

$$\sum_{x=10}^{20} \frac{20!}{x!(20-x)!} (0.30)^x (0.70)^{20-x} = 0.0480,$$

found directly from the table which is entered for $N = 20$, $k = 10$, and $p = 0.30$.

EXAMPLE 2

If a pair of dice is rolled 12 times, what is the probability that the sum 5 or 6 appears fewer than the expected number of times?

Here $N = 12$ and $p = 0.25$, whence $E(x) = 3$. Therefore

$$P(x < 3) = \sum_{x=0}^{2} P(x) = 1 - \sum_{x=3}^{12} P(x)$$

$$= 1 - 0.6093 = 0.3907.$$

EXAMPLE 3

For $N = 15$ and $p = 0.60$, find the probability for 12 or more successes. Since values for $p > 0.50$ are not found in the table, we note that 12 or more successes is equivalent to 3 or fewer failures, so we make use of $q = 1 - p = 0.40$.

$$\sum_{x=12}^{15} \frac{15!}{x!(15-x)!} (0.60)^x(0.40)^{15-x} = \sum_{x=0}^{3} \frac{15!}{x!(15-x)!} (0.40)^x(0.60)^{15-x}$$

$$= 1 - \sum_{x=4}^{12} \frac{15!}{x!(15-x)!} (0.40)^x(0.60)^{15-x}$$

$$= 1 - 0.9095 = 0.0905.$$

An individual binomial probability term, $P(x = k)$ can be derived from this table by simple subtraction since

$$P(x = k) = \sum_{x=k}^{N} P(x) - \sum_{x=k+1}^{N} P(x).$$

EXAMPLE 4

For the dice data of example 2, find (from the table) the probability of obtaining the sum 5 or 6 just four times.

$$P(x = 4) = \frac{12!}{4!8!}\left(\frac{1}{4}\right)^4\left(\frac{3}{4}\right)^8$$

$$= \sum_{x=4}^{12} \frac{12!}{x!(12-x)!}\left(\frac{1}{4}\right)^x\left(\frac{3}{4}\right)^{12-x} - \sum_{x=5}^{12} \frac{12!}{x!(12-x)!}\left(\frac{1}{4}\right)^x\left(\frac{3}{4}\right)^{12-x}$$

$$= 0.3512 - 0.1576 = 0.1936.$$

CUMULATIVE BINOMIAL PROBABILITIES*

$$\sum_{x=k}^{N} \frac{N!}{x!(N-x)!} p^x q^{N-x}$$

N	k	0.05	0.10	0.15	0.20	0.25	0.30	0.35	0.40	0.45	0.50
							p				
2	1	0.0975	0.1900	0.2775	0.3600	0.4375	0.5100	0.5775	0.6400	0.6975	0.7500
	2	0.0025	0.0100	0.0225	0.0400	0.0625	0.0900	0.1225	0.1600	0.2025	0.2500
3	1	0.1426	0.2710	0.3859	0.4880	0.5781	0.6570	0.7254	0.7840	0.8336	0.8750
	2	0.0072	0.0280	0.0608	0.1040	0.1562	0.2160	0.2818	0.3520	0.4252	0.5000
	3	0.0001	0.0010	0.0034	0.0080	0.0156	0.0270	0.0429	0.0640	0.0911	0.1250
4	1	0.1855	0.3439	0.4780	0.5904	0.6836	0.7599	0.8215	0.8704	0.9085	0.9375
	2	0.0140	0.0523	0.1095	0.1808	0.2617	0.3483	0.4370	0.5248	0.6090	0.6875
	3	0.0005	0.0037	0.0120	0.0272	0.0508	0.0837	0.1265	0.1792	0.2415	0.3125
	4	0.0000	0.0001	0.0005	0.0016	0.0039	0.0081	0.0150	0.0256	0.0410	0.0625
5	1	0.2262	0.4095	0.5563	0.6723	0.7627	0.8319	0.8840	0.9222	0.9497	0.9688
	2	0.0226	0.0815	0.1648	0.2627	0.3672	0.4718	0.5716	0.6630	0.7438	0.8125
	3	0.0012	0.0086	0.0266	0.0579	0.1035	0.1631	0.2352	0.3174	0.4069	0.5000
	4	0.0000	0.0005	0.0022	0.0067	0.0156	0.0308	0.0540	0.0870	0.1312	0.1875
	5	0.0000	0.0000	0.0001	0.0003	0.0010	0.0024	0.0053	0.0102	0.0185	0.0312
6	1	0.2649	0.4686	0.6229	0.7379	0.8220	0.8824	0.9246	0.9533	0.9723	0.9844
	2	0.0328	0.1143	0.2235	0.3446	0.4661	0.5798	0.6809	0.7667	0.8364	0.8906
	3	0.0022	0.0158	0.0473	0.0989	0.1694	0.2557	0.3529	0.4557	0.5585	0.6562
	4	0.0001	0.0013	0.0059	0.0170	0.0376	0.0705	0.1174	0.1792	0.2553	0.3438
	5	0.0000	0.0001	0.0004	0.0016	0.0046	0.0109	0.0223	0.0410	0.0692	0.1094
	6	0.0000	0.0000	0.0000	0.0001	0.0002	0.0007	0.0018	0.0041	0.0083	0.0156
7	1	0.3017	0.5217	0.6794	0.7903	0.8665	0.9176	0.9510	0.9720	0.9848	0.9922
	2	0.0444	0.1497	0.2834	0.4233	0.5551	0.6706	0.7662	0.8414	0.8976	0.9375
	3	0.0038	0.0257	0.0738	0.1480	0.2436	0.3529	0.4677	0.5801	0.6836	0.7734
	4	0.0002	0.0027	0.0121	0.0333	0.0706	0.1260	0.1998	0.2898	0.3917	0.5000
	5	0.0000	0.0002	0.0012	0.0047	0.0129	0.0288	0.0556	0.0963	0.1529	0.2266
	6	0.0000	0.0000	0.0001	0.0004	0.0013	0.0038	0.0090	0.0188	0.0357	0.0625
	7	0.0000	0.0000	0.0000	0.0000	0.0001	0.0002	0.0006	0.0016	0.0037	0.0078
8	1	0.3366	0.5695	0.7275	0.8322	0.8999	0.9424	0.9681	0.9832	0.9916	0.9961
	2	0.0572	0.1869	0.3428	0.4967	0.6329	0.7447	0.8309	0.8936	0.9368	0.9648
	3	0.0058	0.0381	0.1052	0.2031	0.3215	0.4482	0.5722	0.6846	0.7799	0.8555
	4	0.0004	0.0050	0.0214	0.0563	0.1138	0.1941	0.2936	0.4059	0.5230	0.6367
	5	0.0000	0.0004	0.0029	0.0104	0.0273	0.0580	0.1061	0.1737	0.2604	0.3633
	6	0.0000	0.0000	0.0002	0.0012	0.0042	0.0113	0.0253	0.0498	0.0885	0.1445
	7	0.0000	0.0000	0.0000	0.0001	0.0004	0.0013	0.0036	0.0085	0.0181	0.0352
	8	0.0000	0.0000	0.0000	0.0000	0.0000	0.0001	0.0002	0.0007	0.0017	0.0039
9	1	0.3698	0.6126	0.7684	0.8658	0.9249	0.9596	0.9793	0.9899	0.9954	0.9980
	2	0.0712	0.2252	0.4005	0.5638	0.6997	0.8040	0.8789	0.9295	0.9615	0.9805
	3	0.0084	0.0530	0.1409	0.2618	0.3993	0.5372	0.6627	0.7682	0.8505	0.9102
	4	0.0006	0.0083	0.0339	0.0856	0.1657	0.2703	0.3911	0.5174	0.6386	0.7461
	5	0.0000	0.0009	0.0056	0.0196	0.0489	0.0988	0.1717	0.2666	0.3786	0.5000
	6	0.0000	0.0001	0.0006	0.0031	0.0100	0.0253	0.0536	0.0994	0.1658	0.2539
	7	0.0000	0.0000	0.0000	0.0003	0.0013	0.0043	0.0112	0.0250	0.0498	0.0898
	8	0.0000	0.0000	0.0000	0.0000	0.0001	0.0004	0.0014	0.0038	0.0091	0.0195
	9	0.0000	0.0000	0.0000	0.0000	0.0000	0.0000	0.0001	0.0003	0.0008	0.0020

* From *Handbook of Probability and Statistics with Tables* by R. S. Burington and D. C. May. Copyright, 1953. McGraw-Hill Book Company. By permission.

TABLE B (*Continued*)

N	k	0.05	0.10	0.15	0.20	0.25	0.30	0.35	0.40	0.45	0.50
						P					
10	1	0.4013	0.6513	0.8031	0.8926	0.9437	0.9718	0.9865	0.9940	0.9975	0.9990
	2	0.0861	0.2639	0.4557	0.6242	0.7560	0.8507	0.9140	0.9536	0.9767	0.9893
	3	0.0115	0.0702	0.1798	0.3222	0.4744	0.6172	0.7384	0.8327	0.9004	0.9453
	4	0.0010	0.0128	0.0500	0.1209	0.2241	0.3504	0.4862	0.6177	0.7340	0.8281
	5	0.0001	0.0016	0.0099	0.0328	0.0781	0.1503	0.2485	0.3669	0.4956	0.6230
	6	0.0000	0.0001	0.0014	0.0064	0.0197	0.0473	0.0949	0.1662	0.2616	0.3770
	7	0.0000	0.0000	0.0001	0.0009	0.0035	0.0106	0.0260	0.0548	0.1020	0.1719
	8	0.0000	0.0000	0.0000	0.0001	0.0004	0.0016	0.0048	0.0123	0.0274	0.0547
	9	0.0000	0.0000	0.0000	0.0000	0.0000	0.0001	0.0005	0.0017	0.0045	0.0107
	10	0.0000	0.0000	0.0000	0.0000	0.0000	0.0000	0.0000	0.0001	0.0003	0.0010
11	1	0.4312	0.6862	0.8327	0.9141	0.9578	0.9802	0.9912	0.9964	0.9986	0.9995
	2	0.1019	0.3026	0.5078	0.6779	0.8029	0.8870	0.9394	0.9698	0.9861	0.9941
	3	0.0152	0.0896	0.2212	0.3826	0.5448	0.6873	0.7999	0.8811	0.9348	0.9673
	4	0.0016	0.0185	0.0694	0.1611	0.2867	0.4304	0.5744	0.7037	0.8089	0.8867
	5	0.0001	0.0028	0.0159	0.0504	0.1146	0.2103	0.3317	0.4672	0.6029	0.7256
	6	0.0000	0.0003	0.0027	0.0117	0.0343	0.0782	0.1487	0.2465	0.3669	0.5000
	7	0.0000	0.0000	0.0003	0.0020	0.0076	0.0216	0.0501	0.0994	0.1738	0.2744
	8	0.0000	0.0000	0.0000	0.0002	0.0012	0.0043	0.0122	0.0293	0.0610	0.1133
	9	0.0000	0.0000	0.0000	0.0000	0.0001	0.0006	0.0020	0.0059	0.0148	0.0327
	10	0.0000	0.0000	0.0000	0.0000	0.0000	0.0000	0.0002	0.0007	0.0022	0.0059
	11	0.0000	0.0000	0.0000	0.0000	0.0000	0.0000	0.0000	0.0000	0.0002	0.0005
12	1	0.4596	0.7176	0.8578	0.9313	0.9683	0.9862	0.9943	0.9978	0.9992	0.9998
	2	0.1184	0.3410	0.5565	0.7251	0.8416	0.9150	0.9576	0.9804	0.9917	0.9968
	3	0.0196	0.1109	0.2642	0.4417	0.6093	0.7472	0.8487	0.9166	0.9579	0.9807
	4	0.0022	0.0256	0.0922	0.2054	0.3512	0.5075	0.6533	0.7747	0.8655	0.9270
	5	0.0002	0.0043	0.0239	0.0726	0.1576	0.2763	0.4167	0.5618	0.6956	0.8062
	6	0.0000	0.0005	0.0046	0.0194	0.0544	0.1178	0.2127	0.3348	0.4731	0.6128
	7	0.0000	0.0001	0.0007	0.0039	0.0143	0.0386	0.0846	0.1582	0.2607	0.3872
	8	0.0000	0.0000	0.0001	0.0006	0.0028	0.0095	0.0255	0.0573	0.1117	0.1938
	9	0.0000	0.0000	0.0000	0.0001	0.0004	0.0017	0.0056	0.0153	0.0356	0.0730
	10	0.0000	0.0000	0.0000	0.0000	0.0000	0.0002	0.0008	0.0028	0.0079	0.0193
	11	0.0000	0.0000	0.0000	0.0000	0.0000	0.0000	0.0001	0.0003	0.0011	0.0032
	12	0.0000	0.0000	0.0000	0.0000	0.0000	0.0000	0.0000	0.0000	0.0001	0.0002
13	1	0.4867	0.7458	0.8791	0.9450	0.9762	0.9903	0.9963	0.9987	0.9996	0.9999
	2	0.1354	0.3787	0.6017	0.7664	0.8733	0.9363	0.9704	0.9874	0.9951	0.9983
	3	0.0245	0.1339	0.2704	0.4983	0.6674	0.7975	0.8868	0.9421	0.9731	0.9888
	4	0.0031	0.0342	0.0967	0.2527	0.4157	0.5794	0.7217	0.8314	0.9071	0.9539
	5	0.0003	0.0065	0.0260	0.0991	0.2060	0.3457	0.4995	0.6470	0.7721	0.8666
	6	0.0000	0.0009	0.0053	0.0300	0.0802	0.1654	0.2841	0.4256	0.5732	0.7095
	7	0.0000	0.0001	0.0013	0.0070	0.0243	0.0624	0.1295	0.2288	0.3563	0.5000
	8	0.0000	0.0000	0.0002	0.0012	0.0056	0.0182	0.0462	0.0977	0.1788	0.2905
	9	0.0000	0.0000	0.0000	0.0002	0.0010	0.0040	0.0126	0.0321	0.0698	0.1334
	10	0.0000	0.0000	0.0000	0.0000	0.0001	0.0007	0.0025	0.0078	0.0203	0.0461
	11	0.0000	0.0000	0.0000	0.0000	0.0000	0.0001	0.0003	0.0013	0.0041	0.0112
	12	0.0000	0.0000	0.0000	0.0000	0.0000	0.0000	0.0000	0.0001	0.0005	0.0017
	13	0.0000	0.0000	0.0000	0.0000	0.0000	0.0000	0.0000	0.0000	0.0000	0.0001

TABLE B (*Continued*)

N	k	0.05	0.10	0.15	0.20	0.25	0.30	0.35	0.40	0.45	0.50
14	1	0.5123	0.7712	0.8972	0.9560	0.9822	0.9932	0.9976	0.9992	0.9998	0.9999
	2	0.1530	0.4154	0.6433	0.8021	0.8990	0.9525	0.9795	0.9919	0.9971	0.9991
	3	0.0301	0.1584	0.3521	0.5519	0.7189	0.8392	0.9161	0.9602	0.9830	0.9935
	4	0.0042	0.0441	0.1465	0.3018	0.4787	0.6448	0.7795	0.8757	0.9368	0.9713
	5	0.0004	0.0092	0.0467	0.1298	0.2585	0.4158	0.5773	0.7207	0.8328	0.9102
	6	0.0000	0.0015	0.0115	0.0439	0.1117	0.2195	0.3595	0.5141	0.6627	0.7880
	7	0.0000	0.0002	0.0022	0.0116	0.0383	0.0933	0.1836	0.3075	0.4539	0.6047
	8	0.0000	0.0000	0.0003	0.0024	0.0103	0.0315	0.0753	0.1501	0.2586	0.3953
	9	0.0000	0.0000	0.0000	0.0004	0.0022	0.0083	0.0243	0.0583	0.1189	0.2120
	10	0.0000	0.0000	0.0000	0.0000	0.0003	0.0017	0.0060	0.0175	0.0426	0.0898
	11	0.0000	0.0000	0.0000	0.0000	0.0000	0.0002	0.0011	0.0039	0.0114	0.0287
	12	0.0000	0.0000	0.0000	0.0000	0.0000	0.0000	0.0001	0.0006	0.0022	0.0065
	13	0.0000	0.0000	0.0000	0.0000	0.0000	0.0000	0.0000	0.0001	0.0003	0.0009
	14	0.0000	0.0000	0.0000	0.0000	0.0000	0.0000	0.0000	0.0000	0.0000	0.0001
15	1	0.5367	0.7941	0.9126	0.9648	0.9866	0.9953	0.9984	0.9995	0.9999	1.0000
	2	0.1710	0.4510	0.6814	0.8329	0.9198	0.9647	0.9858	0.9948	0.9983	0.9995
	3	0.0362	0.1841	0.3958	0.6020	0.7639	0.8732	0.9383	0.9729	0.9893	0.9963
	4	0.0055	0.0556	0.1773	0.3518	0.5387	0.7031	0.8273	0.9095	0.9576	0.9824
	5	0.0006	0.0127	0.0617	0.1642	0.3135	0.4845	0.6481	0.7827	0.8796	0.9408
	6	0.0001	0.0022	0.0168	0.0611	0.1484	0.2784	0.4357	0.5968	0.7392	0.8491
	7	0.0000	0.0003	0.0036	0.0181	0.0566	0.1311	0.2452	0.3902	0.5478	0.6964
	8	0.0000	0.0000	0.0006	0.0042	0.0173	0.0500	0.1132	0.2131	0.3465	0.5000
	9	0.0000	0.0000	0.0001	0.0008	0.0042	0.0152	0.0422	0.0950	0.1818	0.3036
	10	0.0000	0.0000	0.0000	0.0001	0.0008	0.0037	0.0124	0.0338	0.0769	0.1509
	11	0.0000	0.0000	0.0000	0.0000	0.0001	0.0007	0.0028	0.0093	0.0255	0.0592
	12	0.0000	0.0000	0.0000	0.0000	0.0000	0.0001	0.0005	0.0019	0.0063	0.0176
	13	0.0000	0.0000	0.0000	0.0000	0.0000	0.0000	0.0001	0.0003	0.0011	0.0037
	14	0.0000	0.0000	0.0000	0.0000	0.0000	0.0000	0.0000	0.0000	0.0001	0.0005
	15	0.0000	0.0000	0.0000	0.0000	0.0000	0.0000	0.0000	0.0000	0.0000	0.0000
16	1	0.5599	0.8147	0.9257	0.9719	0.9900	0.9967	0.9990	0.9997	0.9999	1.0000
	2	0.1892	0.4853	0.7161	0.8593	0.9365	0.9739	0.9902	0.9967	0.9990	0.9997
	3	0.0429	0.2108	0.4386	0.6482	0.8029	0.9006	0.9549	0.9817	0.9934	0.9979
	4	0.0070	0.0684	0.2101	0.4019	0.5950	0.7541	0.8661	0.9349	0.9719	0.9894
	5	0.0009	0.0170	0.0791	0.2018	0.3698	0.5501	0.7108	0.8334	0.9147	0.9616
	6	0.0001	0.0033	0.0235	0.0817	0.1897	0.3402	0.5100	0.6712	0.8024	0.8949
	7	0.0000	0.0005	0.0056	0.0267	0.0796	0.1753	0.3119	0.4728	0.6340	0.7228
	8	0.0000	0.0001	0.0011	0.0070	0.0271	0.0744	0.1594	0.2839	0.4371	0.5982
	9	0.0000	0.0000	0.0002	0.0015	0.0075	0.0257	0.0671	0.1423	0.2559	0.4018
	10	0.0000	0.0000	0.0000	0.0002	0.0016	0.0071	0.0229	0.0583	0.1241	0.2272
	11	0.0000	0.0000	0.0000	0.0000	0.0003	0.0016	0.0062	0.0191	0.0486	0.1051
	12	0.0000	0.0000	0.0000	0.0000	0.0000	0.0003	0.0013	0.0049	0.0149	0.0384
	13	0.0000	0.0000	0.0000	0.0000	0.0000	0.0000	0.0002	0.0009	0.0035	0.0106
	14	0.0000	0.0000	0.0000	0.0000	0.0000	0.0000	0.0000	0.0001	0.0006	0.0021
	15	0.0000	0.0000	0.0000	0.0000	0.0000	0.0000	0.0000	0.0000	0.0001	0.0003
	16	0.0000	0.0000	0.0000	0.0000	0.0000	0.0000	0.0000	0.0000	0.0000	0.0000

TABLE B (*Continued*)

N	k	0.05	0.10	0.15	0.20	0.25	0.30	0.35	0.40	0.45	0.50
17	1	0.5819	0.8332	0.9369	0.9775	0.9925	0.9977	0.9993	0.9998	1.0000	1.0000
	2	0.2078	0.5182	0.7475	0.8818	0.9499	0.9807	0.9933	0.9979	0.9994	0.9999
	3	0.0503	0.2382	0.4802	0.6904	0.8363	0.9226	0.9673	0.9877	0.9959	0.9988
	4	0.0088	0.0826	0.2444	0.4511	0.6470	0.7981	0.8972	0.9536	0.9816	0.9936
	5	0.0012	0.0221	0.0987	0.2418	0.4261	0.6113	0.7652	0.8740	0.9404	0.9755
	6	0.0001	0.0047	0.0319	0.1057	0.2347	0.4032	0.5803	0.7361	0.8529	0.9283
	7	0.0000	0.0008	0.0083	0.0377	0.1071	0.2248	0.3812	0.5522	0.7098	0.8338
	8	0.0000	0.0001	0.0017	0.0109	0.0402	0.1046	0.2128	0.3595	0.5257	0.6855
	9	0.0000	0.0000	0.0003	0.0026	0.0124	0.0403	0.0994	0.1989	0.3374	0.5000
	10	0.0000	0.0000	0.0000	0.0005	0.0031	0.0127	0.0383	0.0919	0.1834	0.3145
	11	0.0000	0.0000	0.0000	0.0001	0.0006	0.0032	0.0120	0.0348	0.0826	0.1662
	12	0.0000	0.0000	0.0000	0.0000	0.0001	0.0007	0.0030	0.0106	0.0301	0.0717
	13	0.0000	0.0000	0.0000	0.0000	0.0000	0.0001	0.0006	0.0025	0.0086	0.0245
	14	0.0000	0.0000	0.0000	0.0000	0.0000	0.0000	0.0001	0.0005	0.0019	0.0064
	15	0.0000	0.0000	0.0000	0.0000	0.0000	0.0000	0.0000	0.0001	0.0003	0.0012
	16	0.0000	0.0000	0.0000	0.0000	0.0000	0.0000	0.0000	0.0000	0.0000	0.0001
	17	0.0000	0.0000	0.0000	0.0000	0.0000	0.0000	0.0000	0.0000	0.0000	0.0000
18	1	0.6028	0.8499	0.9464	0.9820	0.9944	0.9984	0.9996	0.9999	1.0000	1.0000
	2	0.2265	0.5497	0.7759	0.9009	0.9605	0.9858	0.9954	0.9987	0.9997	0.9999
	3	0.0581	0.2662	0.5203	0.7287	0.8647	0.9400	0.9764	0.9918	0.9975	0.9993
	4	0.0109	0.0982	0.2798	0.4990	0.6943	0.8354	0.9217	0.9672	0.9880	0.9962
	5	0.0015	0.0282	0.1206	0.2836	0.4813	0.6673	0.8114	0.9058	0.9589	0.9846
	6	0.0002	0.0064	0.0419	0.1329	0.2825	0.4656	0.6450	0.7912	0.8923	0.9519
	7	0.0000	0.0012	0.0118	0.0513	0.1390	0.2783	0.4509	0.6257	0.7742	0.8811
	8	0.0000	0.0002	0.0027	0.0163	0.0569	0.1407	0.2717	0.4366	0.6085	0.7597
	9	0.0000	0.0000	0.0005	0.0043	0.0193	0.0596	0.1391	0.2632	0.4222	0.5927
	10	0.0000	0.0000	0.0001	0.0009	0.0054	0.0210	0.0597	0.1347	0.2527	0.4073
	11	0.0000	0.0000	0.0000	0.0002	0.0012	0.0061	0.0212	0.0576	0.1280	0.2403
	12	0.0000	0.0000	0.0000	0.0000	0.0002	0.0014	0.0062	0.0203	0.0537	0.1189
	13	0.0000	0.0000	0.0000	0.0000	0.0000	0.0003	0.0014	0.0058	0.0183	0.0481
	14	0.0000	0.0000	0.0000	0.0000	0.0000	0.0000	0.0003	0.0013	0.0049	0.0154
	15	0.0000	0.0000	0.0000	0.0000	0.0000	0.0000	0.0000	0.0002	0.0010	0.0038
	16	0.0000	0.0000	0.0000	0.0000	0.0000	0.0000	0.0000	0.0000	0.0001	0.0007
	17	0.0000	0.0000	0.0000	0.0000	0.0000	0.0000	0.0000	0.0000	0.0000	0.0001
	18	0.0000	0.0000	0.0000	0.0000	0.0000	0.0000	0.0000	0.0000	0.0000	0.0000

TABLE B (*Continued*)

N	k	0.05	0.10	0.15	0.20	0.25	0.30	0.35	0.40	0.45	0.50
19	1	0.6226	0.8649	0.9544	0.9856	0.9958	0.9989	0.9997	0.9999	1.0000	1.0000
	2	0.2453	0.5797	0.8015	0.9171	0.9690	0.9896	0.9969	0.9992	0.9998	1.0000
	3	0.0665	0.2946	0.5587	0.7631	0.8887	0.9538	0.9830	0.9945	0.9985	0.9996
	4	0.0132	0.1150	0.3159	0.5449	0.7369	0.8668	0.9409	0.9770	0.9923	0.9978
	5	0.0020	0.0352	0.1444	0.3267	0.5346	0.7178	0.8500	0.9304	0.9720	0.9904
	6	0.0002	0.0086	0.0537	0.1631	0.3322	0.5261	0.7032	0.8371	0.9223	0.9682
	7	0.0000	0.0017	0.0163	0.0676	0.1749	0.3345	0.5188	0.6919	0.8273	0.9165
	8	0.0000	0.0003	0.0041	0.0233	0.0775	0.1820	0.3344	0.5122	0.6831	0.8204
	9	0.0000	0.0000	0.0008	0.0067	0.0287	0.0839	0.1855	0.3325	0.5060	0.6762
	10	0.0000	0.0000	0.0001	0.0016	0.0089	0.0326	0.0875	0.1861	0.3290	0.5000
	11	0.0000	0.0000	0.0000	0.0003	0.0023	0.0105	0.0347	0.0885	0.1841	0.3238
	12	0.0000	0.0000	0.0000	0.0000	0.0005	0.0028	0.0114	0.0352	0.0871	0.1796
	13	0.0000	0.0000	0.0000	0.0000	0.0001	0.0006	0.0031	0.0116	0.0342	0.0835
	14	0.0000	0.0000	0.0000	0.0000	0.0000	0.0001	0.0007	0.0031	0.0109	0.0318
	15	0.0000	0.0000	0.0000	0.0000	0.0000	0.0000	0.0001	0.0006	0.0028	0.0096
	16	0.0000	0.0000	0.0000	0.0000	0.0000	0.0000	0.0000	0.0001	0.0005	0.0022
	17	0.0000	0.0000	0.0000	0.0000	0.0000	0.0000	0.0000	0.0000	0.0001	0.0004
	18	0.0000	0.0000	0.0000	0.0000	0.0000	0.0000	0.0000	0.0000	0.0000	0.0000
	19	0.0000	0.0000	0.0000	0.0000	0.0000	0.0000	0.0000	0.0000	0.0000	0.0000
20	1	0.6415	0.8784	0.9612	0.9885	0.9968	0.9992	0.9998	1.0000	1.0000	1.0000
	2	0.2642	0.6083	0.8244	0.9308	0.9757	0.9924	0.9979	0.9995	0.9999	1.0000
	3	0.0755	0.3231	0.5951	0.7939	0.9087	0.9645	0.9879	0.9964	0.9991	0.9998
	4	0.0159	0.1330	0.3523	0.5886	0.7748	0.8929	0.9556	0.9840	0.9951	0.9987
	5	0.0026	0.0432	0.1702	0.3704	0.5852	0.7625	0.8818	0.9490	0.9811	0.9941
	6	0.0003	0.0113	0.0673	0.1958	0.3828	0.5836	0.7546	0.8744	0.9447	0.9793
	7	0.0000	0.0024	0.0219	0.0867	0.2142	0.3920	0.5834	0.7500	0.8701	0.9423
	8	0.0000	0.0004	0.0059	0.0321	0.1018	0.2277	0.3990	0.5841	0.7480	0.8684
	9	0.0000	0.0001	0.0013	0.0100	0.0409	0.1133	0.2376	0.4044	0.5857	0.7483
	10	0.0000	0.0000	0.0002	0.0026	0.0139	0.0480	0.1218	0.2447	0.4086	0.5881
	11	0.0000	0.0000	0.0000	0.0006	0.0039	0.0171	0.0532	0.1275	0.2493	0.4119
	12	0.0000	0.0000	0.0000	0.0001	0.0009	0.0051	0.0196	0.0565	0.1308	0.2517
	13	0.0000	0.0000	0.0000	0.0000	0.0002	0.0013	0.0060	0.0210	0.0580	0.1316
	14	0.0000	0.0000	0.0000	0.0000	0.0000	0.0003	0.0015	0.0065	0.0214	0.0577
	15	0.0000	0.0000	0.0000	0.0000	0.0000	0.0000	0.0003	0.0016	0.0064	0.0207
	16	0.0000	0.0000	0.0000	0.0000	0.0000	0.0000	0.0000	0.0003	0.0015	0.0059
	17	0.0000	0.0000	0.0000	0.0000	0.0000	0.0000	0.0000	0.0000	0.0003	0.0013
	18	0.0000	0.0000	0.0000	0.0000	0.0000	0.0000	0.0000	0.0000	0.0000	0.0002
	19	0.0000	0.0000	0.0000	0.0000	0.0000	0.0000	0.0000	0.0000	0.0000	0.0000
	20	0.0000	0.0000	0.0000	0.0000	0.0000	0.0000	0.0000	0.0000	0.0000	0.0000

TABLE C

CRITICAL VALUES FOR THE SIGN TEST

For N differences, where x is the number of occurrences of the less frequent sign, the column values under the headings 0.005, 0.025, 0.05, yield the values of r such that $P(x \leq r) = 0.005, 0.025, 0.05$, respectively (see Section 8.15).

N \ P	0.005	0.025	0.05	N \ P	0.005	0.025	0.05
6		0	0	50	15	17	18
7		0	0	51	15	18	19
8	0	0	1	52	16	18	19
9	0	1	1	53	16	18	20
10	0	1	1	54	17	19	20
11	0	1	2	55	17	19	20
12	1	2	2	56	17	20	21
13	1	2	3	57	18	20	21
14	1	2	3	58	18	21	22
15	2	3	3	59	19	21	22
16	2	3	4	60	19	21	23
17	2	4	4	61	20	22	23
18	3	4	5	62	20	22	24
19	3	4	5	63	20	23	24
20	3	5	5	64	21	23	24
21	4	5	6	65	21	24	25
22	4	5	6	66	22	24	25
23	4	6	7	67	22	25	26
24	5	6	7	68	22	25	26
25	5	7	7	69	23	25	27
26	6	7	8	70	23	26	27
27	6	7	8	71	24	26	28
28	6	8	9	72	24	27	28
29	7	8	9	73	25	27	28
30	7	9	10	74	25	28	29
31	7	9	10	75	25	28	29
32	8	9	10	76	26	28	30
33	8	10	11	77	26	29	30
34	9	10	11	78	27	29	31
35	9	11	12	79	27	30	31
36	9	11	12	80	28	30	32
37	10	12	13	81	28	31	32
38	10	12	13	82	28	31	33
39	11	12	13	83	29	32	33
40	11	13	14	84	29	32	33
41	11	13	14	85	30	32	34
42	12	14	15	86	30	33	34
43	12	14	15	87	31	33	35
44	13	15	16	88	31	34	35
45	13	15	16	89	31	34	36
46	13	15	16	90	32	35	36
47	14	16	17				
48	14	16	17				
49	15	17	18				

For values of $N > 90$, approximate values of r may be found by taking the nearest integer less than $\frac{1}{2}(N - 1) - k\sqrt{N + 1}$, where k is 1.29, 0.980, 0.822, for $P = 0.005, 0.025, 0.05$, respectively.

Reproduced in modified form with permission from W. J. Dixon and A. M. Mood, "The Statistical Sign Test," *Journal of the American Statistical Association*, Vol. 41 (1946), p. 560.

ORDINATES OF THE NORMAL CURVE

$$\phi(z) = \frac{1}{\sqrt{2\pi}} e^{-\frac{1}{2}z^2}$$

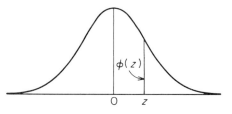

z	0.00	0.01	0.02	0.03	0.04	0.05	0.06	0.07	0.08	0.09
0.0	0.3989	0.3989	0.3989	0.3988	0.3986	0.3984	0.3982	0.3980	0.3977	0.3973
0.1	0.3970	0.3965	0.3961	0.3956	0.3951	0.3945	0.3939	0.3932	0.3925	0.3918
0.2	0.3910	0.3902	0.3894	0.3885	0.3876	0.3867	0.3857	0.3847	0.3836	0.3825
0.3	0.3814	0.3802	0.3790	0.3778	0.3765	0.3752	0.3739	0.3725	0.3712	0.3697
0.4	0.3683	0.3668	0.3653	0.3637	0.3621	0.3605	0.3589	0.3572	0.3555	0.3538
0.5	0.3521	0.3503	0.3485	0.3467	0.3448	0.3429	0.3410	0.3361	0.3372	0.3352
0.6	0.3332	0.3312	0.3292	0.3271	0.3251	0.3230	0.3209	0.3187	0.3166	0.3144
0.7	0.3123	0.3101	0.3079	0.3056	0.3034	0.3011	0.2989	0.2966	0.2943	0.2920
0.8	0.2897	0.2874	0.2850	0.2827	0.2803	0.2780	0.2756	0.2732	0.2709	0.2685
0.9	0.2661	0.2637	0.2613	0.2589	0.2565	0.2541	0.2516	0.2492	0.2468	0.2444
1.0	0.2420	0.2396	0.2371	0.2347	0.2323	0.2299	0.2275	0.2251	0.2227	0.2203
1.1	0.2179	0.2155	0.2131	0.2107	0.2083	0.2059	0.2036	0.2012	0.1989	0.1965
1.2	0.1942	0.1919	0.1895	0.1872	0.1849	0.1826	0.1804	0.1781	0.1758	0.1736
1.3	0.1714	0.1691	0.1669	0.1647	0.1626	0.1604	0.1582	0.1561	0.1539	0.1518
1.4	0.1497	0.1476	0.1456	0.1435	0.1415	0.1394	0.1374	0.1354	0.1334	0.1315
1.5	0.1295	0.1276	0.1257	0.1238	0.1219	0.1200	0.1182	0.1163	0.1145	0.1127
1.6	0.1109	0.1092	0.1074	0.1057	0.1040	0.1023	0.1006	0.0989	0.0973	0.0957
1.7	0.0940	0.0925	0.0909	0.0893	0.0878	0.0863	0.0848	0.0833	0.0818	0.0804
1.8	0.0790	0.0775	0.0761	0.0748	0.0734	0.0721	0.0707	0.0694	0.0681	0.0669
1.9	0.0656	0.0644	0.0632	0.0620	0.0608	0.0596	0.0584	0.0573	0.0562	0.0551
2.0	0.0540	0.0529	0.0519	0.0508	0.0498	0.0488	0.0478	0.0468	0.0459	0.0449
2.1	0.0440	0.0431	0.0422	0.0413	0.0404	0.0396	0.0387	0.0379	0.0371	0.0363
2.2	0.0355	0.0347	0.0339	0.0332	0.0325	0.0317	0.0310	0.0303	0.0297	0.0290
2.3	0.0283	0.0277	0.0270	0.0264	0.0258	0.0252	0.0246	0.0241	0.0235	0.0229
2.4	0.0224	0.0219	0.0213	0.0208	0.0203	0.0198	0.0194	0.0189	0.0184	0.0180
2.5	0.0175	0.0171	0.0167	0.0163	0.0158	0.0154	0.0151	0.0147	0.0143	0.0139
2.6	0.0136	0.0132	0.0129	0.0126	0.0122	0.0119	0.0116	0.0113	0.0110	0.0107
2.7	0.0104	0.0101	0.0099	0.0096	0.0093	0.0091	0.0088	0.0086	0.0084	0.0081
2.8	0.0079	0.0077	0.0075	0.0073	0.0071	0.0069	0.0067	0.0065	0.0063	0.0061
2.9	0.0060	0.0058	0.0056	0.0055	0.0053	0.0051	0.0050	0.0048	0.0047	0.0046
3.0	0.0044	0.0043	0.0042	0.0040	0.0039	0.0038	0.0037	0.0036	0.0035	0.0034
3.1	0.0033	0.0032	0.0031	0.0030	0.0029	0.0028	0.0027	0.0026	0.0025	0.0025
3.2	0.0024	0.0023	0.0022	0.0022	0.0021	0.0020	0.0020	0.0019	0.0018	0.0018
3.3	0.0017	0.0017	0.0016	0.0016	0.0015	0.0015	0.0014	0.0014	0.0013	0.0013
3.4	0.0012	0.0012	0.0012	0.0011	0.0011	0.0010	0.0010	0.0010	0.0009	0.0009
3.5	0.0009	0.0008	0.0008	0.0008	0.0008	0.0007	0.0007	0.0007	0.0007	0.0006
3.6	0.0006	0.0006	0.0006	0.0005	0.0005	0.0005	0.0005	0.0005	0.0005	0.0004
3.7	0.0004	0.0004	0.0004	0.0004	0.0004	0.0004	0.0003	0.0003	0.0003	0.0003
3.8	0.0003	0.0003	0.0003	0.0003	0.0003	0.0002	0.0002	0.0002	0.0002	0.0002
3.9	0.0002	0.0002	0.0002	0.0002	0.0002	0.0002	0.0002	0.0002	0.0001	0.0001
4.0	0.0001	0.0001	0.0001	0.0001	0.0001	0.0001	0.0001	0.0001	0.0001	0.0001
z	0.00	0.01	0.02	0.03	0.04	0.05	0.06	0.07	0.08	0.09

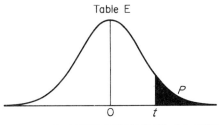

Table E

TABLE E

AREA UNDER THE NORMAL CURVE

$$A = \int_z^\infty \phi(z)\, dz$$

z	0.00	0.01	0.02	0.03	0.04	0.05	0.06	0.07	0.08	0.09
0.0	0.5000	0.4960	0.4920	0.4880	0.4840	0.4801	0.4761	0.4721	0.4681	0.4641
0.1	0.4602	0.4562	0.4522	0.4483	0.4443	0.4404	0.4364	0.4325	0.4286	0.4247
0.2	0.4207	0.4168	0.4129	0.4090	0.4052	0.4013	0.3974	0.3936	0.3897	0.3859
0.3	0.3821	0.3783	0.3745	0.3707	0.3669	0.3632	0.3594	0.3557	0.3520	0.3483
0.4	0.3446	0.3409	0.3372	0.3336	0.3300	0.3264	0.3228	0.3192	0.3156	0.3121
0.5	0.3085	0.3050	0.3015	0.2981	0.2946	0.2912	0.2877	0.2843	0.2810	0.2776
0.6	0.2743	0.2709	0.2676	0.2643	0.2611	0.2578	0.2546	0.2514	0.2483	0.2451
0.7	0.2420	0.2389	0.2358	0.2327	0.2296	0.2266	0.2236	0.2206	0.2177	0.2148
0.8	0.2119	0.2090	0.2061	0.2033	0.2005	0.1977	0.1949	0.1922	0.1894	0.1867
0.9	0.1841	0.1814	0.1788	0.1762	0.1736	0.1711	0.1685	0.1660	0.1635	0.1611
1.0	0.1587	0.1562	0.1539	0.1515	0.1492	0.1469	0.1446	0.1423	0.1401	0.1379
1.1	0.1357	0.1335	0.1314	0.1292	0.1271	0.1251	0.1230	0.1210	0.1190	0.1170
1.2	0.1151	0.1131	0.1112	0.1093	0.1075	0.1056	0.1038	0.1020	0.1003	0.0985
1.3	0.0968	0.0951	0.0934	0.0918	0.0901	0.0885	0.0869	0.0853	0.0838	0.0823
1.4	0.0808	0.0793	0.0778	0.0764	0.0749	0.0735	0.0721	0.0708	0.0694	0.0681
1.5	0.0668	0.0655	0.0643	0.0630	0.0618	0.0606	0.0594	0.0582	0.0571	0.0559
1.6	0.0548	0.0537	0.0526	0.0516	0.0505	0.0495	0.0485	0.0475	0.0465	0.0455
1.7	0.0446	0.0436	0.0427	0.0418	0.0409	0.0401	0.0392	0.0384	0.0375	0.0367
1.8	0.0359	0.0351	0.0344	0.0336	0.0329	0.0322	0.0314	0.0307	0.0301	0.0294
1.9	0.0287	0.0281	0.0274	0.0268	0.0262	0.0256	0.0250	0.0244	0.0239	0.0233
2.0	0.0228	0.0222	0.0217	0.0212	0.0207	0.0202	0.0197	0.0192	0.0188	0.0183
2.1	0.0179	0.0174	0.0170	0.0166	0.0162	0.0158	0.0154	0.0150	0.0146	0.0143
2.2	0.0139	0.0136	0.0132	0.0129	0.0125	0.0122	0.0119	0.0116	0.0113	0.0110
2.3	0.0107	0.0104	0.0102	0.0099	0.0096	0.0094	0.0091	0.0089	0.0087	0.0084
2.4	0.0082	0.0080	0.0078	0.0075	0.0073	0.0071	0.0069	0.0068	0.0066	0.0064
2.5	0.0062	0.0060	0.0059	0.0057	0.0055	0.0054	0.0052	0.0051	0.0049	0.0048
2.6	0.0047	0.0045	0.0044	0.0043	0.0041	0.0040	0.0039	0.0038	0.0037	0.0036
2.7	0.0035	0.0034	0.0033	0.0032	0.0031	0.0030	0.0029	0.0028	0.0027	0.0026
2.8	0.0026	0.0025	0.0024	0.0023	0.0023	0.0022	0.0021	0.0021	0.0020	0.0019
2.9	0.0019	0.0018	0.0018	0.0017	0.0016	0.0016	0.0015	0.0015	0.0014	0.0014
3.0	0.0013	0.0013	0.0013	0.0012	0.0012	0.0011	0.0011	0.0011	0.0010	0.0010
3.1	0.0010	0.0009	0.0009	0.0009	0.0008	0.0008	0.0008	0.0008	0.0007	0.0007
3.2	0.0007	0.0007	0.0006	0.0006	0.0006	0.0006	0.0006	0.0005	0.0005	0.0005
3.3	0.0005	0.0005	0.0005	0.0004	0.0004	0.0004	0.0004	0.0004	0.0004	0.0003
3.4	0.0003	0.0003	0.0003	0.0003	0.0003	0.0003	0.0003	0.0003	0.0003	0.0002
3.5	0.0002	0.0002	0.0002	0.0002	0.0002	0.0002	0.0002	0.0002	0.0002	0.0002
3.6	0.0002	0.0002	0.0001	0.0001	0.0001	0.0001	0.0001	0.0001	0.0001	0.0001
3.7	0.0001	0.0001	0.0001	0.0001	0.0001	0.0001	0.0001	0.0001	0.0001	0.0001
3.8	0.0001	0.0001	0.0001	0.0001	0.0001	0.0001	0.0001	0.0001	0.0001	0.0001
3.9	0.0000	0.0000	0.0000	0.0000	0.0000	0.0000	0.0000	0.0000	0.0000	0.0000
z	0.00	0.01	0.02	0.03	0.04	0.05	0.06	0.07	0.08	0.09

VALUES OF FISHER'S t

P equals the probability of exceeding a given positive value of t corresponding to n degrees of freedom. (One-tailed probability.)

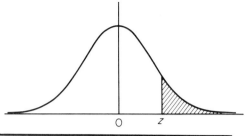

n \ P	0.45	0.40	0.35	0.20	0.15	0.10	0.05	0.025	0.01	0.005
1	0.158	0.325	0.510	1.376	1.963	3.078	6.314	12.71	31.82	63.66
2	0.142	0.289	0.445	1.061	1.386	1.886	2.920	4.303	6.965	9.925
3	0.137	0.277	0.424	0.978	1.250	1.638	2.353	3.182	4.541	5.841
4	0.134	0.271	0.414	0.941	1.190	1.533	2.132	2.776	3.747	4.604
5	0.132	0.267	0.408	0.920	1.156	1.476	2.015	2.571	3.365	4.032
6	0.131	0.265	0.404	0.906	1.134	1.440	1.943	2.447	3.143	3.707
7	0.130	0.263	0.402	0.896	1.119	1.415	1.895	2.365	2.998	3.499
8	0.130	0.262	0.399	0.889	1.108	1.397	1.860	2.306	2.896	3.355
9	0.129	0.261	0.398	0.883	1.100	1.383	1.833	2.262	2.821	3.250
10	0.129	0.260	0.397	0.879	1.093	1.372	1.812	2.228	2.764	3.169
11	0.129	0.260	0.396	0.876	1.088	1.363	1.796	2.201	2.718	3.106
12	0.128	0.259	0.395	0.873	1.083	1.356	1.782	2.179	2.681	3.055
13	0.128	0.259	0.394	0.870	1.079	1.350	1.771	2.160	2.650	3.012
14	0.128	0.258	0.393	0.868	1.076	1.345	1.761	2.145	2.624	2.977
15	0.128	0.258	0.393	0.866	1.074	1.341	1.753	2.131	2.602	2.947
16	0.128	0.258	0.392	0.865	1.071	1.337	1.746	2.120	2.583	2.921
17	0.128	0.257	0.392	0.863	1.069	1.333	1.740	2.110	2.567	2.898
18	0.127	0.257	0.392	0.862	1.067	1.330	1.734	2.101	2.552	2.878
19	0.127	0.257	0.391	0.861	1.066	1.328	1.729	2.093	2.539	2.861
20	0.127	0.257	0.391	0.860	1.064	1.325	1.725	2.086	2.528	2.845
21	0.127	0.257	0.391	0.859	1.063	1.323	1.721	2.080	2.518	2.831
22	0.127	0.256	0.390	0.858	1.061	1.321	1.717	2.074	2.508	2.819
23	0.127	0.256	0.390	0.858	1.060	1.319	1.714	2.069	2.500	2.807
24	0.127	0.256	0.390	0.857	1.059	1.318	1.711	2.064	2.492	2.797
25	0.127	0.256	0.390	0.856	1.058	1.316	1.708	2.060	2.485	2.787
26	0.127	0.256	0.390	0.856	1.058	1.315	1.706	2.056	2.479	2.779
27	0.127	0.256	0.389	0.855	1.057	1.314	1.703	2.052	2.473	2.771
28	0.127	0.256	0.389	0.855	1.056	1.313	1.701	2.048	2.467	2.763
29	0.127	0.256	0.389	0.854	1.055	1.311	1.699	2.045	2.462	2.756
30	0.127	0.256	0.389	0.854	1.055	1.310	1.697	2.042	2.457	2.750
40	0.126	0.255	0.388	0.851	1.050	1.303	1.684	2.021	2.423	2.704
60	0.126	0.254	0.387	0.848	1.046	1.296	1.671	2.000	2.390	2.660
120	0.126	0.254	0.386	0.845	1.041	1.289	1.658	1.980	2.358	2.617
∞	0.126	0.253	0.385	0.842	1.036	1.282	1.645	1.960	2.326	2.576
n \ P	0.45	0.40	0.35	0.20	0.15	0.10	0.05	0.025	0.01	0.005

Table F is abridged from Table IV of Fisher: *Statistical Methods for Research Workers*, Oliver and Boyd, Ltd., Edinburgh, by permission of the author and publishers.

TABLE G

VALUES OF χ^2

P equals the probability of exceeding a given value of χ^2 corresponding to n degrees of freedom.

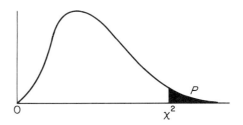

P / n	0.99	0.98	0.95	0.90	0.50	0.10	0.05	0.02	0.01
1	0.0002	0.0006	0.0039	0.0158	0.455	2.706	3.841	5.412	6.635
2	0.0201	0.0404	0.103	0.211	1.386	4.605	5.991	7.824	9.210
3	0.115	0.185	0.352	0.584	2.366	6.251	7.815	9.837	11.34
4	0.297	0.429	0.711	1.064	3.357	7.779	9.488	11.67	13.28
5	0.554	0.752	1.145	1.610	4.351	9.236	11.07	13.39	15.09
6	0.872	1.134	1.635	2.204	5.348	10.64	12.59	15.03	16.81
7	1.239	1.564	2.167	2.833	6.346	12.02	14.07	16.62	18.48
8	1.646	2.032	2.733	3.490	7.344	13.36	15.51	18.17	20.09
9	2.088	2.532	3.325	4.168	8.343	14.68	16.92	19.68	21.67
10	2.558	3.059	3.940	4.865	9.342	15.99	18.31	21.16	23.21
11	3.053	3.609	4.575	5.578	10.34	17.28	19.68	22.62	24.72
12	3.571	4.178	5.226	6.304	11.34	18.55	21.03	24.05	26.22
13	4.107	4.765	5.892	7.042	12.34	19.81	22.36	25.47	27.69
14	4.660	5.368	6.571	7.790	13.34	21.06	23.68	26.87	29.14
15	5.229	5.985	7.261	8.547	14.34	22.31	25.00	28.26	30.58
16	5.812	6.614	7.962	9.312	15.34	23.54	26.30	29.63	32.00
17	6.408	7.255	8.672	10.08	16.34	24.77	27.59	31.00	33.41
18	7.015	7.906	9.390	10.86	17.34	25.99	28.87	32.35	34.80
19	7.633	8.567	10.12	11.65	18.34	27.20	30.14	33.69	36.19
20	8.260	9.237	10.85	12.44	19.34	28.41	31.41	35.02	37.57
21	8.897	9.915	11.59	13.24	20.34	29.62	32.67	36.34	38.93
22	9.542	10.60	12.34	14.04	21.34	30.81	33.92	37.66	40.29
23	10.20	11.29	13.09	14.85	22.34	32.01	35.17	38.97	41.64
24	10.86	11.99	13.85	15.66	23.34	33.20	36.42	40.27	42.98
25	11.52	12.70	14.61	16.47	24.34	34.38	37.65	41.57	44.31
26	12.20	13.41	15.38	17.29	25.34	35.56	38.88	42.86	45.64
27	12.88	14.13	16.15	18.11	26.34	36.74	40.11	44.14	46.96
28	13.57	14.85	16.93	18.94	27.34	37.92	41.34	45.42	48.28
29	14.26	15.57	17.71	19.77	28.34	39.09	42.56	46.69	49.59
30	14.95	16.31	18.49	20.60	29.34	40.26	43.77	47.96	50.89
n / P	0.99	0.98	0.95	0.90	0.50	0.10	0.05	0.02	0.01

For $n > 30$, let $z = \sqrt{2\chi^2} - \sqrt{2n - 1}$, and use the normal probability function, $\phi(z)$.

Table G is abridged from Table III of Fisher: *Statistical Methods for Research Workers*, Oliver & Boyd, Ltd., Edinburgh, by permission of the author and publishers.

TABLE H
95% CONFIDENCE LIMITS FOR p
Each number attached to a curve denotes the sample size, N.

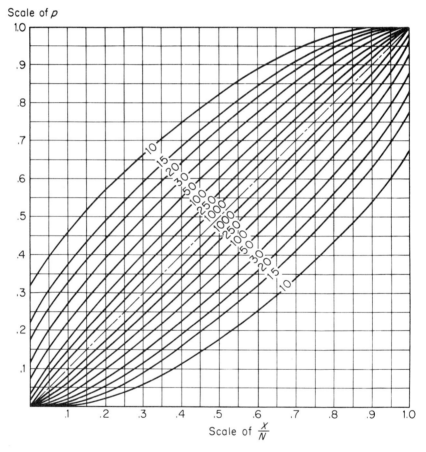

Scale of p

Scale of $\frac{X}{N}$

Reproduced by permission of E. S. Pearson from the paper by C. J. Clopper and E. S. Pearson, "The use of Confidence or Fiducial Limits Illustrated in the Case of the Binomial," *Biometrika*, Vol. 26 (1934), p. 410.

Table I

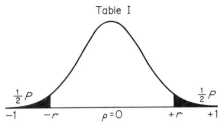

TABLE I
CRITICAL VALUES OF r WHEN $\rho = 0$

P equals the probability of exceeding numerically a given value of r corresponding to n degrees of freedom. (Two-tailed probability.) For simple correlation $n = N - 2$ where N is the number of paired variates in the sample.

P n	0.10	0.05	0.02	0.01
1	0.988	0.997	1.000	1.000
2	0.900	0.950	0.980	0.990
3	0.805	0.878	0.934	0.959
4	0.729	0.811	0.882	0.917
5	0.669	0.754	0.833	0.874
6	0.622	0.707	0.789	0.834
7	0.582	0.666	0.750	0.798
8	0.549	0.632	0.716	0.765
9	0.521	0.602	0.685	0.735
10	0.497	0.576	0.658	0.708
11	0.476	0.553	0.634	0.684
12	0.458	0.532	0.612	0.661
13	0.441	0.514	0.592	0.641
14	0.426	0.497	0.574	0.623
15	0.412	0.482	0.558	0.606
16	0.400	0.468	0.542	0.590
17	0.389	0.456	0.528	0.575
18	0.378	0.444	0.516	0.561
19	0.369	0.433	0.503	0.549
20	0.360	0.423	0.492	0.537
25	0.323	0.381	0.445	0.487
30	0.296	0.349	0.409	0.449
35	0.275	0.325	0.381	0.418
40	0.257	0.304	0.358	0.393
45	0.243	0.288	0.338	0.372
50	0.231	0.273	0.322	0.354
60	0.211	0.250	0.295	0.325
70	0.195	0.232	0.274	0.302
80	0.183	0.217	0.256	0.283
90	0.173	0.205	0.242	0.267
100	0.164	0.195	0.230	0.254

Table I is reprinted from Table V.A. of Fisher: *Statistical Methods for Research Workers*, Oliver and Boyd, Ltd., Edinburgh, by permission of the author and publishers.

TABLE J

95% CONFIDENCE LIMITS FOR ρ

Each number attached to a curve denotes the sample size, N.

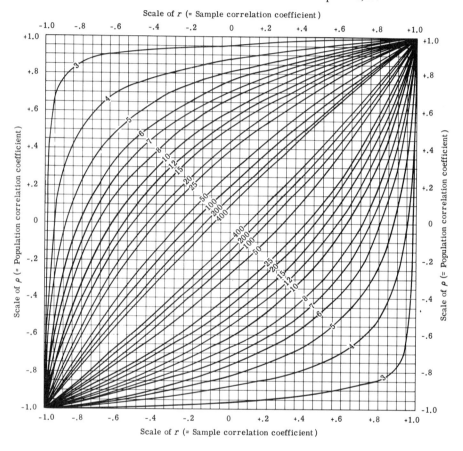

Scale of r (= Sample correlation coefficient)

Scale of ρ (= Population correlation coefficient)

Scale of r (= Sample correlation coefficient)

Reproduced by permission of E. S. Pearson on behalf of the *Biometrika* Trustees from F. N. David's *Tables of the Correlation Coefficient*. New York: Cambridge University Press (1938).

Answers to Odd-Numbered Exercises

CHAPTER 2

1. (a) $\{2,3,4,6,9,12,18\}$.
   (b) {penny, nickel, dime, quarter, half dollar, silver dollar}.
   (c) $\varnothing$
   (d) $\{1,\frac{1}{2},\frac{1}{3},\frac{1}{4},\,,\,\}$.
   (e) {tetrahedron, cube, octahedron, dodecahedron, icosahedron}.
   (f) $\{2,3,4,5,6,7,8,9,10,11,12\}$.

3. (a) $\{123, 132, 213, 312, 231, 321\}$.
   (b) $\{557, 575, 755\}$.
   (c) $\{ab,ac,ad,bc,bd,cd,ba,ca,da,cb,db,dc\}$.

5. $\{AA,BB,OO,AB,AO,BO\}$.

7. $\{GGGG, GGGD, GGDG, GDGG, DGGG, GGDD, GDGD, DGGD, GDDG,$
   $DGDG, DDGG, DDDG, DDGD, DGDD, GDDD, DDDD\}$.

9. $\{r\}$, $\{s\}$, $\{t\}$, $\{r,s\}$, $\{r,t\}$, $\{s,t\}$, $\{r,s,t\}$.

11. (a) $\{s,t,u,v,w,x,y,z\}$.
    (b) $\{x,y,z\}$.
    (c) $\{u,v,w,x,y,z\}$.
    (d) $\varnothing$.

13. (a) {parallelograms}.
    (b) {rectangles}.
    (c) {parallelograms}.
    (d) {rectangles}.
    (e) {quadrilaterals}.

15. (a) Complementary, provided suburban voters are included among urban voters.
    (b) Not complementary; quadrilaterals with nonparallel sides are omitted.

(c) Complementary, provided male smokers and male nonsmokers are implied.

(d) Not complementary; integers can be expressed as quotients of integers.

17. 15.   19. 31.   23. $\{ae,af,ag,be,bf,bg,ce,cf,cg,de,df,dg\}$.

25. $\{rg,ry,ro,wg,wy,wo,bg,by,bo\}$.

27. (b) does not constitute a partition because $A_2 \cap A_3 = \{y\} \neq \varnothing$ or $A_1 \cap A_3 = \{x\} \neq \varnothing$.

29. (a) $\{a\}, \{b\}, \{c\}; \{a,b\}, \{c\}; \{a\}, \{b,c\}; \{b\}, \{a,c\}$.
    (b) $\{a\}, \{b\}, \{c\}, \{d\}; \{a\}, \{b,c,d\}; \{b\}, \{a,c,d\};$
        $\{c\}, \{a,b,d\}; \{d\}, \{a,b,c\}; \{a,b\}, \{c,d\}; \{a,c\}, \{b,d\}; \{a,d\}, \{b,c\}$.

31. Not a partition, $E_2 \cap E_3 \neq \varnothing$.

33. (a) $\{HHH\}, \{HHT, HTH, THH\}, \{HTT, THT, TTH\}, \{TTT\}$.
    (b) $\{HHH, HHT, HTH, HTT\}, \{THH, THT\}, \{TTH\} \{TTT\}$.

35. 24.   37. (a) 360.   (b) 720.   39. 6840.   41. 55.   43. 126.

45. 35.   47. (a) 21.   (b) For example,

	A	B	or		O	O
A	AA	AB		A	AO	AO
B	AB	BB		B	BO	BO

49. 720.   51. 126.   53. 8820.   55. 1680.

CHAPTER 3

3. (a) $\{HHH, HHT, HTH, THH, HTT, THT, TTH, TTT\}$.
   (b) $\frac{3}{8}$.   (c) $\frac{1}{2}$.   (d) 1.

5. $\{A_1B_1, A_2B_2, A_3B_3, A_1B_2, A_2B_1, A_1B_3, A_3B_1, A_2B_3, A_3B_2\}$.
   (a) $\frac{4}{9}$.   (b) $\frac{1}{3}$.

7. (a) $\frac{2}{13}$.   (b) $\frac{4}{13}$.

9. $\frac{1}{4}$.   11. $\frac{1}{4}$.   13. 0.000495.   15. $\frac{1}{4}$.   17. (a) $\frac{1}{6}$.   (b) $\frac{1}{2}$.

19. (a) $\frac{2}{7}$.   (b) $\frac{6}{7}$.   21. 0.332.   23. $\frac{2}{5}$.   25. $\frac{5}{26}$.

CHAPTER 4

1. 73.3%.   3. 0.60.   5. 0.14.   9. $\frac{5}{12}$.   11. 0.179.   13. 0.015.

15. (a) $\frac{1}{3}$.   (b) $\frac{1}{2}$.   17. 0.106.   19. 0.064.   21. 0.086.

23. (a) 0.16.   (b) 0.30.   (c) 0.040.   (d) 0.08.   (e) 0.625.

25. (a) Unfair; $P = \frac{25}{52}$.   (b) Fair.   (c) Unfair; $P = \frac{4}{9}$.

27. $\frac{2}{9}$; 0.214.   29. 0.545.   31. (a) 0.25.   (b) R; 41.5%.

33. 0.36.   35. 0.340.   37. 0.432.   39. 0.0000015.

CHAPTER 5

1. (a) 0.618.   (b) 0.954.   (c) 1.   3. (a) 0.0444.   (b) 0.0631.
5. 0.493.   7. (a) 0.00120.   (b) 0.00200.   9. 0.133.   11. 0.245.
13. 0.157.   15. (a) 0.0081.   (b) 0.81.   (c) 0.0000081.

CHAPTER 6

1. One method used is the following. Take five shovels of coal, one from each corner and one from the center of the car. Place in a heap, pulverize, mix, and divide into four quarters. Save one-quarter, pulverize further, mix, and divide into quarters. Repeat the process a few more times, then spoon out the required 10 grams.

3. No. A county having a relatively small number of dairies would have a representation in the sample of greater importance than was due it. The number from each county should be proportional to the number of dairies in it. It might be necessary to take into account the sizes of the dairies.

5. The only way for no classes to be below the average is to have them all the same, and that is practically impossible.

7. Draw out every 40th card.

27. (a) 20; (b) 5; (c) 96; (d) 55; (e) 32; (f) 100; (g) 15.

29. (a) 10; (b) 37 − 34 = 3.   33. 4.41%.   35. 1.68.   37. (a) 4.93 gr.
(b) 0.20 gr.

39. (a) 24.2 secs.   (b) 1.9 secs.   41. (a) 23.4; (b) 8.9.

45. (a) $8; (b) $17.93; (c) The median, because of the very large contribution of $150.

47. 2.64.   49. $1.11.

CHAPTER 7

1. About 25 for each digit.

7.

x	2	3	4	5	6	7	8	9	10	11	12
$f(x)$	$\frac{1}{36}$	$\frac{2}{36}$	$\frac{3}{36}$	$\frac{4}{36}$	$\frac{5}{36}$	$\frac{6}{36}$	$\frac{5}{36}$	$\frac{4}{36}$	$\frac{3}{36}$	$\frac{2}{36}$	$\frac{1}{36}$

9. 3.04; 1.2.   11. 5.38.   13. (a) 0.8; 2.160

(b)

x	−2	−1	0	1	2	3
$F(x)$	0.1	0.2	0.4	0.6	0.9	1

15. 1.5; 0.866.   17. $7.   19. 9.   21. $\frac{7}{8}$.   23. $\frac{5}{6}$.

25. $2.75.   27. 0.   29. 24.5 cents.   35. $k = 0.1$.

37. (a)

y	0	3	8	15
$f(y)$	0.1	0.3	0.5	0.1

; (b) 6.4; (c) 16.24.

CHAPTER 8

1. 0.273.   3. 0.230.   5. 0.6257.   7. $P = 0.112$; not biased.

9. 0.0432.   11. (a) 0.0173; (b) 0.6865.   13. 0.0043.

15. 0.6778.   17. (a) 0.0159; (b) 0.867.   19. About 71 times.

21. 25; 4.33.   23. 7 or 8.   25. (a) approximately 7; (b) approximately 6; (c) 7.   27. (a) 4; 1.79; (b) 0.0001; (c) 1.05×10^{-14}; (d) 1.15×10^{-2}.

29. (a) $P \geq \frac{3}{4}$; (b) $P \geq \frac{5}{9}$.   31. $r \leq 1$ for $P \leq 0.05$; accept H_0.

33. $r = 3$; $P_{0:50}$ requires $r = 0$; accept H_0.

CHAPTER 9

7. 4.905 gr.   9. $2,188.   15. Between 55 and 59 years; 56.4 yrs.

17. (a) 0.561; (b) 0.104.   19. $\frac{1}{2}$.

CHAPTER 10

1. (a) 0.3521; (b) 0.3867; (c) 0.1989; (d) 0.0147.

3. (a) 0.0031; (b) 0.2323; (c) 0.3209; (d) 0.0067.

5. (a) 0.0034; (b) 0.0030; (c) 0.0190.

7. (a) 0.0168; (b) 0.8413; (c) 0.0455.

9. (a) 0.694; (b) 2.75.   13. About 68%.   15. 66.   17. 789.

19. 18 times.   21. 0.524.   23. 433.   25. 6.81%.   27. 0.044.

29. 0.464.   31. $z = -4.19$; yes.   33. Acceptance region: $50.4 < \bar{x} < 69.6$; accept.

35. One-tail $P = 0.0068$; result is unusual.   37. 0.869.

39. $z = 4.11$; very unusual.   41. 0.0367.   43. 16.7; 3.33; two-tail $P = 0.02$, an unusual result.

45. (a) 51; (b) 0.76.

CHAPTER 11

1. 0.0756.   3. 0.036.   5. $\chi^2 = 5.97$; not an unusual result.

7. (i) H_0: persons cannot discriminate between A and B;
$\chi^2 = 2.83$; $P > 0.05$; accept.
(ii) H_0: persons who did discriminate showed no preference;
$\chi^2 = 41.2$; $P < 0.01$; reject.
(iii) H_0: preferences were the result of chance, $\chi^2 = 89$;
$P < 0.01$; reject.

9. $\chi^2 = 4.66$; $P < 0.05$; treatment is effective.

11. $\chi^2 = 1.35$; accept hypothesis of independence.

13. $\chi^2 = 5.87$; $P < 0.02$; yes.

15. $P = 0.099$ (one-tail); hypothesis accepted.

17. (i) H_0: Day of the week immaterial; assume a 5-day week; $\chi^2 = 10.38$;
$P < 0.01$; reject H_0; note that actual frequencies exceeded the theoretical for Mondays and Fridays.
(ii) H_0: Hour of the day immaterial; assume an 8-hour day; $\chi^2 = 5.61$;
$P > 0.05$; accept H_0.
(iii) H_0: Accidents equally frequent hour by hour; $\chi^2 = 16.36$; $P < 0.05$;
reject H_0.
(iv) H_0: Accident frequencies for the hours of the day are independent of the day of the week; assume a 40-hour week; $\chi^2 = 0.512$; H_0 not refuted;
unusually close agreement.
(v) H_0: The 4–5 hour accident frequency is not different from the other hours; $\chi^2 = 5.08$; $P < 0.05$, H_0 refuted.

19. $\chi^2 = 6.635$; reject hypothesis; the cell frequencies are fairly large.

21. $\chi^2 = 15.90$; accept H_0.   23. Estimate is $186 < \sigma^2 < 730$; no.

CHAPTER 12

1. $z = 1.82$; if $\alpha = 0.05$ and H_1: $p > 0.25$, result is not due to chance; if H_1:
$p \neq 0.25$, result is due to chance.

3. $z = -2.36$; yes.   5. 0.0655.   7. (a) 152; (b) 171.

9. $z = -1.74$; accept H_0.   11. $z = -0.76$; no.

13. H_0: $\hat{p}_1 = \hat{p}_2$, H_1: $\hat{p}_1 > \hat{p}_2$; $z = 4.24$. Inoculation aids recovery; correction factor negligible for such a large z.

15. $\bar{x} = 0.34$, $s^2 = 0.28$; theoretical frequencies: 24.8, 8.5, 1.5, 0.2.

17. $\bar{x} = 0.93$, $s^2 = 0.94$; theoretical frequencies: 228, 211, 98.5, 30.5, 6.9, 1.2.

19. Poisson $P = 0.130$; binomial $P = 0.129$; no.

21. 0.175.   23. $\mu = 0.9$, $\sigma = 0.7$.

25. The Poisson law. The "expected" number of times for 4 or more murders to occur in a year is about one.

CHAPTER 13

3. (a) $\mu_x = 0.1$, $\sigma_x^2 = 0.89$;
   (b)

$\bar{x}$	-1	$-\dfrac{2}{3}$	$-\dfrac{1}{3}$	0	$\dfrac{1}{3}$	$\dfrac{2}{3}$	1	$\dfrac{4}{3}$	$\dfrac{5}{3}$	2
$f(\bar{x})$	0.027	0.108	0.198	0.235	0.204	0.132	0.065	0.024	0.006	0.001

   (c) $\mu_{\bar{x}} = 0.1$, $\sigma_{\bar{x}}^2 = 0.297$.

5. (a) 25; (b) 20; (c) 10.   7. $z = 2.25$; yes.

9. 16.   11. 22.   13. Rejection: $\bar{x} > 53.3$; acceptance: $\bar{x} \leq 53.3$; β;
    0.56; 0.20.   15. 0.15; 0.85.

19. $z = -1.25$; no.

21. $z = -6.85$; reject the hypothesis.

23. $z = -1.91$; two-tail $P = 0.0562$; probably no unusual difference.

25. $t = -2.61$; accept H_1: $\mu \neq 15$.

27. $t = 2.06$; H_0: $\mu \leq 0$; assertion is substantiated for $\alpha = 0.05$.

29. $t = 1.50$; accept H_0: $\mu \geq 27,000$.

31. $t = 1.54$; no.

33. $t = 1.70$; no.

35. $t = -3.26$; reject H_0.

37. (a) $\alpha = 0.04$; (b) $\beta = 0.69$; 0.23; 0.0006.

39. (a) A one-tail test, because the danger lies in the grenade exploding too soon. (b) A larger α because then β would be smaller and there would be less danger of accepting lots that should be rejected.

41. H_1: $\mu_0 \neq 50$, i.e. $\mu_0 < 50$ or $\mu_0 > 50$.

CHAPTER 14

1.

Trial 1 \ Trial 2	$+$	$-$	$f(x)$
$+$	0.3	0.3	0.6
$-$	0.3	0.1	0.4
$g(y)$	0.6	0.4	

3.

y / x	S HH	F HT, TH, or TT	$f(x)$
H	$\frac{1}{4}$	$\frac{1}{4}$	$\frac{1}{2}$
T	0	$\frac{1}{2}$	$\frac{1}{2}$
$g(y)$	$\frac{1}{4}$	$\frac{3}{4}$	

7. $P = \dfrac{20!}{10!1!2!7!}(0.4)^{10}(0.2)(0.1)^2(0.3)^7$

9. $\frac{1}{2}$.   11. (i) $-\frac{3}{50}$; (ii) $-\frac{3}{304}$; (iii) $\frac{1}{8}$.

13. (i) $-\frac{1}{4}$; (ii) $-\frac{1}{19}$; (iii) $\sqrt{3}/3$; (vii) $\sqrt{6}/6$.

15. 0.60; Probably fairly accurate since cell frequencies are large.

CHAPTER 15

1. (a)

x	1	2
$f(x)$	0.4	0.6

;

y	0	1	3	4
$g(y)$	0.4	0.1	0.2	0.3

(b) $\frac{1}{3}$; $\frac{1}{4}$.

(c)

y	0	1	3	4
$g(y\mid 1)$	$\frac{1}{4}$	$\frac{1}{4}$	0	$\frac{1}{2}$

;

x	1	2 .
$f(x\mid 4)$	$\frac{2}{3}$	$\frac{1}{3}$

3. (a)

x / y	0	2	$f(y)$
0	0.05	0	0.05
2	0.20	0.15	0.35
4	0	0.60	0.60
$f(x)$	0.25	0.75	

(b) No; $P(x,y) \neq f(x)g(y)$.

5. (a)

y / x	0	1	2	3	$f(x)$
0	$\frac{1}{8}$	$\frac{1}{8}$	0	0	$\frac{1}{4}$
1	0	$\frac{1}{4}$	$\frac{1}{4}$	0	$\frac{1}{2}$
2	0	0	$\frac{1}{8}$	$\frac{1}{8}$	$\frac{1}{4}$
$g(y)$	$\frac{1}{8}$	$\frac{3}{8}$	$\frac{3}{8}$	$\frac{1}{8}$	

(b) See $f(x)$ and $g(y)$ above.

(c)

y	0	1	2	3
$g(y \mid 1)$	0	$\frac{1}{2}$	$\frac{1}{2}$	0

;

x	0	1	2
$f(x \mid 2)$	0	$\frac{2}{3}$	$\frac{1}{3}$

.

(d) No; $P(x,y) \neq f(x)g(y)$.

7. (a)

$u = x + y$	1	2	5	6
$P(u)$	0.1	0.4	0.4	0.1

;

(b)

$u = y - x$	-2	-1	0	1	2	3
$P(u)$	0.3	0.1	0.1	0.2	0.1	0.2

.

9. No; $P(x,y) \neq f(x)g(y)$; Yes; $P(x,y) = f(x)g(y)$ always.

11. 16.5.   13. -0.14.

17. (a) $y = \frac{1}{2}$; (b) $y = 2.83 - 0.583x$.

19. (a)

x	0	1	2	3
$r(x)$	$\frac{7}{3}$	2	2.5	2

(b) $y = 2.29 + 0.00990x$;

(e) 0.0127.

21. -0.162.   23. 0.685.   25. 1.

CHAPTER 16

1. (a) 130.7; (b) 4.90; (c) We would expect the mean blood pressure to be more accurate since it is derived from a larger sample; however, weights of tablets are more stable than the blood pressures of individuals.

3. (a) 62.5%; (b) 66.7%; (c) 64.3%, provided male and female voters are about equal in numbers in the community; otherwise one should use a weighted percentage.

5. $67.4 < \mu < 75.0$.   7. $19.4 < \mu < 27.4$.   9. $79.6 < \mu < 84.4$.

11. $\mu < 35.6$; yes; special training reduces the mean time.

13. $-1.3 < \mu_x - \mu_y < 13.3$.   15. 8718; 93.3.   17. 13.1.

19. Formula (13.13).   21. 1.68.   23. $29.0 < p < 16.4$.

25. Not unless N is large.

CHAPTER 17

1. $y = 1.0 + 0.97x$.   3. (a) $70°$; (b) four chirps per min.

5. $y = 7.19 - 0.234x$; 0.234%.   7. $y = 11.4 + 0.675x$.

9. $y = -12.1 + 0.265x$; MLD $= 64.5$.

11. (i) The second method took a shorter time.
    (ii) There was a mean decrease of 16% effected by retraining.

13. $t = 4.47$; reject H_0: $\beta = 0.80$.

15. $1.40 < \beta < 1.50$.

CHAPTER 18

1. 0.984.   3. 1.00.   7. (a) About 0.9; (b) -0.3 to -0.1; (c) 0.4 to 0.6.

9. (a) Literature and verbal scores correspond fairly well.
   (b) Chemistry and verbal scores do not correspond very well.

11. (a) There is a moderate tendency for other sales to vary as prescription sales
        do; since $r^2 = 0.20$, about 20% of the variance of other sales can be
        attributed to the variability of prescription sales.
    (b) $z' = 0.244$; H_0 not refuted.

13. (a) $-0.03 < \rho < 0.78$; (b) $-0.63 < \rho < 0.12$; (c) $0 < \rho < 0.93$.

15. $-0.03 < \rho < 0.74$.

CHAPTER 19

1. (a) and (d), because the rows add to 1.

3. (a) $\begin{pmatrix} 0 & 7 \\ -1 & 2 \end{pmatrix}$;   (b) $\begin{pmatrix} \frac{7}{24} & \frac{17}{24} \\ \frac{17}{60} & \frac{43}{60} \end{pmatrix}$.

5. (a) $(5,3)$; (b) $\left(\frac{29}{60}, \frac{31}{60}\right)$

7. $\begin{pmatrix} -1 & 2 & 4 \\ 2 & 0 & -2 \\ 1 & 4 & 5 \end{pmatrix}$.   11. $p_1^{(3)} = \frac{43}{128}$; $p_2^{(3)} = \frac{85}{128}$.

13. (a) 0.624; (b) 0.626.   15. $p_{11}^{(4)} = \frac{3}{8}$; $p_{12}^{(4)} = \frac{5}{8}$; $p_{22}^{(4)} = \frac{11}{16}$.

29. $\frac{1}{2}$.   31. (a) $\frac{18}{125}$; (b) 0.00922.

Index